A series of student texts in

CONTEMPORARY BIOLOGY

General Editors:
Professor E. J. W. Barrington, F.R.S.
Professor Arthur J. Willis

64409

The Chemotaxonomy
of Plants

Philip M. Smith

Ph.D.
Department of Botany
University of Edinburgh
Edinburgh, Scotland

Elsevier, New York

American Elsevier Publishing Company, Inc.
52 Vanderbilt Avenue, New York, N.Y. 10017

First published 1976 in Great Britain
by Edward Arnold (Publishers) Limited

Boards edition ISBN: 0–444–19454–1
Paper edition ISBN: 0–444–19455–X
Library of Congress Catalog Card Number: 76–25310

Printed in Great Britain by
J. W. Arrowsmith Ltd.,
Bristol, England

Preface

Chemotaxonomy is a field of scientific investigation which has attracted students and researchers from diverse academic disciplines. Taxonomists and chemists represent obvious end points of the spectrum of interests now brought to bear on the application of chemical evidence to taxonomic studies. In some ways taxonomists and chemists are very different kinds of scientist, and the philosophical meeting ground between them is small and inadequately explored. Yet, if the hybrid subject of chemotaxonomy is to manifest full hybrid vigour, the chemist and the taxonomist must begin to understand each other better.

In most first degree courses it is inappropriate or impossible to pursue both disciplines beyond an elementary level. Often the aspiring taxonomist may have little time and perhaps less taste for elementary chemistry in the early stages of his career. Nevertheless, he must understand something of the strengths and limitations of chemical methodology and data, if he wishes eventually to evaluate chemotaxonomic evidence relating to the organisms which he studies. Similarly the chemist who realizes that his techniques or results have a taxonomic or evolutionary relevance is seldom trained to appreciate the different demands and approaches of the biological subject.

It is hoped that this book may enable chemists and taxonomic biologists to glimpse possible areas where they may cooperate with mutual profit. To this end, facts and methods of chemistry and taxonomic principles are both gently introduced, and then integrated. Copious references are cited to facilitate subsequent penetration into either chemical or taxonomic literature.

Chemotaxonomic facts are used to illustrate principles and problems in chemotaxonomy, but no attempt is made to discuss chemosystematics *in extenso*. *Chemotaxonomy*—the subject of the book — is here regarded as the practice by which is produced *chemosystematics*—a body of chemical evidence and the classifications in which it is employed. Evolutionary significance of chemical data is considered when relevant, but taxonomic and phylogenetic problems are regarded as distinct, if sometimes related, matters. Functions of chemical characters are discussed.

Though chemotaxonomy has been well provided with research-orientated texts in the past, often in the form of symposium reports or multi-author, multi-level compilations (e.g. *Chemistry in Botanical Classifications*, ed. Bendz and Santesson 1973), I have felt for some time that a more introductory, homogeneous and relatively inexpensive treatment was needed, especially for students. The various past reviews have not been particularly accessible to the embryo chemotaxonomist, and much relevant material has been widely scattered. Alston and Turner's *Biochemical Systematics*[12] had an introductory, even pioneering function, but progress since 1963 has been rapid. Multi-volume encyclopaedias of chemosystematic data, such as Hegnauer's monumental *Chemotaxonomie der Pflanzen*[221] and Gibbs' *Chemotaxonomy of Flowering Plants*[179] have little discussion of taxonomic principles and problems. They are primarily reference books. Several excellent handbooks on chemical procedures are available (e.g. Harborne[209]), so it has not in general been thought necessary to include the minutiae of analytical methods in the present work.

I am grateful to various people for helping me to write about chemotaxonomy. I thank particularly Dr P. H. Davis, Dr R. O. D. Dixon and Professor G. L. Stebbins for reading draft material; Professor A. J. Willis for his careful editorial scrutiny, suggestions and encouragement; and Edward Arnold Ltd, for their calm efficiency. Finally and fundamentally, I thank my wife and family for their forebearance.

Edinburgh, 1975   P. M. S.

Contents

PREFACE

PART 1

Possibilities and Problems

I

Introduction

Taxonomy is the theory and practice of classification, and **chemotaxonomy** incorporates the principles and procedures involved in the use of chemical evidence for classificatory purposes. **Chemical Systematics** is the study of the chemical variation in a diversity of organisms, and of their relationships. This book does not aim to give accounts of the systematics of any group of plants but rather to introduce and illustrate the ways in which chemical data may be used with profit to taxonomists. Most taxonomists strive to produce **natural classifications**, that is, classifications based on consideration of as many features of the organisms as possible, which it is *hoped* will reflect their evolutionary relationships. Features used in a classification are termed **taxonomic characters**. All sources of taxonomic evidence are scanned in the search for taxonomic characters, and among the richest have been the fields of morphology, anatomy, cytology, ecology and genetics. The widespread use of chemical data as taxonomic characters marks a recent extension of the range of recognized sources of taxonomic evidence—a range which has been widening for several hundred years.

Most taxonomists are interested in the relationships of the organisms which they study, as well as in the best ways to classify them. It is very difficult to produce a natural classification without being aware of the possible affinities of the species or other groups which are recognized. Chemical taxonomy, like any other contributory discipline, will provide evidence for or against schemes of relationship between the taxonomic groups (taxa) which it helps to define. The extent to which chemical data may be useful in suggesting or testing schemes of relationship will therefore be considered in the chapters which follow.

To speak of relationship without qualifying the meaning further is to introduce a vagueness which has characterized certain work in the field of chemical taxonomy. There is the relationship between all plants which have descended from a common ancestor which we describe as **evolutionary** or **phylogenetic relationship**. There is also a relationship between plants in terms of some shared feature or features, regardless of the reason for the sharing, based simply on the resemblances which they show in the features studied. Such relationships based upon perceived similarities are described as **phenetic.** Chemical analyses might show that certain plant species were all very similar in terms of the polysaccharides stored in their seeds. This would reveal a phenetic relationship but not necessarily a phylogenetic one. Many workers in chemical taxonomy have become interested in the problems of plant evolution and in many cases the aim of their studies seems not to be the provision of chemical evidence for better classification, but to shed light upon the phylogeny of the plant taxa with which they work. These different purposes are not always stated clearly. Our knowledge of the origin and evolution, i.e. the phylogeny, of many plant groups is so sparse that we must welcome any further knowledge from chemical analysis of living plants which may reinforce other comparative phenetic studies and the impoverished fossil record. As with comparative morphology, that main-stay of phylogenetic speculations, the evidence of the chemist and biochemist must be scrutinized with great care.

The distinctions between phenetic, phylogenetic and natural classifications are fully discussed in recent taxonomic works[118,230,233].

The principles, procedures and results of investigations into the chemical variation of plant taxa are therefore applied mainly for two different purposes: first, to provide taxonomic characters which may improve existing plant classification, i.e. a strict taxonomic purpose, and second, to add to knowledge of phylogeny or evolutionary relationship. An introduction to chemotaxonomy must explore the potential contribution and usefulness of chemical evidence to both.

Perhaps a brief word on the status of the two purposes of chemotaxonomy would be appropriate here. Phylogeny and evolution have always been compellingly interesting to biologists, and it is noteworthy that the fascination of the subject has recently diverted many chemists and biochemists from their orthodox enquiries.

Knowledge of phylogeny in any group aids genetic manipulation of the species in the group for human gain, particularly important when the group in question includes cultivated plants. The classification of plants, or of any other objects, seems to be a basic human behaviour pattern which we cannot avoid—we have an urge to classify. So necessary is the recognition of the entities in our environment to our survival, to efficient communication and to optimal exploitation of resources, that our art or science of taxonomy by which we achieve this recognition must be a fundamental reason for our success as a species.

THE PLACE OF CHEMISTRY IN TAXONOMY AND SYSTEMATICS

Studies of chemical variation have been suggested to be one of the principal growing points in the field of taxonomy and systematics. Reasons why chemotaxonomy seems so exciting at present will be reviewed in the next chapter. Here we should relate the subject to the other activities of taxonomists in order to place it in perspective.

Figure 1.1 is a 'taxonomic flow chart' which shows that though chemotaxonomy has become such a large and useful treasury of new facts for the taxonomist, it must not be thought of as a replacement for his traditional work. At best it is a major source of new characters and information. All other sources of taxonomic evidence still exist and are still producing new ideas and facts which cannot be ignored. Chemical facts are not vital to the continuation of improvement in taxonomy, except in the case of bacteria and some other microorganisms, but are extremely helpful and stimulating. The taxonomic contributions of cytology and of genetics, both still comparatively new fields, have been enormous. It is likely that chemical taxonomy or chemotaxonomy, by whatever name it is finally known, will make at least an equally great impact on our ideas of classification, and of phylogeny.

The 'whole' taxonomist, a hypothetical person, includes in his research some work in all the departments mentioned in the flow chart (Fig. 1.1). In most cases, the taxonomist is unable through lack of time, knowledge or skill to produce evidence of all the different types personally. Instead he will try to integrate all available evidence in his final conclusions about the classification and the evolutionary relationships of the group of plants concerned. Many scientists produce contributory taxonomic evidence almost as a by-product of their own work—on cytology or genetics, for

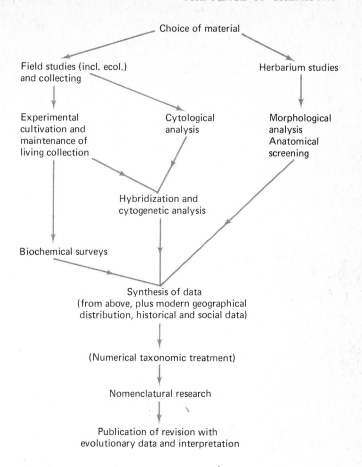

Fig. 1.1   A taxonomic 'flow chart'.

example. In the case of chemical evidence, the situation is often one where chemists or biochemists furnish chemical facts, which are then available for a taxonomist to consider subsequently. It would be profitable if both parties involved knew of the needs and problems of the other.

As a contributory discipline in both taxonomic and evolutionary studies, chemotaxonomy is now very important. Chemical characters have provided valuable clues to unsuspected or only half-suspected evolutionary relationships and in some cases have removed problems which have lain unsolved for many years. Chemical characters of plants can often be used in a classification almost or quite as readily as familiar features such as those of leaf arrangement, chromosome number and indumentum. In future, chemical characters will be essential components in systems of natural classification. In **artificial classifications**, based on one or only a few characters, and usually having a limited application in keys for identification, or in defining groups of plants in commerce, chemical features have long been of practical value. In identifying members of the Umbelliferae, the smells arising from the crushed foliage may be a quicker guide than the relatively homogeneous gross morphology of the plants, for elementary students and Early Man. *Sison amomum,* the Stone Parsley, smells of nutmeg mixed with petrol, while Coriander (*Coriandrum sativum*) gives off the smell of bed-bugs. These are practical, if curious, chemical characters. In commerce, chemical characters underly the taste or smell of different varieties or grades of tea and tobacco.

INFORMATION FROM MOLECULES

What form does chemical evidence take? Often it is presented as a statement that a given taxonomic group (taxon, pl. taxa) does or does not contain a certain chemical constituent. The distribution of the constituent becomes better known as a wider range of plants are analysed. Eventually it may become clear that, for example, certain species in a genus contain the constituent, while certain other species do not. More often, chemical evidence is more complicated than a single presence or absence character. Several or many chemical substances may be involved in the analysis, and the chemical characters may consist of the different *combinations* in which these are found to occur. More rarely, the character may be quantitative, i.e. one group may consistently contain much more of a substance than another group.

Not all kinds of chemical substance present in plants reveal information useful to the taxonomist. They are by no means all equal in the amount and value of taxonomic information conveyed. Part of this book is concerned with assessing the value of taxonomic evidence gleaned from the occurrence and distribution of the various kinds of chemical substances.

Unlike biochemists, taxonomists and evolutionists are only incidentally interested in molecules from the standpoint of how they may be synthesized, or what their function may be. Instead they are primarily concerned with the molecule as a carrier of information. Zuckerkandl and Pauling[514] have defined information-carrying molecules as **semantides**. Deoxyribonucleic acid (DNA) is now widely recognized as the physical basis of the genetic code—the information necessary to construct a new individual. This information is similar in similar organisms, and hence also in plants in similar species and similar genera. As the specification for an individual in all respects, DNA is a primary source of taxonomic information, as well as being the blue-print for development and differentiation. Evolutionists believe that similarity between organisms is normally proportional to the number of ancestors which they share, and to the age of their most recent common ancestor. Therefore DNA is also a primary source of information relating to phylogeny. Zuckerkandl and Pauling characterize it as a **primary semantide**. Ribonucleic acid (RNA) is a secondary source of this information (a **secondary semantide**) while the translation of the code into sequences of amino acids provides the taxonomist with **tertiary semantides** in the form of proteins. All chemical materials synthesized by an organism reflect the information in the semantide molecules to a greater or lesser degree. To varying extents all therefore contain useful information for taxonomy which may also have a bearing on phylogeny.

Other chapters examine the significance of the information in different types of naturally occurring substances, and comment on its value in studies of taxonomy or evolution in terms of its accessibility and ease of interpretation. Taxonomic information cannot always be readily extracted from the most obvious chemical sources. Improvements in analytical techniques have been so great in the recent past, providing so much of value to systematics, that taxonomists can look forward with high hopes of receiving more taxonomic or evolutionary evidence at present locked up in molecules. It will be freed completely only by substantial advances in technology and in methods of interpretation.

Further researches into techniques, and further use of available methods of analysis, will be most effective only if the aims and requirements of evolutionists and taxonomists are fully appreciated. They have not always been understood in the past. Chapter 3 attempts to define the kinds of chemical evidence most needed and also to emphasize the quite strict requirements necessary for chemical techniques and investigations if they are to gain acceptance by taxonomists in general. When the objectives and problems of taxonomists are better understood by technologists, perhaps 'purpose-built' techniques for chemical taxonomy will come forward. They are urgently needed.

CHEMICAL CHARACTERS, THE TAXONOMIC HIERARCHY, AND THE PLANT KINGDOM

How far may chemical evidence be useful throughout the Plant Kingdom? We have no reason to suppose that chemical evidence is limited in its applicability in any way to only part of the Plant Kingdom or to only part of the hierarchy of taxonomic categories. Numerous examples of taxonomically useful chemical facts can be cited in most groups of plants. Chemical evidence is of particular significance in the simplest organisms—the bacteria—and it has been used effectively in all more complex groups from the fungi to the most highly specialized angiosperms.

The identification, rather than the classification, of lichens has been considerably aided by the use of simple microchemical tests and crystallization reactions. Lichens form complicated organic molecules ('lichen substances') which produce colour reactions with simply applied test reagents such as potassium hydroxide and calcium hypochlorite. Some variation of the colour reaction within populations of certain species of lichen has been detected, and taxonomic problems arise from it.[109,139,197]

In the case of bacteria, the taxonomic characters provided by chemistry have long been vital to classification. These primitive organisms have so few structural features, even when viewed with the electron microscope, that their chemical properties have provided much of the evidence for delimitation of species, genera and higher categories. A glance through Bergey's fascinating *Manual of Determinative Bacteriology*[71] furnishes endless instances of the value of biochemical evidence in bacterial taxonomy. For example, the tribe Nitrobacterieae is defined largely on the ability of the members to gain energy from the oxidation of ammonia to nitrite or from nitrite to nitrate. Genera in this tribe are characterized partly by the rates at which they are able to carry out these oxidations.

Even in the bacteria, where the importance of chemical characters is well established, the newer concepts and techniques of chemotaxonomy are making significant contributions to improvement in classification. Certain features of chemical synthesis, on which the limits of some genera have traditionally been based, are now known to be determined by single genes, and are hence trivial as taxonomic characters, and as evidence of phylogenetic relationship. An example is the capacity to ferment lactose, long regarded as a generic property in the coliform bacteria.

A further problem in the taxonomy of bacteria is that many of the chemical characters traditionally used do not correlate well with structural features. Campbell and Postgate[84] discuss an example of this in the sulphate-reducing bacteria *Desulphovibrio* and *Desulphotomaculum*. Both use sulphate as the terminal electron acceptor in anaerobic respiration, but they appear unrelated to each other on criteria of cell structure. Their morphological aberrations and locomotory behaviour also differ. Perhaps this is an example of convergent evolution in biochemical behaviour.

Difficulties of this kind should eventually be resolved by approaches like that of Stanier[449]. Here the biochemical characters most valued in determining the best classification of bacterial groups are highly complex metabolic processes, governed by many genes. Stanier has worked on the ways in which different bacteria use aromatic compounds such as hydroxybenzoic acid as respiratory substrates. In the genus *Pseudomonas*, one group of species converted *p*-hydroxybenzoate into pyruvate by a short pathway, while a second group converted it via a more involved pathway, to succinate and acetyl-CoA. The groups so separated appear in Fig. 1.2. They differ also in the manner in which the constituent species metabolize tryptophan. Stanier points out that this separation is based only on a fragment of the total metabolism of the organisms, and it may well show that *Pseudomonas,* a large genus, is biochemically very heterogeneous. Perhaps, when more work has been completed, the genus may need to be split into several smaller ones, on biochemical characters.

In the taxonomy of higher plants, complexity of structure and behaviour has provided much evidence on which to base natural classifications. The groups recognized often seem likely to have arisen from a common ancestor. The richness of characters and variation has meant that, unlike workers on bacteria, taxonomists investigating higher plants have only fairly recently begun to study chemical variation systematically, though it has been recognized for millenia.

An example of the application of chemical methods in higher plant taxonomy is provided by work on tea.[406] Tea plants are

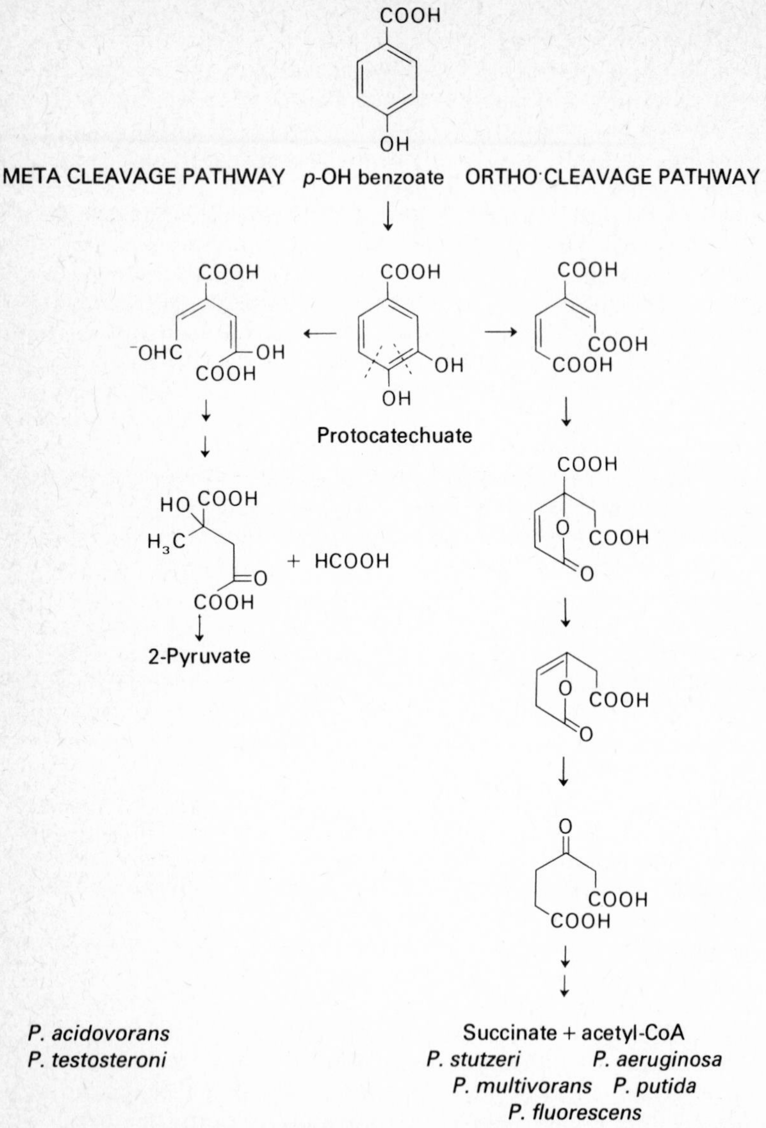

Fig. 1.2 The two pathways for the dissimilation of *p*-hydroxybenzoate in the genus *Pseudomonas*. (From Stanier.[449])

generally classified as *Camellia sinensis*. In this species it is usual to include the two main kinds of tea, China Tea and Assam Tea, as subspecies *sinensis* and *assamica* respectively. These two teas differ in leaf and shoot morphology. Tea plantations in India consist of both teas, and of hybrids between them, together forming large inter-grading populations. There are also suspected hybrids with other less well known species of tea. When standard techniques of morphological comparison are applied, the recognition and delimitation of taxa of tea are frustrated almost completely by past and present hybridizations. Wild tea plants may also contribute to the confusion by chance hybridizations with cultivated forms. Some further form of taxonomic evidence is clearly needed. It is essential to have the taxonomy of tea as clear as possible because it is an important commodity, which has to be defined in terms of type, quality and source in the tea markets of the world.

Using paper chromatography, Roberts *et al.*[406] studied the phenolic content of the young leafy shoots of tea plants, and of related, 'non-tea' species of *Camellia*. Some of their results appear in

Table 1.1 Occurrence of triglycosides of quercetin and kaempferol, 'IC' and depsides in extracts of tea shoots. (From Roberts *et al.*[406]).

Taxonomic category	Depsides	'IC'	Triglycosides
China tea (*Camellia sinensis* subsp. *sinensis*)			
Sample 1	+	−	+++
Sample 2	+	−	+++
Assam tea (*C. sinensis* subsp. *assamica*)			
Sample 1	++	?	?
Sample 2	++	?	?
Artificial Assam × China F₁	+	−	+++
'China Hybrid tea'			
Sample 1	+	?	+++
Sample 2	+++	+	+
Sample 3	++	+	+++
'Southern Form'			
Sample 1	+++	+++	−
Sample 2	+++	+++	−
Sample 3	+++	+++	−
Camellia irrawadiensis	++	+	−
Camellia taliensis	+++	+++	−

Key: +++, strong; ++, medium; +, weak; ?, near level of detectability; −, not detected.

Table 1.1. They found that the tea Camellias (*Camellia* section *Thea*) were all generally similar in phenolic content, and showed no obvious chemical relationship to the other *Camellia* species which were analysed. Table 1.1 shows the variation in three types of phenolic molecules among the tea taxa, omitting all the other phenolics which did not show differences. China tea, obtained in as pure a form as possible, with typical dull, microphyllous leaves, contained glycosides of quercetin and kaempferol, and depsides. Plants of Assam tea entirely unaffected by past hybridization with China tea were not available, but the purest forms used contained only traces of the triglycosides. It was assumed that these were introduced by the hybridization, and that typical Assam tea lacked triglycosides of this type. An unidentified phenolic, called 'IC', was also present in trace form. A third kind of tea, with a southern distribution, completely lacked the triglycosides but contained large amounts of depsides and 'IC'. This possibly discrete form of tea, which has broad glossy leaves like Assam tea but much red pigment, may be related to other species of tea, e.g. *Camellia taliensis* and *C. irrawadiensis*. Since 'IC' occurred in trace quantities in the Assam tea samples, it is likely that they contained genes from this southern tea, rather than typical China Tea.

So far the three confused forms of tea are easily separable on the basis of phenolic pattern. One further problem was resolved. Tea plantations include many bushes referred to as 'China Hybrid' tea. They are very heterogeneous and are widely thought to be hybrids of Assam and China teas. The phenolic patterns show that it is much more likely that they are hybrids of China tea with some taxon containing 'IC' because they contain triglycosides, 'IC' and higher concentrations of depsides than artificial Assam × China hybrids.

The findings from this very simple and rapid demonstration of chemical variation in a complex group are most helpful. Assam and China teas are recognizably distinct. The 'southern form' is seen to be different in phenolic pattern as well as in morphology of the shoot. Perhaps it should be recognized as a third sub-species of *Camellia sinensis*. The 'southern form' of tea, the 'China Hybrid' teas, and two separate tea species (*C. taliensis* and *C. irrawadiensis*) form an 'IC' group. Perhaps the genes for 'IC' production originate from *C. taliensis* or *C. irrawadiensis*, implying that some cultivated teas are of interspecific hybrid origin. Processed tea leaf material may be analysed by these methods, so that the chemical characters are not only taxonomically enlightening but have a practical application in the identification of tea offered for sale.

Chemical evidence is applicable to taxonomy at all levels of the hierarchy of classification. Varietal differences in proteins are well known in plants, and are of potential value in speeding up identifications of samples of cereals, for example. Minor variants of bread wheat (*Triticum aestivum*) may be recognized on the basis of electrophoretic variation in seed proteins.[146] Examples of the usefulness of chemical characters at the level of species, genus, family and order will be found throughout the text, but it is worth noting that even the highest levels of the hierarchy, the Divisions of plants, are usually separated at least in part on biochemical criteria. Divisions of algae are separated in part by the pigments they produce, and also by the nature of the storage products which they assemble (lipids and different polysaccharides). These characters correlate well with morphological and reproductive characters and with variation in the fine structure of the cells. One of the most satisfactory criteria for recognizing an organism as a plant rather than an animal is a biochemical one—the ability to synthesize a cellulose cell wall.

This width of possible application for chemical evidence is a feature making it most attractive to taxonomists. In principle all known plants might be assayed for the presence of a particular substance, or combination of substances, and might therefore be compared in a uniform manner. So wide a survey is possible with very few other characters. Certain proteins, such as cytochrome *c*, may be recognizably homologous in almost all plants, and so be a basis for comprehensive taxonomic comparisons. Such widespread employment of many useful morphological and anatomical characters is frustrated by the absence of homologous parts throughout the range of plants to be compared. Even the application of genetics to taxonomy, which resulted in the growth of the modern subject of biosystematics, is circumscribed. Genetic relationships of taxa, established by artificial breeding experiments, can contribute to taxonomy only at or beneath the levels at which some gene exchange is possible, i.e. the species or more rarely the genus.

Comparisons of homologous chemical characters throughout the Plant Kingdom, where possible, will not be carried out very often despite the potential interest. This is because the labour and time involved in such a project make it daunting. Uniform chemical analysis of smaller, but still substantial, groups, such as families or orders, are both practical and useful. The work on the family Umbelliferae at the University of Reading[232] is an example of this. Another way in which the possibility of widespread surveys of chemical variation may be realized within a reasonable time is to select only a few representatives of each group of plants, and to compare these. Given that homology of the compared molecules is established, the limits to the range of plants which may be investigated in a chemical taxonomic project are set not by the variation of the plants or by technical difficulties, but by the patience and resourcefulness of the taxonomist himself.

CHEMICAL EVIDENCE OF PHYLOGENY

We have been careful to distinguish between the taxonomy of organisms, that is the theory and practice of their classification, and the study of their phylogeny, i.e. of their origin and evolution. Much of the promise in chemical data from plants lies in the possibility that certain kinds of chemical evidence may be a reliable guide to phylogenetic relationships of living species. This possibility has perhaps been the greatest single reason for the current interest and involvement of chemists and biochemists in this field of biology.

Quicker methods of determining the sequences of amino acids in proteins now offer the exciting possibility of comparing the sequence in a homologous protein from a wide range of plants. The numbers of differences in amino acid sequence between samples of the protein from two species are assumed to be proportional to the number of mutations of the gene responsible for coding for the sequence in the protein, which have occurred since the two species diverged from a common ancestor. If the protein sequences of larger numbers of species are compared in all possible pairs, it should be a simple matter to arrange the species in groups showing minimal differences of amino acid sequence, in that particular protein. Similarly these groups could be arranged in a hierarchy of minimal difference categories. This hierarchy may be converted into a 'phylogenetic tree' representing the path of descent of the species from which the homologous proteins were extracted[158] (see Chapter 15).

In work on animals, sufficient evidence has already accumulated to show that the method produces phylogenies which are similar to those already well established on the basis of fossils and comparative morphology. Work on plants has started more recently but already it is known that the sequences of amino acids in cytochrome c from plants can be used to construct interesting schemes.[66]

If the rate of mutation during the past can be reliably estimated, then the sequence data could be used to show the probable times of origin of modern plant groups. Since the fossil record of plants is relatively sparse and incomplete, it will be difficult to estimate mutation rates, but the information on the age of groups coming from sequence data will *ipso facto* be more than usually interesting and important.

CORRELATIONS OF CHEMOTAXONOMIC CHARACTERS

Taxonomists and evolutionists are strongly encouraged to seek out and use chemical evidence in their work by the positive correlations which are often shown with other kinds of information. If it were to conflict with the great mass of evidence from other sources, its value would be very hard to estimate. Fortunately, the conflicts are no more common than occur between any other types of data. Marked correlations of chemical evidence with morphological and genetic evidence are shown in work involving serological analysis of proteins.[177,444] Genetic relationships between varieties of oats have been predicted from protein data,[267] In many cases, known hybrids have been found to be chemically, as well as morphologically intermediate between their parents.[9,199,344] Intermediacy of hybrids has been shown in respect of many different kinds of substance, from proteins to terpenes and phenolic molecules. The early work of Rives[405] illustrated a correlation of protein variation with the ability to form grafts among hybrids of grape-vines.

There seems to be every reason to seek chemical evidence of all kinds in taxonomic and in evolutionary studies of plants.

2

The Origins of Chemotaxonomy

Although chemotaxonomy is apparently a very recently developed field, chemical evidence has been applied in plant classification from early times. The chief importance of botanical study to early man was that it generated knowledge about edible or medical properties of plants which might stave off extinction. Both kinds of property depend on chemical content, which is hence the basis for simple classifications of plants as herbs of healing or as plants of no medicinal use, and, more fundamentally, into poisonous and non-poisonous categories. Early man, with an interest in experimental chemotaxonomy, must have paid a high price for knowledge of the edibility of wild plants!

Primitive chemotaxonomy was thus an applied science, with extremely practical aims and benefits. Plants with similar medicinal qualities would have been grouped together by these early botanists, and the resulting artificial classification, together with others based on categories of food plant, will have been one of the first ever.

Through the subsequent millenia of human social evolution, the elaboration of these classifications steadily increased.[178] By the late seventeenth century a strong association had developed between medicine and botany, and between the people who studied them. Herbals summarized the knowledge gained over centuries, and illustrated the useful plants of the most developed countries. They were the fore-runners of modern Floras (see Fig. 2.1). Physic Gardens were established for the preservation and dissemination of valuable plants. All this time the kinds of taxonomic evidence were

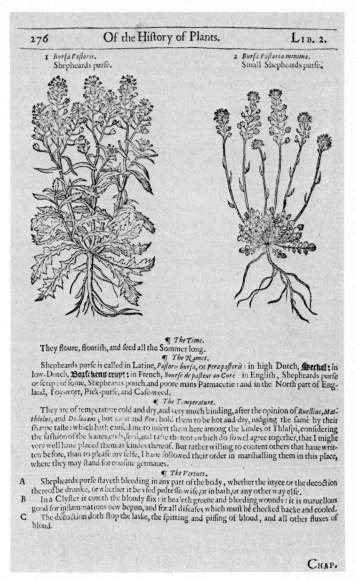

276   Of the History of Plants.   Lıв. 2.

1 *Bursa Pastoris.*
Shepheards purse.

2 *Bursa Pastoria minima.*
Small Shepheards purse.

¶ *The Time.*

They floure, flourish, and feed all the Sommer long.

¶ *The Names.*

Shepheards purse is called in Latine, *Pastoris bursa,* or *Pera pastoris* : in high Dutch, **Seckel** : in low-Dutch, **Borsekens cruyt** : in French, *Bourse de pasteur ou Cure* · in English , Shepheards purse or scrip : of some, Shepheards pouch,and poore mans Parmacetie : and in the North part of England, Toy-wort, Pick-purse, and Cafe-weed.

¶ *The Temperature.*

They are of temperature cold and dry,and very much binding,after the opinion of *Ruellius,Matthiolus,* and *Dodonaeus* ; but *Lovet* and *Pena* hold them to be hot and dry, iudging the same by their sharpe taste : which hath caused me to insert them here among the kindes of Thlaspi,considering the fashion of the leaues,cods,seed,and taste thereof : which do so wel agree together,that I might very well haue placed them as kindes thereof. But rather willing to content others that haue written before, than to pleafe my selfe, I haue followed their order in marshalling them in this place, where they may stand for coufine germanes.

¶ *The Vertues.*

A   Shepheards purfe stayeth bleeding in any part of the body , whether the iuyce or the decoction thereof be dranke , or whether it be vfed pulteffe-wife,or in bath,or any other way elfe.

B   In a Clyster it cureth the bloudy flix : it hea'eth greene and bleeding wounds : it is maruellous good for inflammations new begun,'and for all difeafes which muft be checked backe and cooled.

C   The decoction doth stop the laske, the spitting and piffing of bloud , and all other fluxes of bloud.

Cʜᴀᴘ•

Fig. 2.1   The treatment of *Capsella bursa-pastoris* in Gerard's *Herball,* 1597.

multiplying. Nehemiah Grew (1641–1712) is mainly remembered for his pioneering work on anatomy, but in commenting on the predictive value of taxonomic characters[193] he chose some chemical examples: 'The Natures of Umbelliferous Plants we know are various; yet 'tis most probable that they all agree in this one, *scil*, in being Carminative . . .'.

The London apothecary James Petiver was asked how to predict the medicinal property ('virtue') characteristic of particular plants, and responded:[378] '. . . Plants of the same *Figure* or likeness, have for the generallity much the same *Vertues* and *Use*: Especially if we consider, that the *Organs* or *Structure* of ye *Plants* of the same Family or *Class*, must have much the same *Vessels* and *Ductus's* to consummate that Regular formation and consequently the *Juices* Circulated and strained thro' then cannot be very *Heterogeneous*'.

In picturesque words, Petiver was implying that natural groups of plants have chemical as well as morphological and anatomical similarities.

William Withering, the Birmingham physician and botanist, best known for his accidental discovery of digitalis treatment for heart disease, eventually considered[505] that the previously unknown properties of the foxglove might have been predicted from those of its relatives in the 'Luridae' (mainly Solanaceae) had he but applied his mind to it. In his *Botanical Arrangement*[504] Withering attributed to Linnaeus and his school the demonstration that '. . . the Medical properties of plants are not the only circumstances worthy their attention'. Chemical properties of plants must evidently have held considerable sway in the eighteenth century.[224]

The year 1804 saw the publication in France by A. P. de Candolle of a far-sighted paper[85] relating natural plant classification to medicinal properties of plant species (e.g. the febrifuge quality of all species of the genus *Cinchona*), and the association soon became widely recognized. The significance of this correlation, and of the correlation of other kinds of evidence, however, was not appreciated until after the Darwinian period.

In the nineteenth century attempts were made by chemists to characterize the chemical constituents of plants more precisely and to investigate their occurrence in different species. At first the results were inevitably inconclusive, and not many people were persuaded of the merit of a formal chemical approach to taxonomy. Only after the publications by Darwin[116] and Wallace did taxonomists see the true significance of the occurrence of the same or similar substances in similar plants. Evolution by natural selection, and the common ancestry of similar organisms, were rapidly accepted as the explanation of the character correlations already discovered in morphology and anatomy.

Helen Abbott's paper on 'Certain chemical constituents of plants considered in relation to their morphology and evolution'[1] can be taken as the beginning of the modern phase of chemotaxonomy. Although the work reported was used to support an over-valuation of saponins as taxonomic characters, Abbott made some interesting comments:

'... the theory of evolution in plant life is best illustrated by the chemical constituents of plant form'.

Therefore the notion that studies of the chemical content of plants could be of value not only as a source of evidence for classification, but also in understanding evolution, was forcibly stated as early as 1886.

In the later part of the nineteenth century more and more chemical evidence accumulated, though much of it was still sought for the potential pharmacological importance of the materials discovered. Alkaloids were studied by Eykman[153] and by Greshoff[191] who was interested also in plant poisons. The term 'comparative phytochemistry' is due to Greshoff, who defined it[192] as 'the knowledge of the connection between the natural relationships of plants and their chemical composition'. He wanted the chemical facts about a plant to be a normal part of its scientific description.

It was recognized quite early that not all the diverse chemical constituents of plants would be equally useful as sources of taxonomic evidence, or as guides to evolutionary relationship. Common, widespread materials would not demonstrate many potentially informative discontinuities in distribution. Abbott indicated that chlorophyll would be of little value in distinguishing between categories of green plant, which by definition all possess chlorophyll.[1] She was less correct in her similar statement about 'albuminous compounds'. Though certainly widespread, they soon proved to be complicated and extremely diverse molecules, which we now call proteins.

One of the earliest methods of detecting protein differences was by using the recognition properties of animal antibodies. Protein extracts were used to immunize the animal, and then the antibodies formed in its bloodstream were extracted for use as a kind of 'taxonomic reagent'.

Other methods involved using the physiological reaction of the immunized animal itself to injection of protein extracts from other sources. The use of antiserum *in vitro* became known as serology.

Ehrlich discovered that animals would produce antibodies to injected plant proteins,[144] and Kraus[281] that combining the serum antibodies (antiserum) with the original protein extract (antigen) in a liquid medium produced a visible precipitate. The 'precipitin test' was born. It was quickly seen as a rapid method of checking the similarities of proteins of diverse plant and animals. Kowarski[280] writing about plants, and Nuttall in a classic paper on the blood relationships of primates,[365] were among the first to apply serological methods to the study of classification and of phylogeny.

Plant serology developed fastest in Germany during the early part of the twentieth century.[90] A group at Königsberg (Kaliningrad), including Göhlke, Mez and Ziegenspeck, was the pioneer school, although much of their work was refuted by a rival group at Berlin, headed by Gilg and Schurhoff. Chester[90] gives a comprehensive account of the acrimonious exchanges between the two schools. The culmination of this phase of chemotaxonomy was the publication of the 'Stammbaum', a family tree of plant relationships, based largely on the results of serological tests[337] (see Fig. 2.2). Unfortunately, the crudity of the methods, and the poor state of knowledge of the principles underlying the immune response so reduce the value of the 'Stammbaum' that today it is only of historical interest. Serological methods fell into general disfavour for a considerable period. The ideas and techniques of serology were considerably developed during the twenties and thirties by such workers as Boyden in America[68] and Moritz in Germany.[345] Over the last twenty years the discipline has gradually been rehabilitated.

Comparative chemistry as an aid to taxonomy was a cause championed for many years by McNair, who published papers on the taxonomic usefulness of variations of fat or oil content in plants[330] and of alkaloid content.[331] His statement[332] that: '. . . a chemical classification may be compared with or used as a supplement to morphological classification and may be of some importance in the development of the true natural system of angiosperm phylogeny' would find many supporters today. It is clear that McNair saw chemotaxonomy not as a replacement for existing systems of plant classifications, but as a force contributing to their improvement. Even so he made certain extravagant claims for it, particularly in relation to the significance of molecular size and of iodine numbers of lipids. Some of his work, together with the ambitious activities of the Königsberg serologists, exemplifies the beginning of the phase of over-optimism which usually accompanies the spread of new methods and ideas.

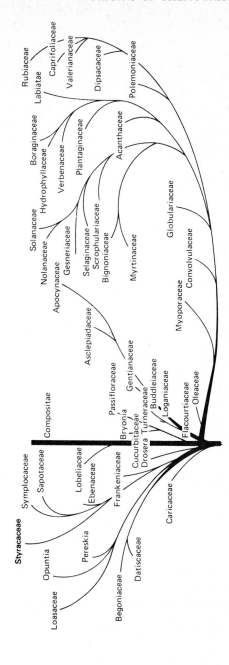

Fig. 2.2 A portion of the 'Stammbaum'. (After Mez and Ziegenspeck.[337])

Baker and Smith[21] worked on the taxonomy of the large genus
Eucalyptus, basing almost all their conclusions on their own studies of
interspecific variation in content of essential oils. The dangers
inherent in so narrow an approach were made plain when it was
shown by Penfold and Morrison[373,374] that Baker and Smith had in
many cases greatly underestimated the intraspecific variation in
essential oils. Their taxonomic conclusions were quickly over-
shadowed by work based on a wider range of taxonomic characters.
However promising the chemotaxonomic approach may often
seem, it is rash indeed to ignore other available evidence.

Recent developments in chemotaxonomy have involved the application of an ever-widening range of biochemical techniques to the
study of taxonomy, and of evolutionary relationship. The details are
reviewed in subsequent chapters but an outline of the general
situation is appropriate here.

Today, the relationship of chemistry and plant taxonomy is seen
less and less as leading to advance in pharmacology, and more in
terms of a source of valuable or vital new character correlations
which may improve classification and perhaps shed light on
phylogeny. Nevertheless, the old connections of medicine and
taxonomic botany are far from being broken completely. The
Institut für Pharmakognosie of the University of Kiel, Germany, has
long been a centre of research into applications of chemistry to
taxonomy. Plants are still screened for their drug properties, and
the surest guide to predicting the best drug plants is still by reference
to their classificatory position. An example of this is to be found in
the current search for safer and more effective oral contraceptives.
Plants with oestrogenic properties have been selected, on a trial and
error basis, and used to limit population size in many primitive
human societies. It is interesting to note that in lists of species
reputed to contain effective contraceptive principles[292] the same
genera and families occur repeatedly.

The recent growth of chemotaxonomy as a popular field of
research is largely due to the development of rapid analytical
techniques, such as chromatography and electrophoresis. These
methods permit the screening of many species or samples in a
reasonably short time. Taxonomists typically have many species to
study and little time for laborious chemical analysis. If such fast
methods had been available in the early years of the century
chemotaxonomy might perhaps have been a favourite field of
research much earlier.

The most recent developments in the technology of automatic
protein 'sequenators' have exciting possibilities for chemo-

taxonomy. By the use of the new equipment, the sequences of amino acids in proteins may be compared relatively quickly. With improvements of the apparatus the time taken for the complete analysis of larger proteins is likely to become acceptably small, even for busy taxonomists. No similar methods for rapid sequencing of nucleic acids are yet in view but perhaps they will be developed ultimately. It is less than satisfactory that the technological developments underlying new methods of interest to chemotaxonomists seem to be associated with wars (e.g. paper chromatography) or space programmes (protein sequencers).

The growth of interest in biology in secondary and tertiary education has almost inevitably led to a greater consideration of the biological applications of chemistry and physics. Possibilities of experimental approaches to taxonomy, and the possibility of phylogenetic explanations of chemical variation have attracted the attention of people trained primarily as chemists or biochemists. On the whole they have, so far, been drawn to the study of phylogeny, rather than the practical but more spartan topic of classification.

Other reasons for the popularity of chemotaxonomy arise from factors internal to the science of systematics. Taxonomists and evolutionists are constantly searching for new characters and variation patterns. The powerful stimulus to both kinds of worker given by the inception of genetics in the early part of the century has waned somewhat after fifty years of fervent application to systematics. Genetic principles, applied to taxonomy and evolution, have developed into the discipline of biosystematics. But studies of genetic relationships are possible only within the limits of gene exchange, and hence taxa at or above generic level are usually excluded. The necessarily lengthy programmes of research into the biosystematics of large groups are difficult to plan, finance and sustain. Consideration of variation within fertility limits has generated the view that genetic data do not offer the sure guide to Absolute Truth which was at first expected. For these reasons the advance of biosystematists towards the Perfect System[452] has run out of steam. All developing subjects provide a new faith when the old one crumbles. For this position in modern systematics, chemotaxonomy now stands as a principal contender.

3

Chemotaxonomic Investigation

It could be said that chemotaxonomic investigations are hybrids, partaking of the nature of both chemical and taxonomic research. Hybrids are often characterized by hybrid vigour but unfortunately hybrid sterility is quite as common. Both the contributory kinds of study, taxonomic and chemical, need to be thoroughly understood and well-planned before a productive chemotaxonomic exercise can be undertaken.

Extra difficulty in research projects must be expected when two kinds of work have to be integrated, and in chemotaxonomy it is further heightened by the fact that skills in the two departments of knowledge are only rarely well-developed in one person. Taxonomic research is not at all similar in aims and methods to chemistry or biochemistry. There are differences of attitude, philosophy and temperament between the chemist and the taxonomist. Misunderstandings, and disagreements based on them, might have been expected in chemotaxonomy. This chapter comments on difficulties confronting the chemotaxonomist, suggests some possible solutions, and discusses the heterogeneous purposes which chemotaxonomists seem to have.

One obvious solution to the problem of personnel is to adopt a team approach. A chemist or biochemist interested in taxonomic problems which may relate to his work can hire a taxonomist to interpret the data for him or, better still, to ensure that the plan of work adopted is taxonomically sound at the outset. In similar ways, taxonomists interested in getting chemical evidence may employ a

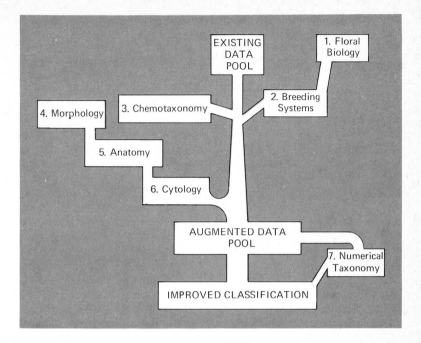

Fig. 3.1 Seven lines of enquiry in a team approach to investigation of the Umbelliferae.

chemist to advise them on the planning and execution of the chemical work. Teams of workers covering all aspects of a research project might be assembled in this way. A fine example of this method was the work on the Umbelliferae carried out by Heywood and a team of people with different skills[231,232]. Perhaps this is the most efficient way to plan taxonomic projects (Fig. 3.1).

The team approach depends for success on a supply of money, good administration and sustained enthusiasm. This approach is not always possible for many chemists and taxonomists who nevertheless wish to explore the potential of chemotaxonomy.

Chemotaxonomic work by taxonomists in isolation carries with it the danger that chemical techniques may be applied improperly or ineptly. Only comparatively recently, with the publication of books[209] and a journal devoted to chemotaxonomy, has there been a concentrated source of technical information intelligible to the taxonomist unfamiliar with the language and complexity of biochemical literature.

Other problems confront the chemotaxonomist who has been trained as a chemist or biochemist. The education of such people rarely includes any component of systematic biology. As a result, many chemists wishing to study the taxonomic or phylogenetic significance of chemical investigations find that they are uncertain of the principles of taxonomy and of mechanisms and pathways of evolution.

The consequences of the gulf in education and attitudes between trained taxonomists and trained chemists are often serious, and will not disappear rapidly. Taxonomists may rashly apply a chemical technique which seems attractive, overlooking some vital precaution. Sometimes a new method is accepted far too readily, before its basis is properly understood. The early German serologists, perhaps forgivably, fell into this trap (see Chapter 2 and Chapter 11). A chemist may apply an elaborate technique quite brilliantly, but to an unacceptably small sample of plant material or may even mistake the identity of the plants investigated. The rigour of taxonomic work must not be underestimated.

Chemists rightly pour scorn on the apparent conservatism of taxonomy. Some spurn a discipline which seems sluggish in terms of production, but yet which suspects the technology which it is supposed may emancipate its workers from centuries of drudgery, i.e. monographic work. But it is a serious and common observation that these new disciples show at the same time a wonderful faith in the taxonomic systems which have been produced, in the specific delimitations of long dead botanists, and in the statements of affinity made by the curators of herbaria.

There are unfortunate and wholly unnecessary obstacles to communication between chemists and taxonomists, which must be corrected if chemotaxonomy is to grow into a meaningful component of systematics and not merely a decoration.

It may be useful, before treating the detailed applications and methods of chemotaxonomy, to present a plan of an idealized chemotaxonomic investigation, which indicates where problems of understanding and methodology may arise. Hegnauer has reviewed some of these matters.[224]

Six main stages can be recognized in a chemotaxonomic investigation which reconciles the necessity for informed chemical procedure and a project design which satisfies formal taxonomic requirements. These are:

(a) Choice of group, taxonomic survey and sound sampling

    (b) Choice, mastery and modification of suitable chemical techniques in a pilot survey
    (c) Full analysis of all material
    (d) Interpretation and comparison with data from all other sources
    (e) Adjustment of classification as necessary
    (f) Treatment of any evolutionary relationship indicated by the new data.

These stages are rarely all incorporated in chemotaxonomic work, which is thereby reduced in value. The aims of the project in hand must constantly be kept in mind, and the relative importance of the stages may seem to vary according to whether the investigator is primarily interested in evidence for taxonomy, for phylogeny or for both.

STAGES IN CHEMOTAXONOMIC INVESTIGATION

(a) Taxonomic survey

This stage covers the choice of the taxonomic group to be investigated, studying its variation and its size. Only when this taxonomic outline has been thoroughly understood can the best method of sampling be devised.

Often the choice of material for chemotaxonomic research has been expedient. Researchers have approached the problem not by asking themselves where there might be an interesting taxonomic problem, but rather by looking for a group of plants well suited to some technique they wished to try out. Much work has concentrated on the Leguminosae mainly because the seeds of these plants have large quantities of easily extracted albumins and globulins[67] or merely because they and the Gramineae are readily available in bulk.[45] With such an approach the tendency is often just to assemble plant material on an empirical basis, and perhaps to rest content with whatever species may be obtained from commercial houses. There are practical reasons for such choice and restriction of materials to investigate, but the enduring taxonomic value of the work may be small because the sample was too narrow.

Chemists may have difficulty in identifying taxonomic problems. There are many ready to advise them, and plenty of information exists in the literature. Taxonomic problems abound where there are restrictions on gene flow in a plant group, for instance in autogamous plants[439,444] and apomictic groups, or in taxa where polyploidy is known. Hybridizing populations always generate taxonomic difficulties which might be reduced by chemotaxonomic enquiries. Alston and Turner and their collaborators have produced classic work on the applications of chemical evidence to hybridization in *Baptisia*.[10] Mystery often surrounds taxonomically isolated groups. Such taxa can rarely be assigned to an agreed position in a classification, and are a source of dispute. Chemical evidence might help assign them accurately and quickly, but at the very least would provide more information just where it is most needed. Finally, there are problems which concern the attribution of rank to taxa which have been reliably delimited, and the testing of numerical classifications.[395]

It is not difficult to obtain living stocks of a wide range of species in most genera and families from the great plant collections maintained in most countries, or by contacting professional plant collectors and explorers. The botanic gardens of the world remain the great treasure houses of materials for the experimentalist, just as they were for Eykman and Greshoff in the nineteenth century (see Chapter 2). Museums and plant breeding stations are subsidiary sources of material and for advice on where or whom to ask for further help. Commercial plantsmen are, of course, excellent sources for many economically important species.

The greatest snag with this phase of the research is the painfully slow accumulation of material. Years may elapse before a collection is complete. Another method of obtaining plants or seeds is by personal travel and collection, but this is expensive in time and money. It is by far the best way, however, because the origins of the material used will be completely known to the researcher. If resources are not equal to personal expeditions, plant collectors can be approached via national herbaria, and may be willing to help. Experimenters are sometimes driven to advertise for their desiderata in the columns of taxonomic journals. It is hardly surprising that the herbarium forms such an important focus for much taxonomic research.

The time taken to assemble a good collection is therefore another reason why sampling for chemotaxonomic experiments is often quite unsatisfactory. As a result chemical assays of only small samples of material, perhaps of only a few genera in a family or a few species in a genus, are published prematurely. Results may never be integrated into taxonomy because they are too incomplete, though they remain preserved in the literature.[221] Taxonomy can only slowly approach its goal of optimal natural classification of all biota, living or dead, because *sampling* the diversity of nature is not possible. *Everything* must be considered in detail. The task is 'attractively infinite'.[98] Chemotaxonomists can make an important contribution by studying a sample providing it is a taxonomically informed and intelligent one, which can be fitted into place at some future date.

An understanding of natural variation within a group, and some knowledge of previously suggested phylogenies are both vital to good sampling. Breadth of sampling will depend on the rank of the taxa of interest. If only one or a few species are to be studied then the samples need to be taken from a range of habitats, over a wide geographical area. If a genus is to be investigated, as many species as possible should be analysed, and any infrageneric taxa should be fully represented in the sample. Many genera should be considered where a tribe is the object of the work, and also where an entire family is concerned. Another useful technique is to include some rather different taxon after the sample has been defined, to lend a perspective to the results. If all the species in a genus are being looked at, for example, it is very interesting to have just one or two species from a related genus included as a reference point. A small amount of extra work may be rewarded liberally.

A practical problem arises when the sample has been taken, and the materials are either all collected or still accumulating. This is the prime necessity for accurate identification. Reliance cannot be placed on the identifications of the material provided by collectors or curators of plant collections. The responsibility falls squarely on the chemotaxonomist. If identification cannot be verified, at least voucher specimens should be grown and preserved for later checking. Specialists in different groups will often identify material, if it is in reasonable condition. If the identification stage fails, or is omitted, correlating the chemical results with data from other fields, and with existing classifications seems pointless.

(b) Chemical techniques and pilot surveys

Not all chemical techniques are equally suited to a taxonomic project. Theoretically all chemical constituents of a plant can be assayed and compared for taxonomic purposes. The investigator has to choose what class of materials is likely to exhibit useful variation at the taxonomic level (i.e. family, genus or species, etc.) at which he has already elected to work. Relative values of different kinds of substance, in terms of taxonomic discontinuities, are reviewed in later chapters.

Once chosen, the distribution of the chemical material within the individual must be established. Are the compounds present in every organ or tissue? Where are they most concentrated? From which part of the plant may they most easily be extracted in the native state? A pilot survey must answer these and other questions in advance of the main investigation, as well as provide practice in technique.

Qualitative variation between different parts of the same plant is well established for many compounds, in many plants. Kloz *et al.*[271] showed how different plant organs varied in their protein content. Quantitative variations in content of particular substances among different parts of a plant are even better established. Alkaloids are often found in highest concentration in storage organs or flowers, though they are present everywhere in the plant at lower concentration.

Pilot surveys should also establish the seasonal and environmental fluctuation, if any, in the chemical content of plants. Iodine numbers of fats and oils are notoriously variable with temperature. The incidence of cyanogenesis in clover varies with changes of altitude[113] and soil moisture.[163] In his work on the taxonomic significance of turpentines in *Pinus*, Mirov[342] was careful to investigate the seasonal, geographical and environmental variations within species. Physiological forms of the same species are well known, and the possibility of this kind of variation must be fully explored.[375] Mirov demonstrated physiological forms in *Pinus ponderosa* by careful study of the turpentines from different individuals. Intraspecific chemical variation is well known in many higher plant groups (e.g. *Solanum*,[218] *Phaseolus*[270]), while chemotypes in lichen species are also widely recognized.[109,139] Intraspecific variation is obscured by bulking supplies of plant material from different individuals. Since such bulking is often the only way that sufficient material can be obtained for an analysis, it is useful to determine at the outset how much internal diversity characterizes each taxon. At the generic level, intra-taxon variation can be estimated by taking a good sample of species from each genus, not relying on just one representative species.

Whatever plant group is chosen for study, the chemical techniques which are to be applied to it must be well worked out in the pilot survey. Most methods will need modifications for use with particular plant material, if only in terms of how the chemical substances are best extracted. Popular chemotaxonomic techniques have a number of properties in common. Most of them fall into a category which might be termed 'biochemical short-cuts'. These are rapid analyses which provide a certain amount of information about the compounds studied, but not necessarily all that could be elicited given a longer time of analysis. Electrophoresis is a case in point. Molecules are fractionated on the criterion of net electrical charge, not on precise chemical configuration. In chromatography, materials are rapidly separated on the basis of their different partition coefficients. The chemical structure and precise identity of the separated molecules are not established. The *pattern* produced in electrophoretic and chromatographic analyses is usually sufficient evidence for taxonomic purposes. Other 'short-cuts' include the colour tests for lichen substances, and the comparison of protein extracts by serology and by fingerprinting (*q.v.*). All these methods give an acceptable return of taxonomic information for the time invested.

The 'short-cut' approach is anathema to some chemists and biochemists whose preference is for fully comprehensive analyses which finally identify each chemical constituent and establish its structure. Fully comprehensive analyses are not widely applied by taxonomists because they cannot afford time to look into the precise chemical details of each constituent which their analyses may show, unless it is vital for some taxonomic gain to be realized. Elaborate chemical analysis, involving careful study of the molecules present in plant extracts, is often a lengthy process, unless the molecules are comparatively simple, like phenols for example. The time taken for sequence analyses of protein extracts means that only one or two proteins, perhaps from only one or two species in a genus, or one or two genera in a family, might be studied in a project of reasonable duration. The taxonomist's respect for the diversity of the living world inhibits him from taking so sketchy a sample of it.

Another common feature of the popular chemotaxonomic methods is cheapness. All the short-cut techniques need only a small capital outlay, generate small maintenance costs, and usually require a single operator.

A third property of the ideal chemical technique is that it requires only small amounts of plant material to complete an analysis. This feature reduces the problem, mentioned previously, of accumulating and storing experimental stocks. All the short-cut methods are satisfactorily economical in this respect. Herbarium material can be used for some tests. Protein sequencing, even on the efficient micro-scale recently announced,[403] still requires kilogram quantities of plant material. Rarely will such quantities be available from an acceptably large sample of taxa at any level of the hierarchy.

A last feature of the most favoured chemotaxonomic methods is simplicity of operation. Only taxonomists will be motivated to carry out sustained taxonomic investigations, but they generally lack deep chemical knowledge, insight, and interest. This is why the team approach was recommended earlier. Sadly, teams are more ephemeral than taxonomic problems.

(c) Full analysis of all material

Pilot projects will have indicated the course to be followed in the main investigation, and will have reduced or removed technical difficulties. Once adopted, the plan of campaign should be adhered to with grim determination. All the customary safeguards of scientific experimentation, e.g. controls, replications and accurate records, apply to chemotaxonomic work. It is an attractive property of many chemical methods that the physical record of the results can be preserved. Protein spectra produced by electrophoresis, chromatograms and fingerprints can be kept and re-interpreted later, if desired.

Technical snags inevitably creep in during the course of the study. Typical cases involve refractory accessions of material which cannot be analysed properly due to low concentration of constituent chemicals, or interfering substances. Some accessions of seed normally fail to germinate at the critical stage. With a poor initial sample of material, incompleteness of data may vitiate the whole investigation.

It is not a good plan to exhaust all the plant material in the analysis. Some results may seem anomalous later, and warrant further checking. If the sample material is used up, it may be impossible to repeat the work. It is often awkward to duplicate material, even from the original source. Taxonomists normally retain some material for stock maintenance and voucher purposes.

(d) Interpretation and comparison of data

Assessment of taxonomic significance of chemical variation demands great circumspection. Full weight must be given to any environmental or developmental variation shown up in stage (b). Variation within the taxonomic boundary drawn in stage (a) is the principal item of concern, but plants beyond this boundary may also have been studied.

Chemotaxonomists will look for discontinuities in the chemical variation. Their size must be assessed in relation to the variation across the taxonomic boundary defined for the project. They can then be compared with discontinuities in all other kinds of available taxonomic evidence. If chemical facts are considered in isolation, their full meaning may not be understood.

Unfortunately much relevant taxonomic evidence is scattered and hard to assemble. This is especially true of archaeological and linguistic data. Though the chemotaxonomist may have gained a general appreciation of the taxonomic background in stage (a), he may feel reluctant to interpolate his conclusions into a taxonomic system with which he has limited experience. These two factors together may mean that chemical data are considered in terms of one established classification, which is thereby the sole basis for comparison, or that no taxonomic consideration is attempted. In the latter case, the result is a paper about comparative biochemistry, not chemotaxonomy. Chemically orientated chemotaxonomists can often profit from orthodox taxonomic advice at this stage of work.[16]

The final synthesis must draw attention to discrepancies between the chemical variation and the variation in other characters. Whatever the measure of agreement or disagreement, significant conclusions should be possible. If the chemical evidence conflicts markedly with other data, the taxonomy of the group concerned should be reconsidered. The chemical evidence should itself receive equally searching scrutiny. If only minor discrepancies occur in the match of chemical and other variation, then the classification is essentially confirmed. The minor areas of disagreement then become extremely interesting, and critical study may be rewarded by the development of a more useful or a more natural classification. Discrepancies should always be followed up by further work.

(e) Taxonomic changes

A principal reason for chemotaxonomic research is the need for new taxonomic evidence. Stages (a) to (c) provide the evidence, while stage (d) relates it to taxonomy. Taxonomic change is the natural outcome of greater knowledge of diversity. It demands a degree of technical skill which inhibits many chemotaxonomists from attempting it themselves. It would be ideal if the workers who produce chemical evidence would also make themselves taxonomically competent and responsible for integrating it fully into classification, not merely commenting on its possible taxonomic relevance. Though taxonomists can be employed to do this phase of the work it is an inefficient system. The greatest danger is that if this phase of the investigation is not completed, and necessary adjustments to taxonomy are not made, valuable evidence may be overlooked for years. At the very least, the chemotaxonomist should suggest what changes are to be made, in as strident a fashion as possible.[311]

(f) Phylogenetic interpretation

Though chemical data are not always fully integrated with other taxonomic evidence or used to improve classification, they are usually inspected for any bearing which they may have on phylogeny. Some workers scorn to consider evolutionary aspects of new knowledge, believing that phylogenetic speculation in the absence of fossil records is unworthy of scientific men. That is an extreme view. To discount the evidence of possible phylogenetic relationship revealed by careful analysis of chemical, or any other natural variation, is to reject much of value and interest. It must be confessed nevertheless that in the past some phylogeneticists have contributed less to science than to Romance. It is if anything more important to consider all available lines of evidence in phylogenetic study than in taxonomy. Chemical facts alone are unlikely to be satisfactory.

There are theoretically many ways in which modern plants may have been derived from previously existing ones. When comparative phenetic data are critically examined, it is soon obvious that reasonable hypotheses of phylogeny are few in number. The wider the basis for comparison, the lower this number becomes. Chemical facts may comprise important material favouring one of only two likely phylogenies. Though conclusive evidence may never be available, botanists want to know what the possibilities may be.

PART 2

The Sources of Evidence

4

Taxonomic Evidence from Amino Acid Distribution

Amino acids are best known as the building units from which proteins are synthesized. They are ubiquitous constituents of plant tissue. Considerable variation exists in the chemical structure of the compounds included in this category, and there is some difficulty in defining it satisfactorily. For taxonomic purposes it is important that chemical comparisons are made between strictly homologous groups of compounds.

α-Amino acids have a primary amino group ($-NH_2$) and a carboxyl group ($-COOH$) attached to the same carbon atom. Glycine (I) (Figure 4.1) is the simplest example. The amino group and carboxyl group are separately located in β-alanine (II). Additional amino groups may be present, as for instance in arginine (III). Some compounds have an imino group ($-NH$) instead of the amino group, and are most correctly called imino acids. In Fig. 4.1, proline (IV) and azetidine-2-carboxylic acid (V) are strictly α-imino acids. In practice, cyclic compounds with imino groups are included in the general definition of amino acids, for convenience. Of course, not all molecules with carboxyl and amino groups are classed as amino acids. Anthranilic acid (VI), with the amino group on an aromatic ring, is *not* an amino acid. By contrast, phenylalanine (VII) is classified as an amino acid, having an amino group on a side chain. Amides of amino acids, such as asparagine (VIII) and glutamine, are

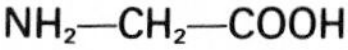

$$NH_2-CH_2-COOH$$

I   Glycine

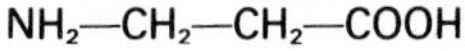

$$NH_2-CH_2-CH_2-COOH$$

II   β-Alanine

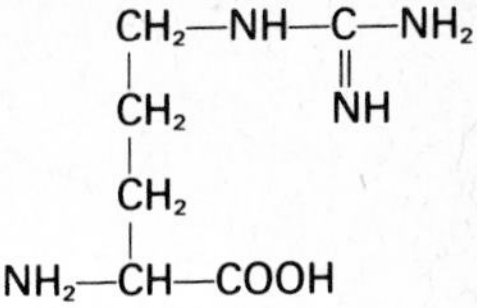

$$CH_2-NH-C-NH_2$$
$$\qquad\qquad\overset{\|}{NH}$$
$$CH_2$$
$$CH_2$$
$$NH_2-CH-COOH$$

III   Arginine

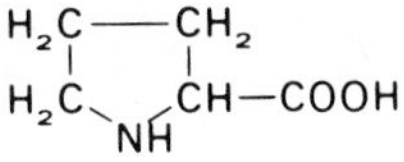

$$H_2C-CH_2$$
$$H_2C\underset{NH}{\diagdown}CH-COOH$$

IV   Proline

$$H_2C\overset{CH_2}{\diagup}CH-COOH$$
$$\qquad NH$$

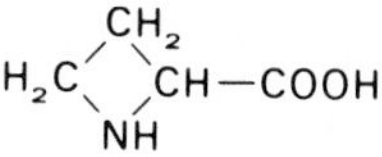

V   Azetidine-2-carboxylic acid

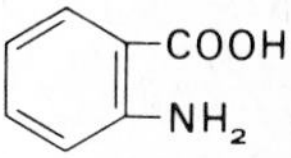

[benzene ring]—COOH
—NH_2

VI   Anthranilic acid

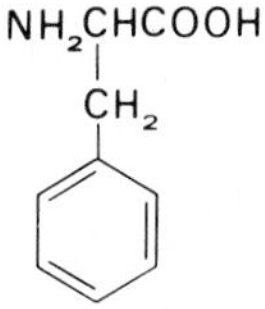

$$NH_2CHCOOH$$
$$CH_2$$
[benzene ring]

VII   Phenylalanine

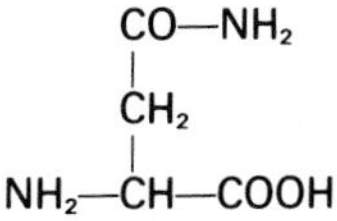

$$CO-NH_2$$
$$CH_2$$
$$NH_2-CH-COOH$$

VIII   Asparagine

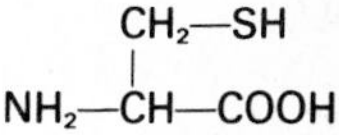

$$CH_2-SH$$
$$NH_2-CH-COOH$$

IX   Cysteine

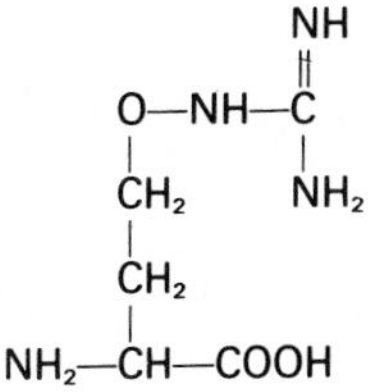

$$O-NH-\overset{\overset{NH}{\|}}{C}$$
$$CH_2\qquad NH_2$$
$$CH_2$$
$$NH_2-CH-COOH$$

X   Canavanine

$$HO-[indole ring]-CH_2-\overset{NH_2}{CH}$$
$$\qquad\qquad\qquad\qquad COOH$$

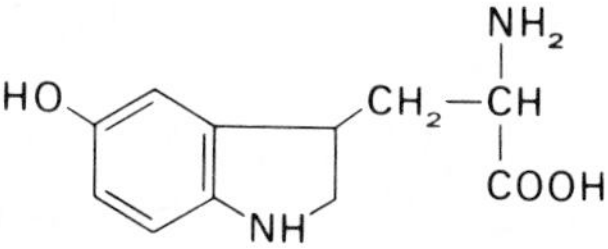

XI   5-Hydroxytryptophan

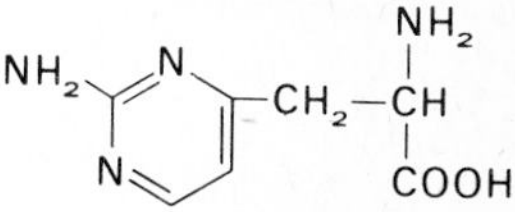

$$NH_2-[pyrimidine ring]-CH_2-\overset{NH_2}{CH}$$
$$\qquad\qquad\qquad\qquad\qquad COOH$$

XII   Lathyrine

Fig. 4.1 Structural formulae of same amino acids and related compounds.

normally considered together with the amino acids themselves. Some amino acids incorporate sulphur: cysteine (IX) is an example. Soluble nitrogenous compounds of plant origin which react with ninhydrin are often considered as a group. Most of those so far identified have proved to be amino acids. Amino acids are optically active. Many are known to occur naturally in both D- and L-enantiomorphs.

Amino acids have been known to occur in plant tissue since asparagine was isolated in 1806. Most of those discovered at first were found to be building units of proteins, and were released when proteins were hydrolysed. Table 4.1 lists these 'protein amino acids'.

Table 4.1   Amino acids derived from proteins.

Glycine	Glutamine
Alanine	Lysine
Valine	Hydroxylysine*
Leucine	Arginine
Isoleucine	Histidine
Serine	Phenylalanine
Threonine	Tyrosine
Cysteine	Diiodotyrosine*
Cystine	Dibromotyrosine*
Methionine	Thyroxine*
Aspartic acid	Tryptophan
Asparagine	Proline
Glutamic acid	Hydroxyproline

*Indicates not recorded from plant tissue.

'Non-protein amino acids' are those so far not found in combination in proteins, but there is always the possibility that some of them will eventually be found. The non-protein amino acids are by far the more numerous of the two groups, and more of them are discovered every year[165]. Before the Second World War, uncombined amino acids were discovered only if they had some notable peculiarity, such as high concentration in a plant, or marked physiological action. Thus the poisonous amino acid canavanine (X) was detected in *Canavalia* (Leguminosae) and found to be present in quantity.[266] Since the wartime advent of paper chromatography[97] numerous non-protein amino acids have been identified in plant tissue.[167] Estimates of the number now recognized vary from two to three hundred.

The recognition of the non-protein amino acids as a distinct group has had interesting consequences for plant taxonomy. If protein amino acids occur in most proteins, it follows that their distribution will be extremely wide, without discontinuities. Non-protein amino acids prove to have a much patchier distribution, and they are, of course, very numerous. Their discontinuous distribution attracts taxonomic attention. Protein amino acids are inevitably closely connected with the metabolic state of the tissue in which they occur. It is possible, *a priori*, that the non-protein amino acids lie in a biochemical 'backwater', less susceptible to rapid change. This stability would increase their taxonomic value.

Amino acids in general are relatively simple molecules. In some cases their biosynthesis has been fully worked out, and in the others elucidation of the pathway would be a reasonable proposition.

Both of these features add to the potential value of amino acids as taxonomic evidence. Biosynthetic knowledge is important because of the ever-present possibility that a compound may not be produced by the same method in two different plants. Only the pathway of synthesis is controlled by genes and therefore only the pathway is of taxonomic interest. If the presence of the compound does not guarantee the operation of the pathway, the taxonomic significance of its occurrence is greatly reduced. At least in the amino acids there is a possibility that the pathway can be checked comparatively quickly.

VARIATION IN AMINO ACID CONTENT

Chapter 3 stressed the need for full knowledge of variation in content and distribution of compounds within the plant. What is known of the variation of the amino acids?

Even though protein amino acids are universally present in plants, and in all parts of the plant, they may show considerable quantitative variation. In *Gilgiochloa indurata* (Gramineae) alanine is the main amino acid in leaf extracts, while in extracts of flowers and of seeds the main components were found to be asparagine and proline respectively.[395] There are similar earlier reports.[401] Some protein amino acids are found to be in unusually high concentration in certain plant groups. Members of the Rosaceae, for instance, are exceptionally rich in arginine.[401] Glutamine, glutamic acid and asparagine are normally the most concentrated simple amino compounds in plant tissue. The difficulty in assessing the significance of quantitative variation in protein amino acids is that the environmental and developmental components in the variation are confounded with any taxonomic component which may be present. It has been established that artificially induced mineral deficiencies are accompanied by changes in the relative and absolute quantities of amino acids in plants.[381,384,479] On the other hand, in a study of *Baptisia leucophaea* (Leguminosae),[12] the amino acid chromatograms of leaf, stem and flower extracts were similar from plants from two widely separated sites. Perhaps the nitrogen metabolism of legumes is less susceptible to variation due to environmental factors because of the availability of nitrogen from nodules.

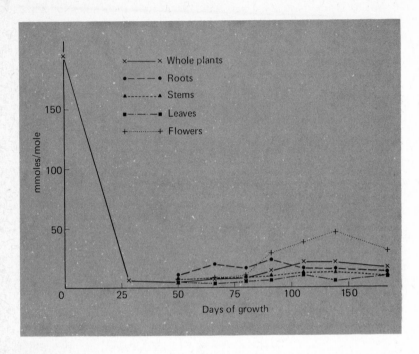

Fig. 4.2 Amount of L-3-carboxy-4-hydroxyphenylalanine + D-3-carboxy-4-hydroxyphenyl-glycine in relation to free α-amino-N in *Reseda odorata L.* (From Larsen.[291])

Variation in non-protein amino acid content is also partly dependent on the metabolic or developmental state of the tissue. Figure 4.2 shows data of Larsen[291] which indicate developmental variation for two non-protein amino acids in different organs of *Reseda* (Resedaceae). In the Leguminosae, non-protein amino acids are more concentrated in the seeds than in the vegetative parts.[40] For this reason much work on non-protein amino acids has involved comparison of seed extracts. Non-protein amino acids are at least not all universally present, and their distribution can be expressed on the presence or absence basis so beloved by taxonomists. It is nevertheless impossible to be certain of the absence of any compound. All that can be said is that a compound was not detectable in an extract, given the method of extraction and analysis employed. It is quite as difficult to assess the taxonomic significance of quantitative variation in non-protein amino acids as in protein amino acids.

FUNCTIONS OF NON-PROTEIN AMINO ACIDS

It might be thought that the function of a taxonomic character is quite irrelevant to consideration of its use and value. This old-fashioned idea should be firmly discounted. By considering the function of a character we may be able to perceive how it might be correlated with the functions, and therefore the incidence, of other characters, or character complexes. Functional analysis enlarges our knowledge of a character. In some instances it may even be possible to predict the total distribution of a character by relating its known or presumed function to the general biology of the plants known to possess it. Such an 'expected' distribution may then be compared with the 'observed' facts.

In the case of protein amino acids, the function is clear, and the reasons for variation in content and distribution are often understandable. As building-blocks of proteins, amino acids would be expected to vary in content and concentration during development, differentiation and senescence. Non-protein amino acids are less well understood. If they are by definition not protein monomers, what is their function in the plant? They are so common and so numerous that it seems unlikely that they have no functions, although it has been suggested that they may be stable end-products without significance, or that they arise accidentally through mistakes made by non-specific enzymes. If they are accidents or redundant end-products, it would appear that many plants are very inefficient, because they produce non-protein amino acids in such quantity. In the latex of *Euphorbia lathyrus* 3,4-dihydroxyphenyl-alanine comprises 2% of the fresh weight.[350] It seems odd that natural selection should have overlooked such gross wastefulness, if that is what it is.

There are so many non-protein amino acids, of such great structural diversity, that it is natural to expect different views on their possible function. It is likely that no single function exists for so diverse a group of molecules. If only a few cases has a function been established for a non-protein amino acid.

It is known that some non-protein amino acids are intermediates in the synthesis or breakdown of protein amino acids. Thus saccharopine was found to be an intermediate in the biosynthesis of lysine by yeast[425]. Many non-protein amino acids are certainly important in the storage and transport of soluble nitrogen. Canavanine (X), so far believed to be restricted to the Leguminosae,[41] contains four nitrogen atoms. It disappears from the seed rapidly during germination. In storage tissues, non-protein amino acids are often present in vast quantities, for example N-acetyl-ornithine in tubers of *Corydalis ochotensis* (Fumariaceae).[318] Miller *et al.*[339] showed that 3-(3-carboxyl-4-hydroxyphenyl)alanine accounts for 0.8% of the total seed nitrogen in *Lunaria annua* (Cruciferae). In groundnuts (*Arachis hypogaea*, Leguminosae), γ-methylene-glutamine has been shown to be the main form of transported nitrogen.[164]

Bell and his co-workers have recently examined the possibility that high concentrations of non-protein amino acids in seeds may confer protection from insect attack. Together with entomologists he has studied the effect of canavanine and 5-hydroxytryptophan (XI) on the larvae of the southern armyworm (*Prodenia eridania*).[396] Both acids when incorporated in diets repelled the larvae at the concentrations in which they occur in certain seeds, which are normally not attacked by the armyworm. The acids caused 100% mortality within three days. Seed powders had similar but less striking effects, causing some mortality but considerable deformity in pupae and adults. The *modus operandi* is presumably that these amino acids are used as homologues for protein amino acids in development sequences, with dire effects. It is highly likely that selection would favour plants containing natural insecticides or materials inhibiting damage by rodents or microorganisms. Rao *et al.*[393] showed that homoarginine inhibited bacterial growth. Perhaps non-protein amino acids are common because of these interesting properties.

A final observation on function may be of even greater significance. Simola demonstrated prevention of germination of foreign pollen by non-protein amino acids occurring in stylar tissue.[435] These acids may therefore be implicated in interspecific isolating mechanisms.

Non-protein amino acids hence appear to have a number of possible functions in plants. It is reasonable to expect that different plants use different non-protein amino acids for these purposes, and perhaps that, in some instances, related plants use the same or similar ones.

TAXONOMIC VALUE OF AMINO ACID STUDIES

Chemotaxonomic studies of amino acids in plants date back to the nineteen-fifties. Reuter identified the 'principal amino acids' (*Hauptaminosauren*) in about fifty families, and thought they might have some systematic significance.[401] Most subsequent work has concentrated on incidence of non-protein amino acids, which both Reuter and later workers have consistently found to vary in different plant taxa. The great interest shown by biochemists in the non-protein amino acids is due partly to their taxonomic potential and partly to a wish to understand their biosynthesis and function.

Bell has made interesting studies on the non-protein amino acids of Leguminosae.[39,41] This family is characterized by unusually high concentrations of these substances in the seeds. Seeds have the merit of being a stable developmental stage on which to base taxonomic comparisons. In both *Lathyrus* and *Vicia*, Bell has been able to construct intriguing infrageneric classifications using biochemical data. Details of his scheme for *Lathyrus* are given in Fig. 4.3. He recognized seven infrageneric groups, each characterized by a different amino acid, or group of associated amino acids.[41] The diagram shows also his ideas on how the genes for production of the amino acids may be distributed in the genus.

Tschiersch and Hanelt (1967) recognized four groups in *Vicia* on the basis of the occurrences of canavanine, β-cyanoalanine, unidentified amino acids A, B and C, and the replacement of non-protein amino acids by high concentrations of arginine.[478] The scheme appears in Fig. 4.4. These groups fit fairly well with classifications founded on morphological and cytological criteria, but the discrepancies warrant further study.

Results of work on the amino acids of *Acacia* (Leguminosae)[430] showed that the amino acid content of seeds in the section Gummiferae was so consistently and clearly different from that in the other sections that it may be possible to assign species to the section solely by reference to the amino acid character. In this example the amino acid properties seem to have a high predictive value, and thus to be just the kind of evidence most sought by taxonomists.

Another type of amino acid evidence is not based on more or less constant associations of different acids, but on the restricted distribution of single ones. Canavanine has not been found outside subfamily Lotoideae of the Leguminosae, despite diligent searches over a reasonable period.[38,53,481] Genes for the production of this amino acid therefore appear to be restricted to this plant group, which is more strongly established by this chemical evidence even

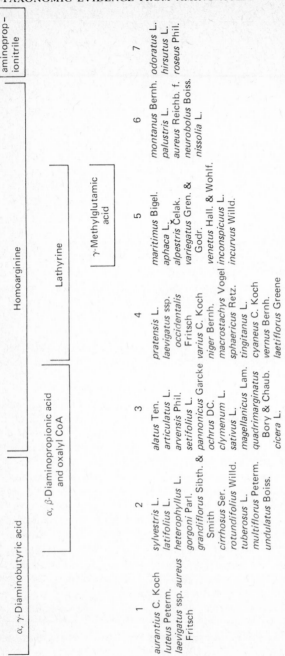

Fig. 4.3 Suggested relationship between gene distribution and amino acid patterns in *Lathyrus*. The groups shown are characterized by the following uncommon amino acids in their seeds. 1. α,γ-diaminobutyric acid; 2. α,γ-diaminobutyric acid and the four oxalyl derivatives of that acid and α,β-diaminopropionic acid; 3. homoarginine and the two oxalyl derivatives of α,β-diaminopropionic acid; 4. homoarginine and lathyrine; 5. homoarginine, lathyrine and γ-methylglutamic acid; 6. homoarginine; 7. γ-glutamyl-β-aminopropionitrile. (From Bell.[40])

GENES CONTROLLING SYNTHESIS OF

α,γ-Diaminobutyric acid

α,β-Diaminopropionic acid and oxalyl CoA

Homoarginine

Lathyrine

γ-Methylglutamic acid

γ-Glutamyl-β-aminopropionitrile

1	2	3	4	5	6	7
aurantius C. Koch	*sylvestris* L.	*alatus* Ten.	*pratensis* L.	*maritimus* Bigel.	*montanus* Bernh.	*odoratus* L.
luteus Peterm.	*latifolius* L.	*articulatus* L.	*laevigatus* ssp.	*aphaca* L.	*palustris* L.	*hirsutus* L.
laevigatus ssp. *aureus* Fritsch	*heterophyllus* L.	*arvensis* Phil.	*occidentalis* Fritsch	*alpestris* Čelak.	*aureus* Reichb. f.	*roseus* Phil.
	gorgoni Parl.	*setifolius* L.	*varius* C. Koch	*variegatus* Gren. & Godr.	*neurobolus* Boiss.	
	grandiflorus Sibth. & Smith	*pannonicus* Garcke	*niger* Bernh.	*venetus* Hall. & Wohlf.	*nissolia* L.	
	cirrhosus Ser.	*ochrus* DC.	*macrostachys* Vogel	*inconspicuus* L.		
	rotundifolius Willd.	*clymenum* L.	*sphaericus* Retz.	*incurvus* Willd.		
	tuberosus L.	*sativus* L.	*tingitanus* L.			
	multiflorus Peterm.	*magellanicus* Lam.	*cyaneus* C. Koch			
	undulatus Boiss.	*quadrimarginatus* Bory & Chaub.	*vernus* Bernh.			
		cicera L.	*laetiflorus* Greene			

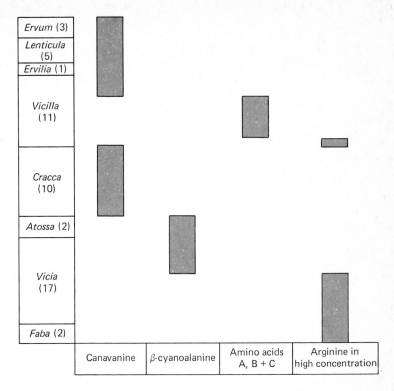

Fig. 4.4 Relationship between biochemical groups and taxonomic sections in *Vicia*. (From Tschiersch and Hanelt.[478])

though only 60% of the species so far examined prove to contain it. The canavanine story exemplifies the difficulty of establishing the absence of a compound beyond doubt. Birdsong *et al.*, commenting on the phylogeny of the Leguminosae, regarded presence of canavanine as an advanced character because it was not known from the primitive tribes Sophoreae and Podalyrieae.[53] It has subsequently been found in both of these tribes.[41] Its presence may equally well be a primitive character. Another famous case of restricted distribution is that of azetidine-2-carboxylic acid, shown to characterize many genera of the related families Liliaceae, Amaryllidaceae and Agavaceae.[170] It has since been reported in the legumes *Delonix* and *Peltophorum*.[460] Perhaps its abundance in the Lilialean families is not without some taxonomic significance nonetheless.

Some non-protein amino acids have even more restricted distributions. Lathyrine (XII) has so far been found only within *Lathyrus*,[41] so the distribution helps us to support the present circumscription of this genus.

There are as many examples of non-protein amino acids which have a very wide distribution, and which occur in plants which are highly unlikely to be closely related. Acetyl ornithine was identified[401] as the 'principal amino acid' in subfamily Fumarioideae of the Fumariaceae but was then found in a number of grasses.[166] There is also a report of it in the fern *Asplenium*.[491] These plant groups are only distantly related.

Occurrence of an amino acid may therefore indicate one of two things. Firstly, it may be that the species containing it are fairly closely related, synthesizing the amino acid in the same fashion. Lathyrine is probably formed in the same way in those species of *Lathyrus* which accumulate it. Secondly, the occurrence may simply mean that different plants can synthesize the same amino acid, perhaps by different pathways. This is probably the case with acetyl ornithine in ferns and grasses. In the latter case, the predictive value of the occurrence of the amino acid is very low.

Which of these two situations exists can be determined only by biochemical study of the method of synthesis. Until the pathways are known there will always be uncertainty about the taxonomic meaning of single amino acid characters, except in the extreme cases such as lathyrine distribution. Biosynthetic studies can be revealing. Ressler showed that the canavanine-containing species of *Vicia* could be divided into those which accumulated γ-glutamyl-β-cyanoalanine, and those which did not.[400] It was later demonstrated that the compound was produced in both groups.[169] Different levels of activity of a nitrilase enzyme were responsible for the rapid conversion of γ-glutamyl-β-cyanoalanine to asparagine in one case, but not the other. This kind of evidence will eventually show to what extent single amino acid characters are fundamental and taxonomically useful.

If species share a number of unusual non-protein amino acids, which are not all necessary components of a single pathway, i.e. which are genetically independent, it is more likely that the species are of common ancestry. In such cases the taxonomic value of the amino acid evidence is high.

All evidence from amino acid distribution, whether of single types or of acids in association, depends for its taxonomic value on the accuracy and refinement of the analytical techniques used. Tiny quantities of amino acids may not be detectable in the fairly small samples which chemotaxonomists apply to their chromatograms and columns. Fowden analysed amino acid fractions from bulk quantities of sugar beet (*Beta vulgaris,* Chenopodiaceae), which were available as a by-product of commercial processing.[168] He found many non-protein amino acids present which would have gone undetected in experiments on the laboratory scale. Among them was azetidine-2-carboxylic acid!

The unusual amino acids may therefore not be so rare after all. Genes for their production are perhaps widespread, but may be fully operative only in certain species. Nevertheless, 'quirks' of metabolism which result in accumulation of non-protein amino acids, or of several of these, presumably have some kind of genetic basis which constitutes a useful taxonomic character. All hinges on how and why the genes are fully 'switched on' in some species and not in others. Perhaps the distant outline of a 'developmental chemotaxonomy' can be discerned in the amino acid field. Certainly there is much yet to be established about the relevance of amino acid distribution to taxonomy. As a source of evidence it can sometimes be clearly significant[430] whereas Reddi and Phipps stigmatized it as 'taxonomic noise'.[395]

5

Evidence from Phenolics and Betalains

No category of small molecule which has been examined from a taxonomic viewpoint has proved so popular as that of the phenolic compounds. The main reason for this popularity is that they are quickly and simply extracted from plant material, easily separated by paper chromatography, and fairly readily identified by location reagents. Plant phenolics are so numerous and varied that it is difficult for the beginner to orientate himself among the different kinds which have been recognized. For this reason a brief review of the major classes of phenolic molecules is offered below. It is not at all complete, and for detailed information monographs on the chemistry of these compounds should be studied.[202,204,402]

Rather little was known about phenolics until paper chromatography was applied to them. It was then soon clear that in plants they are present in considerable numbers, diversity, and quantities, although no single compound is found everywhere, as are the protein amino acids for example. The phenolic compounds of animals are fewer and less diverse, but they have well-established physiological functions. In plants the functions of the majority of phenolics are less obvious.

CHEMICAL STRUCTURE OF PHENOLICS

Phenolics derive their name from the simplest member, phenol (Fig. 5.1), from which many more complex types can be derived

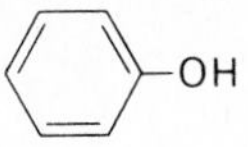

I Phenol 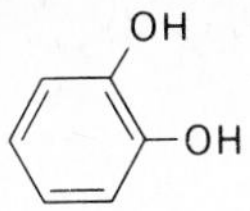　　　　　II Catechol 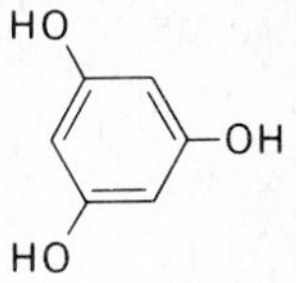　　　　　III Phloroglucinol

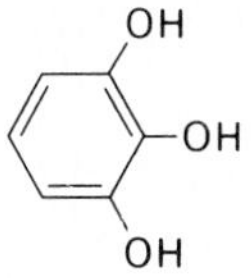

IV Pyrogallol 　　　　V Hydroquinone 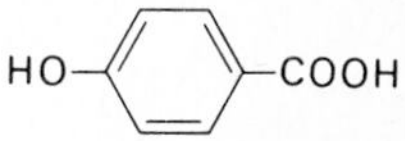　　　VI p-Hydroxybenzoic acid

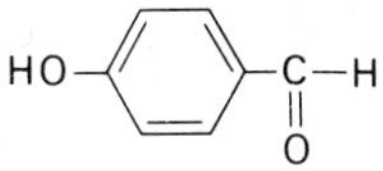

VII p-Hydroxybenzaldehyde 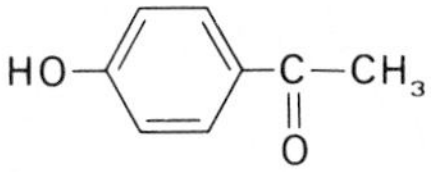　VIII p-Hydroxyacetophenone 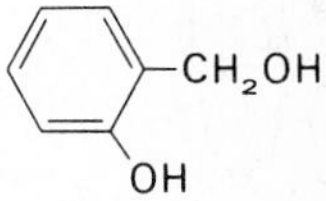　IX Salicyl alcohol

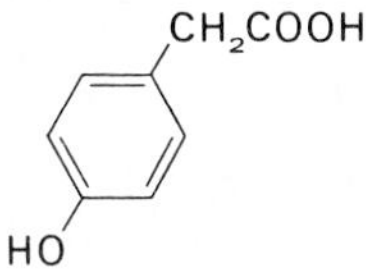

X 4-Hydroxyphenylacetic acid 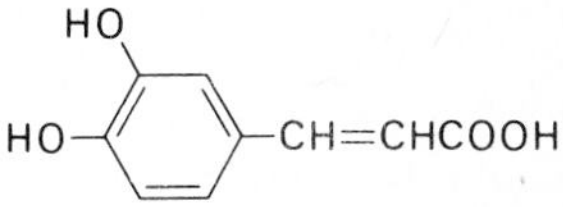　　　XI Caffeic acid

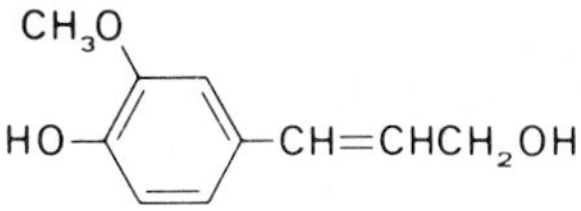

XII Coniferyl alcohol

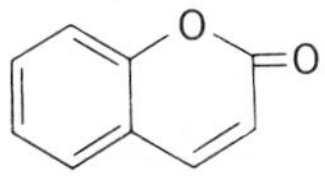

XIII Coumarin 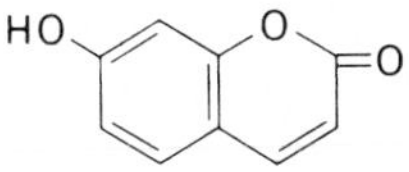　　　　XIV Umbelliferone 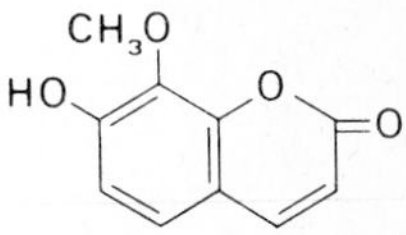　　　XV Scopoletin

Fig. 5.1 Simple phenolics.

structurally, by substitution, polymerization or combination. All phenolics possess an aromatic ring with a hydroxyl substituent. Harborne defines them very broadly as 'all natural substances with a free or masked phenolic function'.[202] Many substances which are phenolic in nature are customarily excluded from the category as used in chemotaxonomic literature. Among these may be mentioned the amino acids tyrosine and dihydroxyphenyl-alanine, and other nitrogen-containing compounds such as the betalains. From chemical studies completed so far, it seems likely that the pathways leading to the synthesis of the phenolics, so defined, are similar in a wide range of plants, and that the diverse types of molecule are inter-related biosynthetically. Metabolic interconvertibility of phenolics helps to demonstrate the homogeneity of a group in which the diversity may at first appear confusing.

Simple phenols

Most of the simple phenols are not common in plant tissue. Phenol (I) occurs in needles and in cones of *Pinus sylvestris* (Pinaceae) and also in other scattered groups of plants (e.g. in tobacco and certain lichens). Catechol (II), phloroglucinol (III) and pyrogallol (IV) are similarly sporadic in distribution. There is not systematic significance in any of these occurrences. Hydroquinone (V) on the other hand, is quite widespread, and in the Rosaceae it seems to be confined to the related genera *Pyrus* and *Docynia*.

Derivatives of simple phenols, with short or long side-chains, are known to occur naturally in the form of acids, aldehydes, ketones or alcohols. These are exemplified in Fig. 5.1 by *p*-hydroxy-benzoic acid (VI), *p*-hydroxybenzaldehyde (VII), *p*-hydroxyaceto-phenone (VIII), salicyl alcohol (IX), and 4-hydroxyphenylacetic acid (X).

Cinnamic acids, such as caffeic acid (XI), are very common in plants as are some of their derivative alcohols, e.g. coniferyl alcohol (XII), which is found in cambial sap. Dimers of the cinnamic acids or their derivatives are called **lignans**.

Coumarins are another group of natural phenolics. Coumarin itself (XIII) is a widely distributed substance, which gives the supposedly characteristic smell of new-mown hay to plants in about thirty angiosperm families. This feature can sometimes be useful in identification. For example, *Anthoxanthum odoratum*, the sweet vernal grass, can be recognized vegetatively by the smell of coumarin arising from the crushed foliage. Umbelliferone (XIV) is widespread in the Umbelliferae, but also occurs elsewhere. Scopoletin

(XV), though common in solanaceous plants, is by no means restricted to that family.

Several groups of simple phenols have not been mentioned here, for example the isocoumarins and chromones. For accounts of their taxonomic significance see Harborne and Simmonds.[211]

Flavonoid compounds

The phenolic molecules most often studied in chemotaxonomy fall into a general class known as the flavonoids. They are the largest group of naturally occurring phenols. All have the characteristic flavonoid C_{15} nucleus (Fig. 5.2, XVI) which seems to be synthesized in a uniform fashion in a wide range of plants. The 'A' benzene ring arises by a condensation of acetate units, while the 'B' benzene ring is a product of the normal pathway of phenolic biosynthesis (the shikimic acid pathway). The two benzene rings are joined by a C_3 structure which may be open or closed. The flavonoid nucleus is normally linked to a sugar, so forming a water-soluble glycoside. Most flavonoids are found in the vacuole of the plant cell.

Structural formulae for some of the commoner types of flavonoid compound are assembled together in Fig. 5.2.

(a) Flavones

Flavone is the root from which the word flavonoid is derived. The commonest flavones are apigenin and luteolin (XVII and XVIII) which are widespread in the leaves and flowers of angiosperms. Flavone itself (XIX) is rarer, but occurs as a white mealy farina on the leaves and stems of certain species of *Primula*.

(b) Flavanones

Flavanones differ from flavones in lacking the double bond in the 2,3-position. Though quite widespread they are especially common in particular families, such as the Rosaceae, Rutaceae, Leguminosae and Compositae. They are also found in the fern family Polypodiaceae and in the Pinaceae. Naringenin (XX) is quite common. Pinocembrin (XXI) is found in *Pinus*.

(c) Isoflavones and isoflavonoids

Isoflavones are isomeric with flavones, having the B ring attached at the 3 position instead of the 2 position. Isoflavonoids have the 2,3-double bond reduced, so that they are related to isoflavones in the same way that flavanones are related to flavones.

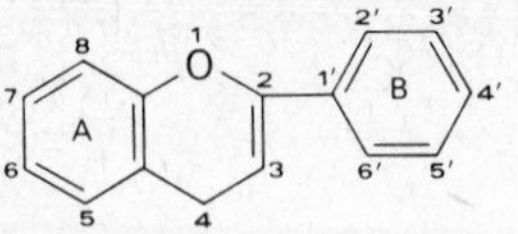

XVI   The flavonoid nucleus

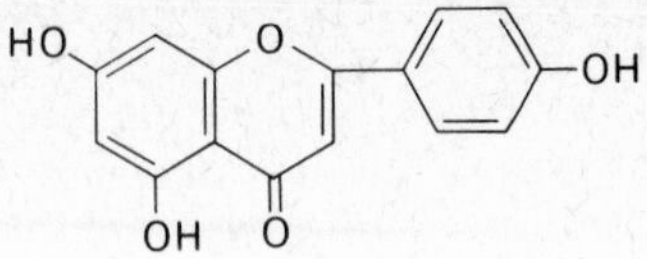

XVII   Apigenin (a flavone)

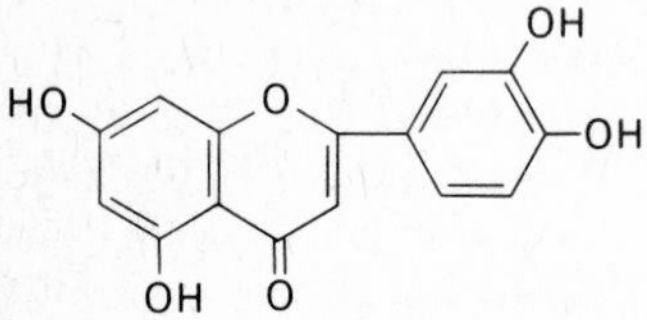

XVIII   Luteolin (a flavone)

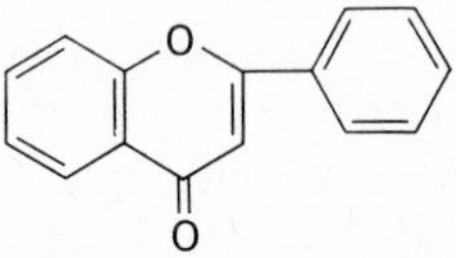

XIX   Flavone (a flavone)

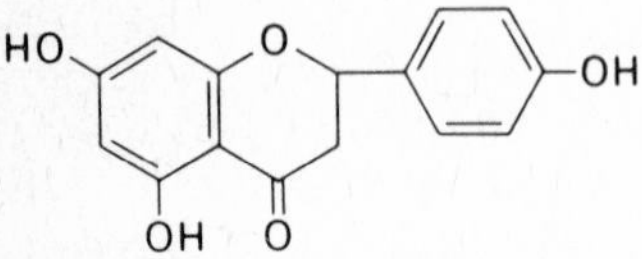

XX   Naringenin (a flavanone)

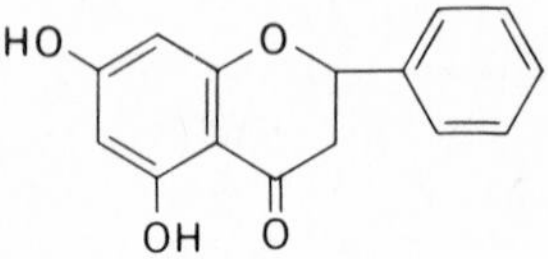

XXI   Pinocembrin (a flavanone)

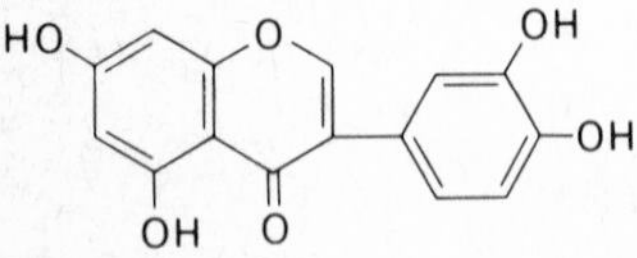

XXII   Orobol (an isoflavone)

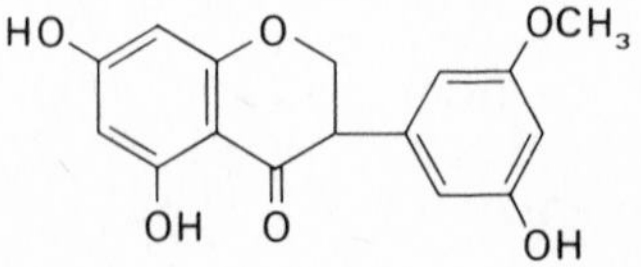

XXIII   Ferreirin (an isoflavonoid)

Fig. 5.2   Types of flavonoid.

XXIV   Kaempferol (a flavonol)

XXV   Cyanidin (an anthocyanidin)

XXVI   Butein (a chalcone)

XXVII   Sulphuretin (an aurone)

XXVIII   Phloretin (a dihydrochalcone)

XXIX   Amentoflavone (a biflavonyl)

Fig. 5.2   *continued*

Isoflavones are most characteristic of subfamily Lotoideae of Leguminosae, though a few have been found elsewhere. Orobol (XXII) is a typical isoflavone. Ferreirin (XXIII) is a simple isoflavonoid from *Ferreira* (Leguminosae). Isoflavonoids are also best known from Leguminosae.

(d) Flavonols

These very common compounds differ from flavones in having a 3-hydroxyl substituent. Numerous flavonols have been identified from plant tissue: kaempferol (XXIV), quercetin and myricetin are by far the commonest.

(e) Anthocyanidins

These materials are normally found as the aglycone (non-sugar moeity) of naturally occurring glycosides with glucose, galactose, arabinose and other mono- and di-saccharide sugars. In other cases the anthocyanidin may be attached to an organic acid (acyl group) such as *p*-hydroxybenzoic acid (VI). Acid hydrolysis of the colourless glycosides, often called leuco-anthocyanins, releases the coloured anthocyanidin aglycone. Unlike all the flavonoids so far considered the anthocyanidins lack the carbonyl group at position 4. Anthocyanidins include most of the natural red and blue pigments. The other flavonoids are mostly pale yellow, cream or colourless ('anthoxanthins').

Cyanidin (XXV), delphinidin and pelargonidin are the three commonest anthocyanidins. They occur in leaves and flowers of most plants. Though only a few anthocyanidins are known, there is much diversity owing to variation in the glycosides which they can form.

(f) Chalcones and aurones

There are the 'anthochlor' pigments—yellow flower pigments which turn orange-red in the presence of ammonia. There is little structural variation in the group, which can be exemplified by the chalcone butein (XXVI) and the aurone sulphuretin (XXVII). Reduction of the double bond in a chalcone gives rise to a dihydrochalcone, a few of which have been found in nature. Phloretin (XXVIII) occurs as the glycoside phloridzin in several species of *Malus* (Rosaceae). In chalcones and dihydrochalcones the heterocyclic C_3 ring is open.

(g) Biflavonyls

Biflavonyls are dimers of the flavone apigenin (XVII). Amentoflavone (XXIX) is the simplest member. It is interesting that biflavonyls seem to be especially common in the gymnosperms.[22]

VARIATION IN PHENOLIC CONTENT

Phenolic constituents are known from the leaves, flowers and fruits of plants. Many complex polyphenols, such as tannins, occur in the bark of trees. Lignins are also phenolic in nature and because of this it is to be expected that some variation in phenolic content will be connected with the physiology of lignification.[78]

Differences in the phenolic content of different plant organs have often been reported. While herbaceous members of the Geraniaceae lack leuco-anthocyanins in the leaves, they are consistently present in the seeds.[34] Bate-Smith has stressed that the incidence of the synthetic process producing leuco-anthocyanins is the important taxonomic character, not merely the presence or absence of the product. Presumably the process can be locally suppressed in some parts of the plant.

Galston has recorded qualitative and quantitative changes in flavonoid content in peas in relation to light and growth.[176] Activation of phytochrome by red light is accompanied by increased synthesis of flavonoids in etiolated peas. Mechanical stimulation of pea tendrils reduced the amount of quercetin which they contained.

Most chemotaxonomic work on phenolics has involved extracts of vegetative tissues because of the great variations which have long been known in the phenolic content of flowers. The flower pigments, which are usually anthocyanins and anthoxanthins, have been shown to be under genetic control. Trivial genetic changes can have considerable effects on them. Single genes regulating the production of different pigments were first demonstrated by Moncrieff.[429] In *Pelargonium zonale*, she showed that a dominant allele controlled the production of malvidin glycoside in the petals. Homozygous recessive plants formed only pelargonidin glycoside. Since then there have been many studies of the genetics of flower pigmentation, in a diversity of plants.[6] The work of Alston and Turner and their collaborators on the hybrids of *Baptisia* (Leguminosae), showing phenolic patterns in hybrids intermediate between the parental patterns, also demonstrates the inheritance of phenolic characters.[9]

It would be wrong to hold that flower colours are inevitably poor taxonomic markers because of the simplicity of their genetic control. Most of the genetic work has been done on cultivars where flower colour variations have been artifically selected. Much greater stability is found in wild populations. In any case the flower colour may often be a complex character, involving genes which control the pH of the vacuolar sap. The colour of anthocyanins varies with pH.

Not all variation in pigment production is genetic in origin. Seedlings of red cabbage developed more anthocyanin between 20°–30°C. than below 10°C.[173] In the yellow-flowered *Dahlia variabilis*, a period of treatment at 30°C changes the anthocyanin content of unopened buds, and the petals emerge red.[213] It is a common observation that increased anthocyanin production often accompanies nutrient deficiencies, particularly of nitrogen and phosphorus.

FUNCTIONS OF PHENOLIC COMPOUNDS

Plant phenolics used to be regarded as inert end products of metabolism,[28] but radioactive tracer techniques show that they are capable of considerable interconversion. They are common in all higher plants and many of the lower groups. It seems unlikely that they have no function, even though they are not involved in the fundamental metabolic processes. They are found, in varying quantities, in most tissues of the plant.

The functions of the flower pigments in pollination are fairly clear: insect and bird pollinators are attracted by coloured petals. There has been a tendency, in the evolution of flower pigments of insect-pollinated plants, towards bluer and more stable colours.[201]

Some phenolics may have no other function than to be intermediates in the biosynthesis of more complex plant products. Coniferyl alcohol (XII) is probably involved in the production of lignins. Gallic acid is a precursor for hydrolysable tannins,[78] while Hillis[238] considered that leuco-anthocyanins polymerized into the condensed tannins of *Eucalyptus*. Polyphenols have been produced by polymerizing leuco-delphinidin with an oak bark polyphenol oxidase.[216] The resulting material had the same absorption spectrum as natural oak bark phlobatannin.

Phenolic glycosides, which are more soluble than the parent phenolic aglycones, may serve as a means of transport of the elaborated phenolic residues about the plant. Possibly the glycosides are a more stable form in which phenolics may be stored. Hillis showed that anthocyanidins were synthesized in leaf tips of *Eucalyptus* and translocated as glycosides down the phloem into the heartwood.[237]

Some phenolics may be implicated in growth and development. Work on pea flavonoids[176] showed that changes in content were rapid enough to be causally related to growth changes. Decreased growth of internodes was related to increased synthesis of kaempferol conjugates. These are known to be co-factors for the oxidative destruction of indole acetic acid (IAA). In peach buds the flavanone naringenin (XX) preserves dormancy by activating IAA oxidase.[226]

Moewus[343] showed that the sex of algal gametes was determined by certain flavonoids. Cross-incompatibility of two varieties of *Forsythia* is related to specific flavonoids in the pollen of each.[285]

The notion that plant phenolics often have the function of deterring would-be predators seems well supported. Bate-Smith comments on the unpleasant astringency of developing pears and persimmons.[31] The taste is due to the presence of tannins in the unripe fruits. When the seeds are fully developed, it is selectively advantageous that the fruit be edible and attractive. Presumably the high tannin concentrations in young fruits are a 'device' which discourages premature seed dispersal. Tannins combine with skin proteins and render them resistant to putrefaction; hence their value in the leather industry. The same kind of effect on proteins of living animal tissue, of the mouth and the alimentary tract, usefully reduces the palatability and digestibility of the plant tissue.

The action of tannins extends to viruses. Allard showed inhibition of tobacco mosaic virus by tannic acid.[4] Inhibition of mechanical transmission of virus has been demonstrated, apparently caused by a reaction between the virus and a polyphenol.[82] Cruickshank and Perrin[108] review the evidence for general pathological functions of the plant phenolics. It seems probable that many phenolics inhibit the germination of fungal spores, and may also be implicated in the host reactions which contain infections which have already begun. Substances which inhibit further development of fungus in hypersensitive host tissue have been defined as **phytoalexins**[353]. Ingham[247] gives a recent review of them. Possibly some of the normal phenolics of plant tissue may act as precursors for phytoalexins, such as pisatin in peas. Pisatin (XXX) is accumulated by pea tissue in the presence of a wide range of fungal species.

XXX   Pisatin

Functions of phenols in wood seem to be connected with decay resistance. Phenolic compounds are particularly concentrated in the heartwood. Most of then have been shown to have antifungal properties. A survey of conifer heartwood extracts showed that those from decay resistant species had greater fungistatic activity.[398]

Muller and Chou[352] discuss a role of secreted phenols as water soluble phytotoxins, preventing establishment of competing vegetation.

Phenolics thus have a wide range of possible functions in plants. Those which are concerned with more basic processes of growth and development may be found to occur widely. Those involved with protection may be as varied as the environmental and ecological pressures which they may help to minimize.

TAXONOMIC VALUE OF PHENOLIC STUDIES

Early applications of evidence from studies on phenolics to taxonomic problems are found in the work of Bate-Smith.[27,28,30] He established background knowledge of the distribution of the commoner plant phenolics. His list of these appears in Table 5.1. Abandoning the flower pigments as too variable, he concentrated on the phenolics of seeds and vegetative tissues. One of his early findings was that presence of leuco-anthocyanins was correlated with the woodiness of the plants. Over 60% of 'woody families' examined contained leuco-anthocyanins, whereas they were detected in only 15% of 'herbaceous families'. Exceptions to the general rule included the herbaceous family Primulaceae, which was rich in leuco-anthocyanins, and the arboreal members of the Oleaceae and Scrophulariaceae, which lacked them completely. A similar but less striking correlation was shown between woody habit and the presence of flavonols. Methoxycinnamic acids were shown to be correlated with the herbaceous habit. These correlations seem merely to reflect the difference in physiology between woody and herbaceous plants. Despite Hutchinson's recognition of two great plant groups, the woody Lignosae and the herbaceous Herbaceae, it is unlikely that presence or absence of woodiness will ever be an acceptable basis for a natural classification.

Bate-Smith also demonstrated the amazing richness of phenolic variation in plants. It is the discontinuous distribution of rarer phenolics and the correlated occurrences or absences of commoner ones which offer potentially valuable evidence to a taxonomist. Ellagic acid (Table 5.1) is absent from all members of subfamily

Table 5.1 The commoner phenolic constituents of plants. (After Bate-Smith.[28])

	Leuco-anthocyanins	Flavonols	Hydroxy-acids
Trihydroxy	Leuco-delphinidin	Myricetin	Ellagic acid (Replaces trihydroxy-acid. Not found in monocots.)
Dihydroxy	Leuco-cyanidin	Quercetin	Caffeic acid
Monohydroxy	(Monohydroxy-representative is rare)	Kaempferol	p-Coumaric acid

Rosoideae of Rosaceae, except for the single tribe Kerrieae.[29] In the genus *Iris*, Bate-Smith compared five phenolic characters of species in seven different sections.[28] Phenolic variation matched the sectional classification quite well, but *Iris flavissima*, originally placed in section *Pogoniris*, resembled species of section *Regelia* in terms of phenolic evidence. The chromosome number has also been found to support transference of *Iris flavissima* to *Regelia*, in which section it is now normally listed. In *Iris*, leuco-anthocyanins were almost completely restricted to the single section *Apogon*.

Table 5.2   Distribution of flavonoids in the Eucryphiaceae (After Bate-Smith, Davenport and Harborne.[33])

| | Distribution in *Eucryphia* | | | | |
| | South America | | Australasia | | |
	cordifolia	*glutinosa*	*moorei*	*milliganii*	*lucida*
Caryatin	+	+	−	−	−
Az 3-galactoside	−	+	−	−	−
Az 3-diglucoside	+	+	−	−	−
Az 3-arabinosylgalactoside	+	−	−	−	−
Azaleatin (Az)	+	+	−	−	−
Unidentified flavonone (?)	+	+	−	−	−
Quercetin 3-galactoside	+	+	−	+	−
Quercetin 3-rhamnoside	+	+	−	−	−
Quercetin 3-diglycoside	+	+	−	−	−
Quercetin 3-triglycoside	−	−	+	−	−
Dihydroquercetin 3-glycoside(s)	−	−	−	+	−
Kaempferol 3,7-dimethyl ether	−	−	−	−	+
Cordifolia constituent	+	−	−	−	−
Unidentified flavan	+	+	−	−	−

Even widespread phenolic types such as leuco-anthocyanins, phenolic acids and flavonols may therefore have taxonomic value in specific cases. Nevertheless, it seems probable that greater taxonomic interest will attach to the occurrences and distribution of rare phenolic aglycones and glycosides. Considering the flavonoid glycosides in leaves of all five known members of Eucryphiaceae (Table 5.2), it was found easy to distinguish the South American from the Australasian species, though all five species are morphologically very similar.[33]

The rare glycoside luteolin-5-glucoside (XXXI) has been found in the umbellifer genera *Chaetosciadium* and *Torilis*.[205]

XXXI   Luteolin-5-glucoside

These genera appeared superficially different in the key characters of fruit morphology. The new biochemical evidence of similarity between them correlates with indications from fruit anatomy, and draws attention to the fact that they are the only genera in the tribe Caucalineae with 12 chromosomes.

In the Coniferae, Erdtman has produced biochemical comparisons of orders, families and genera.[151] He has been able to distinguish very easily between the subgenera *Diploxylon* and *Haploxylon* of *Pinus*. The former contained the flavanones pinobanksin and pinocembrin (XXI), with stilbene derivatives called pinosylvins. The *Haploxylon* pines had in addition flavones and dihydropinosylvins.

However intriguing or suggestive the distribution of particular phenolics may be, their taxonomic value can be assessed only in terms of how they relate to existing classifications. Can they, in particular cases, confirm or extend classifications, or indicate the need for further revision? When phenolic studies are undertaken with the prime aim of validating particular classifications, many gains may be expected. An example is discussed in Chapter 14.[212]

PHENOLICS AND EVOLUTION

Students of the phenolics and their taxonomic value have from the outset also considered how evidence from phenolics may contribute to ideas of phylogeny. Bate-Smith has discussed the possibility that irreversible changes in phenolic biosynthesis have occurred during the evolution of plants.[30] In particular he suggests that the ability to form leuco-anthocyanins and trihydroxy-substituted derivatives, once lost, cannot be regained. Families or other taxa lacking one or both of these classes of compound would be regarded as evolutionarily more advanced than taxa possessing both. Bate-Smith also notes that in plants where the common flavonols and hydroxy-acids (see Table 5.1) are not found, they seem to be replaced either by flavones or by sinapic or ferulic acids, respectively. He believes that the replacements arise from a gradual loss of specific oxidative enzymes during evolution, so preventing development of some or all of the commoner phenolics in more highly evolved plants. Such losses of synthetic power might occur in several unrelated lines of descent, so that it is not suggested, for example, that all plants with flavones are related, merely that they are all to some degree advanced in terms of phenolic metabolism. However, more complex metabolic changes, involving additional stages of hydroxylation or modification of the flavonoid nucleus, might well be rarer, and the plants possessing them thereby more likely to be related phylogenetically. Isoflavone production is quoted by Bate-Smith as a possible example of a rarer evolutionary change which may have phylogenetic meaning.

Consequences of Bate-Smith's ideas include the general point that woody plants (usually containing leuco-anthocyanins) are, on the whole, more primitive than herbs. The Rosales show the greatest consistency in production of leuco-anthocyanins and trihydroxy-acids, irrespective of habit, and so may occupy a central position among orders of dicotyledons. Another corollary would be that taxa characterized by high frequency of unusual phenolics, and deficiencies of the commoner ones, are evolutionarily advanced. Taxa with a wide range of common and more exotic phenolics might perhaps be of great antiquity, and have affinities with many other groups. Bate-Smith cites the Leguminosae as an example of this type. Diversity of phenolics is not just a consequence of size of taxon. The Compositae is larger than the Leguminosae but is biochemically less rich.

Harborne[203] has further developed the suggestions made by Bate-Smith. Table 5.3 lists flavonoid characters which he has categorized as 'primitive', 'advanced' or 'isolated'. 'Isolated' characters appear to be not especially primitive or advanced.

It must be emphasized that the recognition of such characters as primitive or advanced rests largely on their distribution in plants believed to be primitive or advanced on other criteria, and there are exceptions in particular cases. For instance, *loss* of trihydroxylation power may well show advancement in leaf flavonoids, but in petals the *gain* of trihydroxylation (e.g. cyanidin, delphinidin) seems to be an advanced character associated with selection pressure for bluer flowers. Only rarely is there even circumstantial evidence from chemistry itself that the advancement rating of a phenolic character has been correctly assessed. The introduction of a third vicinal

Table 5.3 Primitive and advanced flavonoid characters. (After Harborne.[203])

Primitive characters

1. 3-Deoxyanthocyanidins
2. Flavonols
3. Leuco-anthocyanidins
4. Chalcones, flavanones and dihydrochalcones
5. *C*-substitution (*C*-methylation, *C*-phenylation, *C*-glycosylation, biflavonyl formation)

Advanced characters

Gain mutations

1. Complex *O*-glycosylation (including acylation of sugars)
2. 6- or 8-Hydroxylation
3. *O*-Methylation
4. Oxidation of chalcones→aurones

Loss mutations

1. Replacement of flavonols by flavones
2. Elimination of leuco-anthocyanidins
3. Elimination of trihydroxylation

Isolated characters

1. Replacement of anthocyanin by betacyanin
2. Shift of flavonoid B ring to 3-position: isoflavone formation (Leguminosae)
3. 2'-Hydroxylation
4. Elimination of 5-hydroxyl group

hydroxyl-group into an ortho-dihydroxyphenol has never been managed *in vitro*, or demonstrated *in vivo*.[30] Therefore the natural trihydroxyphenolics probably arise independently, not from mono- or di-hydroxy precursors. This independent pathway of synthesis, once lost, would need to be recreated *de novo*, if loss of trihydroxylation power is reversible. Bate-Smith considers therefore that it is likely to be an irreversible process, as previously mentioned, and hence that elimination of trihydroxylation is an evolutionary advance.

Evolutionary changes in the chemistry of phenols cannot often be related to selection pressure from the environment. Like the modifications which may have been connected with the advantage of having stable, blue petal pigments, replacement of chalcones by the more highly oxidized aurones (see Table 5.3) in highly evolved families may similarly reflect the fact that aurones are more stable yellow pigments. Some advancements may arise simply from the survival value conferred by unpleasant tasting foliage.

BETALAINS

These compounds are excluded from the general definition of phenolics since they contain nitrogen. In the nineteenth century it was recognized that these red and yellow pigments (betacyanins and betaxanthins) occur only in certain families of flowering plants. Early knowledge of betalains is reviewed by Dreiding.[134] Betalains occur in many parts of the plants which synthesize them, but it is their function as flower pigments which gave rise to the expression 'nitrogenous anthocyanins' by which they were known for many years.[407] Only in the late nineteen-fifties was it possible to produce sufficiently pure preparations to determine reliably the structure of betanidin (XXXII) from the chenopod *Beta vulgaris*.[314].

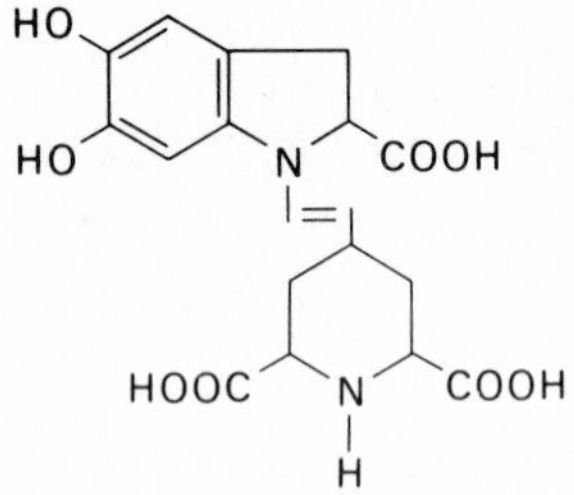

XXXII   Betanidin

The structure is quite unlike that of the anthocyanidins. From 1962 it was clear that a new class of plant pigments had been discovered. They are not flavonoids and, though it seems best to consider them together with the phenolics with which they appear to be functionally equivalent, they may eventually be designated as alkaloids.

Piatelli *et al.* established the structure of a betaxanthin from fruits of *Opuntia ficus-indica* (Cactaceae).[379] It is called indicaxanthin (XXXIII).

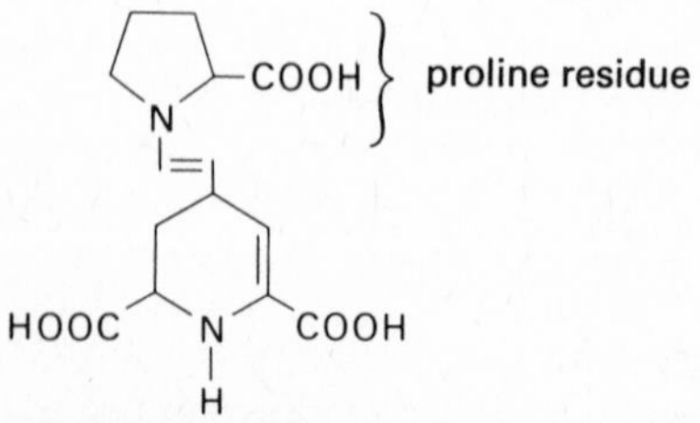

XXXIII   Indicaxanthin

Their work showed that betacyanins and betaxanthins are structurally related and interconvertible. The synthetic pathway of betalains is quite different from that of the anthocyanidins and other flavonoids.

More betalains have been characterized since that time but there seems to be much less diversity in the group than in the anthocyanidins. Betanin, the pigment of red beet (*Beta vulgaris*), is a glucoside of betanidin. Opportunity for variation in betacyanins may come from replacement of the sugar moiety. In the betaxanthins, replacement of proline by other amino acids is a source of variation already known in *Beta vulgaris*.

Betalains are known from only ten families of angiosperms most of which have traditionally been included in a single order, the Centrospermae. The discovery of unique pigments in these families supports the delimitation of the order. Of the ten the Cactaceae have previously had the most chequered taxonomic history, often being placed in an order of their own (Cactales or Opuntiales). With the demonstration that they have betalain pigments, they seem well established as members of Centrospermae. The Caryophyllaceae have customarily been included in the Centrospermae, but are found to lack betalains.

It is interesting that betalain-containing plants lack anthocyanins completely, even though other types of flavonoid are present. The two groups of pigments are mutually exclusive. This fact, the separate biogenetic processes and the extremely limited distribution of betalains have been used to support the exclusion from Centrospermae of all non-betalain families.[313]

It is not possible to state why betacyanins replace anthocyanins in the Centrospermae. Though some members of the order are fairly primitive, no other primitive angiosperms or lower group have so far been found to synthesize them. Anthocyanins, on the other hand, are known from Bryophyta, Pteridophyta and Gymnosperms. In many ways the betacyanins are biologically less satisfactory pigments than anthocyanins: they have a more restricted colour range, produce a less pure blue colour, and are chemically labile.[203] Their nitrogen content may offer a clue to their origins. If they were, or are, always merely pigments, then the nitrogen content makes them rather expensive metabolically. Perhaps they had functions as soluble nitrogen stores and repellents in primitive Centrospermae, and the use of their coincidental chromatophore properties was an economy measure. It should not be difficult to test the idea.

Certainly the betalain story constitutes a notable chemotaxonomic contribution. It raises in an acute form the problem of assessing the relative values of chemical and other kinds of taxonomic evidence. The question of the taxonomic interpretation of betalain distribution is taken up in Chapter 14.

CONCLUSION

The potential value of taxonomic evidence from phenolics and betalains seems to be considerable, despite the fact that they are simple molecules. They are susceptible to environmental effects, and some may be necessary accompaniments of certain physiological processes or states. Nevertheless, the observation that in different plants different phenolics are involved in these processes is undeniably a taxonomic one.

Distribution of some biosynthetic pathways is similarly discontinuous.

It remains to be seen whether bulk assay of plant material will reveal rare phenolics in most plants, comparable to the situation which may be arising in the case of non-protein amino acids. If it does, the discontinuities in phenolic distribution will be shown to be only technically spurious, and taxonomic interest is hardly likely to slacken. Phenolics are of proven convenience and usefulness.

6

Evidence from Plant Oils, Fats and Waxes

Together with the proteins and carbohydrates, the lipids form the bulk of the organic matter of plant tissue. It is not therefore surprising that they have been identified as a potential source of taxonomic evidence. Many plant lipids and waxes are of considerable economic significance, a situation which always usefully boosts efforts to establish the basic facts about the distribution of naturally occurring compounds.

The lipids are a somewhat heterogeneous group defined by their complete or partial solubility in organic solvents such as ethanol, ether or chloroform. They are, by contrast, only feebly soluble in water. Fats are distinguished from oils by their physical state at normal ambient temperatures: fats are solids while oils are liquids.

Simple lipids contain only carbon, hydrogen and oxygen, and are esters of fatty acids with glycerol (Fig. 6.1, I), a trihydric alcohol. Such esters are usually termed 'triglycerides'. Large numbers of different fatty acids have been isolated from plants. Many have an even number of carbon atoms, such as caprylic acid (II) found, for example, in coconut oil. Relatively few fatty acids with odd numbers of carbon atoms are known. Very few naturally occurring fatty acids have branched chains: most are straight-chain types like caprylic acid. Fatty acids differ from each other chiefly in length of the carbon chain and in their level of unsaturation (i.e. the number of double (ethylenic) or triple (acetylenic) bonds which they contain).

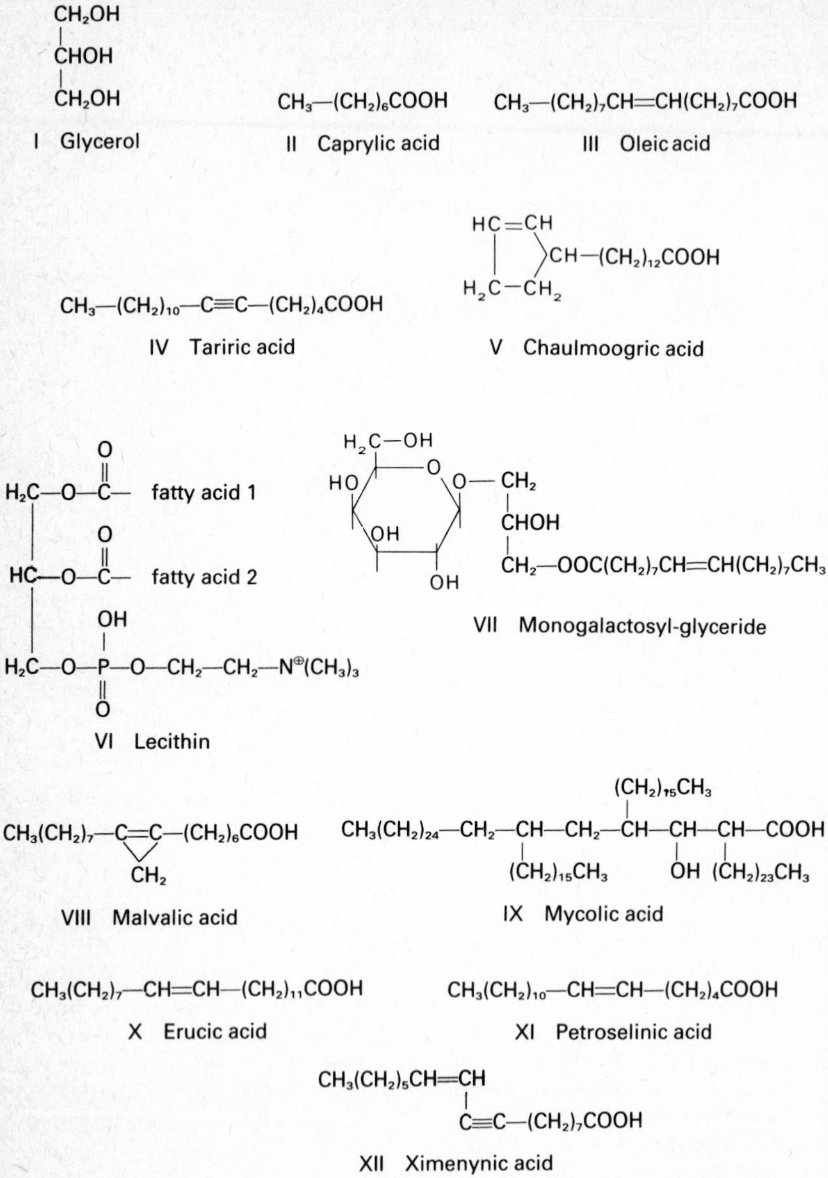

CH₂OH
CHOH
CH₂OH

I Glycerol

CH₃—(CH₂)₆COOH

II Caprylic acid

CH₃—(CH₂)₇CH=CH(CH₂)₇COOH

III Oleic acid

CH₃—(CH₂)₁₀—C≡C—(CH₂)₄COOH

IV Tariric acid

V Chaulmoogric acid

VI Lecithin

VII Monogalactosyl-glyceride

CH₃(CH₂)₇—C=C—(CH₂)₆COOH
        CH₂

VIII Malvalic acid

IX Mycolic acid

CH₃(CH₂)₇—CH=CH—(CH₂)₁₁COOH

X Erucic acid

CH₃(CH₂)₁₀—CH=CH—(CH₂)₄COOH

XI Petroselinic acid

CH₃(CH₂)₅CH=CH
        C≡C—(CH₂)₇COOH

XII Ximenynic acid

Fig. 6.1 Structures of glycerol and fatty acids.

Oleic acid (III) is the commonest unsaturated fatty acid found in plant lipids. Tariric acid (IV) has an acetylenic linkage. A few fatty acids have a cyclic structure (e.g. chaulmoogric acid, V).

Usually the three fatty acids esterified with a molecule of glycerol, forming a triglyceride, are all different. Natural fats and oils are complex mixtures of many such mixed triglycerides, and do not have an absolutely constant composition. Some glycerides may be particularly characteristic in certain lipids, as indicated by the fatty acids which they release when hydrolysed. Oleic acid comprises more than 80% of the total fatty acid released by hydrolysis of olive oil. The greater the proportion of saturated fatty acids in a lipid, the higher is its melting point. Saturation is usually measured by the **iodine number**, that is, the number of grams of iodine absorbed by a hundred grams of the fat or oil, or fatty acid.

Substitutions of hydroxyl or methyl groups along the fatty acid chain provide considerable scope for variation in the detailed secondary structure of fatty acids and the triglycerides which they form.

Some lipids contain nitrogen and/or phosphorus in addition to carbon, hydrogen and oxygen. These are called **phospholipids**. Lecithin (VI) is a widespread phospholipid in plants. Glycolipids, such as monogalactosyl-glyceride (VII), contain sugar units, and occur in green leaves.

The lipids reviewed above are all esters of fatty acids with glycerol. If longer chain alcohols (24–36 carbon atoms) are involved, the resulting compound is a wax. Plant waxes are esters of long-chain alcohols, usually with long-chain fatty acids. These alcohols are often relatively insoluble at room temperature. The C_{36} alcohol is only sparingly soluble even in hot chloroform. From this it can readily be understood why the waxes themselves are normally solids. Free fatty acids are also found in many plant waxes, along with free alcohols, high molecular weight aldehydes, ketones and hydrocarbons. Most plant waxes are hence rather heterogeneous in chemical composition. Carnauba wax (from *Copernica cerifera*, Palmae) contains C_{26}–C_{34} alcohols esterified with fatty acids of the same chain lengths, and also a C_{27} hydrocarbon. Seventyfive percent of the wax is myricyl cerotate, an ester of myricyl alcohol (30 carbon atoms) and cerotic acid (26 carbon atoms).

Although the hydrocarbons of waxes are non-lipid components, they are normally considered with the lipids because of their close association in plant waxes. Mostly they are alkanes (paraffins), remarkable in having odd numbers of carbon atoms (from C_{25}–C_{37}) in their chains. They are normally solid at room temperature.

OCCURRENCE, VARIATION AND FUNCTIONS

Lipids are found in all parts of plants, but occur in highest concentration in storage organs, seeds and fruits. They form droplets suspended in the cytoplasm. Most of the lipid content of plant tissue discharges a storage function and is rapidly depleted when the tissue is kept in the dark. Phospholipids are less readily lost and probably occur in organelles, in association with proteins. Plant waxes are almost entirely connected with the cuticular layers. Either they are incorporated in the cuticle, or they occur as epicuticular rods or plates. Cutin itself is a natural polyester of fatty and hydroxy fatty acids.[19] Suberin from barks is probably similar. The function of the cuticular waxes of fruits, stems and leaves is undoubtedly that of helping to minimize water loss from the plant. Waxes occur only rarely as internal food storage material, for instance in the seeds of *Simmondsia californica* (Buxaceae).[189]

Lipid variation within the plant can be considerable. Shorland[432] records that the lipids from the seeds and leaves of the same plant may differ not only in the proportions of fatty acids which they contain, but also in the type of acid present. He also mentions differences between the fatty acid content of lipids from aquatic and terrestrial plants. Differences in fatty acid content of lipid extracts of the fungus *Neurospora crassa* have been noted when it was cultured on the surface of the medium or submerged.[282]

Lipid production is under genetic control. Selection of high yielding varieties of commercially significant oil plants, such as maize and safflower, has met with considerable success. Though the quantity of oil produced may vary between varieties, the constituent fatty acids usually remain constant. Shorland states that 'seed fats from the same species almost invariably contain the same types of fatty acids'.[432] Gupta and Chakrabarty commented on the inheritance of fatty acid composition, although they attributed some variation to environmental factors.[194]

Levels of saturation in lipids are determined by the proportions of saturated and unsaturated fatty acids which they contain. Lipid saturation, as measured by iodine number, can be shown by experiment to vary with the temperature of the environment. There is corroboration from natural occurrences. Seed oils of legumes are progressively more unsaturated as one proceeds from tropical to temperate zone types.[506] Oils of leguminous trees and vines are more unsaturated than those from herbs. Such observations imply that differences in fatty acid composition may be related to habit.

Plant waxes seem to have constant constituents in some plants but not in others. The alkane content of wax from species in subfamily Sempervivoideae of Crassulaceae remained constant during the life of the plant.[143] Grass plants of various species, grown in controlled conditions, showed only minor quantitative variation in their leaf waxes during development.[476,477] On the other hand, big differences in the wax of *Cortaderia toe-toe* (Gramineae) have been detected at different times of year.[324]

Variation between different parts of the plant is noticeable in surface waxes. Large differences have been found between the petal and leaf waxes of *Aloe kedongensis* (Liliaceae).[228] Cuticular wax from stems, leaves and berries of the sultana vine (*Vitis vinifera* var. *sultana* – Vitaceae) have been found to differ significantly in the proportions of constituent alkanes.[390] Variation has been recorded in leaf waxes at different times of year (in *Betula*), from plants in different localities (*Picea*), on different organs (*Robinia*) and even between the upper and lower surfaces of the same leaf (*Juglans*).[458]

Intra-specific variation in surface waxes is well known. For example, varietal differences in leaf wax were demonstrated to occur between the Copenhagen and Winnigstadt cultivars of cabbage (*Brassica oleracea*).[236] Wax production is known to be controlled, at least partly, by the genotype. Wax-free mutants are known in many species. Martin and Juniper provide a brief review of work on the genetics of wax formation and the inheritance of wax characters.[322] In a non-glaucous mutant of cabbage, a great reduction has been detected in the biosynthesis of C_{29} compounds normally found in cabbage wax (including alkanes, ketones and alcohols).[315]

Much is known of the origins and metabolic intercoversions of the fatty acids. The main pathway of synthesis, involving assembly of 2-carbon units, appears to be almost universal. Fatty acids are therefore probably always metabolically related and hence homologous in different groups of plants. Comparisons of fatty acid content for taxonomic purposes are therefore not invalidated by variations in biogenesis. Presence of a compound is good evidence for presence of an inherited pathway.

TAXONOMIC USEFULNESS OF LIPIDS AND WAXES

Lipids were among the first materials assessed for taxonomic significance by McNair (see Chapter 2). He related the nature of fats and oils to taxonomy and to climate[330] concluding that the oils stored by tropical plants have higher melting points than those of plants growing in temperate conditions. He believed that the iodine number of lipids was higher (i.e. lipids more unsaturated) in more advanced plant groups, an idea which seems attributable to Simonsen and Rau.[436] It has received only fitful support. Mirov assembled evidence correlating saturation level (as shown by the iodine number) with presumed antiquity in gymnosperms.[340] Iodine number has been shown above to be a rather unstable character, varying in changing environments. The association of levels of saturation and evolutionary advancement must be considered dubious until carefully controlled experiments are planned to verify the facts. Goldovskii dismissed the idea in a forthright fashion, pointing out that algae often have very unsaturated lipids, while the highly evolved Compositae do not have the highest levels of unsaturation.[182]

Since lipids are so diverse and inconstant in absolute composition, characters relating to their intact structure are probably not going to be of much value in taxonomy. Iodine number exemplifies this. Only the fatty acid composition of lipids is left as a possible source of taxonomic information.

Systematic variation of fatty acids has been studied for some time.[235,333] Groups of families have been recognized on the basis of the major fatty acids released by hydrolysis of their lipids. Table 6.1 represents such a classification. It can be seen from the table that many 'major fatty acids' occur in several family groups, and that the categories overlap substantially. For instance, oleic acid is a major fatty acid in most groups. Almost all fatty acids occur in all groups at least in low concentration. The concept of this classification recalls Hegnauer's recognition of *Hauptaminosauren* in families (see Chapter 4). Not only do distantly related families sometimes appear in the same group, but variation in lipid composition has the inevitable consequence that a family may appear in more than one group (e.g. the Ulmaceae). A classification where a taxon appears in either of two places is hardly acceptable.

In general it seems therefore that major fatty acids are too continuously distributed to form a satisfactory basis for taxonomic conclusions. The Palmae, however, may be a rare example of a plant group in which the proportions of fatty acids in the lipids are rather constant in both species and genera.[234]

All the work referred to above concerns the lipids of seeds or fruits. Lipids of vegetative tissues are remarkably constant in fatty acid composition in a wide range of plant groups, including angiosperms, mosses and green algae.[360] By contrast, seed oils of the

Table 6.1.   Classification of families on the basis of major fatty acids. (Modified from Shorland.[432])

Group Ia Linolenic-rich seed fats

Pinaceae	Labiatae
Taxodiaceae	Linaceae
Aquifoliaceae	Moraceae
Boraginaceae	Paeoniaceae
Ericaceae	Rhamnaceae

Group Ib Linoleic-rich/oleic-rich seed fats

Podocarpaceae	Juglandaceae	Scrophulariaceae
Agavaceae	Liliaceae	Solanaceae
Amaryllidaceae	Lobeliaceae	Symplocaceae
Asclepiadaceae	Myrtaceae	Theaceae
Compositae	Oleaceae	Typhaceae
Dipsacaceae	Papaveraceae	Ulmaceae
Fagaceae	Passifloraceae	Urticaceae
Hamamelidaceae	Plantaginaceae	
Hippocastanaceae	Polemoniaceae	
Iridaceae	Ranunculaceae	

Group II Seed fats rich in linoleic and oleic acid, with linolenic acid or a conjugated polyethanoic acid as major components

Balsaminaceae	Euphorbiaceae
Bignoniaceae	Rosaceae
Cucurbitaceae	Valerianaceae

Group III Seed fats with palmitic, oleic and linoleic acids as major components

Acanthaceae	Combretaceae	Rutaceae
Amaranthaceae	Fumariaceae	Tiliaceae
Annonaceae	Gramineae	
Berberidaceae	Malvaceae	
Bombacaceae	Portulacaceae	
Buddleiaceae	Rubiaceae	

Group IV Seed fats with characteristic acids other than, or in addition to, oleic, linoleic and palmitic acids

    (a) Petroselinic acid: Araliaceae, Umbelliferae
    (b) Cyclic unsaturated acids: Flacourtiaceae, Malvaceae, Sterculiaceae
    (c) Eicosenoic acid: Buxaceae, Cruciferae, Sapindaceae
    (d) Erucic acid: Cruciferae, Tropaeolaceae
    (e) Arachidic, behenic or lignoceric acids: Leguminosae, Loganiaceae, Sapindaceae
    (f) Stearic acid: Gnetaceae, Dipterocarpaceae, Sapotaceae, Sterculiaceae, Verbenaceae
    (g) Myristic and lauric acids: Lauraceae, Palmae
    (h) Capric acid: Lauraceae, Lythraceae, Ulmaceae

---

angiosperms tested showed marked differences.[362] The photosynthetic parts of plants appear therefore to be conservative in their lipid chemistry. Table 6.2 lists the fatty acid content of broad bean leaves which Nichols quotes as representative of most green plants.[361]

Table 6.2.   Fatty acid composition of broad bean tissues. (From Crombie, W. M. (1958) *J. exp. Bot.* **9**, 254.)

	Fatty acid percentage						
	16 : 0*	16 : 1	18 : 0	18 : 1	18 : 2	18 : 3	22 : 0
Etiolated leaf	16.7	—	4.7	—	33.5	39.4	4.6
Green leaf	11.7	6.9	3.2	3.4	14.3	56.4	4.0
Chloroplasts	7.4	9.2	1.2	5.2	2.6	72.0	1.2

* The figure before the colon indicates the number of carbon atoms; the figure after the colon shows the number of double bonds.

Especial taxonomic significance may attach to cases where unusual fatty acids of the seed oils also occur in the leaves.[432] Such occurrences are atypical. Malvalic acid (VIII) occurs in both seed and leaf lipids in members of the Malvaceae. Another case involved the presence of the rare compounds γ-linolenic acid and an octadecatetraenoic acid in the leaf lipids as well as the seed fats of eight members of the Boraginaceae.[250] Further research revealed the same unusual fatty acids in ten species of the unrelated family Caryophyllaceae.[251] The taxonomic significance of unusual fatty acids in leaves may not, therefore, prove to be very high, when fuller surveys are made.

Fruit fats, except those attributable to the seeds within, have so far revealed little variation of taxonomic interest. They are usually dissimilar to the seed fats. In the Palmae, lauric acid is abundant in the seed lipid hydrolysate, but almost absent from the fruit fat.

Most of the taxonomically interesting variation in fatty acid content arises from work on seed lipids. Early work on the major fatty acids has already been mentioned.[234,235] More of taxonomic value might be expected from the study of the distribution of unusual fatty acids, or of widespread acids which only rarely occur in high concentration. Capric acid was once thought to be a major component only in elms (*Ulmus* spp.). Subsequently it was found richly represented in the seed lipids of *Zelkova* (Ulmaceae), and also in members of the Lythraceae and Lauraceae.[432]

Fatty acids specific to particular plant groups are potentially of interest to the taxonomist. Bacterial lipids contain fatty acids not found in other plants and may be helpful in bacterial taxonomy. Mycolic acid (IX) for instance, is restricted to the mycobacteria. In the flowering plants, the best known example is the restriction of chaulmoogric acid (V) and some related acids to certain species of certain genera in the Flacourtiaceae. Seed oils of this family were used from very early times by Chinese and Hindu physicians in a slow but successful treatment of leprosy. The chaulmoogric acids are now known to have a damaging effect on the envelope of *Bacillus leprae*. Other cases include the almost complete restriction of erucic acid (X) to the Cruciferae, and petroselinic acid (XI) to the Umbelliferae. Ximenynic acid (XII) appears to characterize lipids of the Santalaceae and Olacaceae. 'Unusual' seed oils may have originated in connection with ecological specialization. These examples of restricted distribution of fatty acids are few in number and always open to correction as more analyses are performed.

The taxonomic potential of variation in waxes resides largely in work on the alkane hydrocarbon fraction, mainly since the development of mass spectroscopy and gas chromatography has made rapid analyses possible. Work by Eglinton and his collaborators represents a major contribution to this field.[143] Chemotaxonomic applications of alkane chemistry are frequently reviewed.[133,322,327] Some of the background evidence of variation in alkane characters has been mentioned already.

A general uniformity in proportions of alkane hydrocarbon constituents has been found within genera of the Crassulaceae, and it was considered that this systematic variation augured well for the general use of alkane studies in taxonomy.[143] Discrepancies between alkane distribution and established morphological similarities caused the workers to admit that 'there was only a rough parallelism of hydrocarbon pattern and botanical classification'. Mecklenburg related wax alkane variation to cytogenetics, morphology and protein serology (*q.v.*), in twenty-two tuber-bearing *Solanum* species.[335] There was substantial agreement between the different kinds of evidence. In the Gramineae, Tribe concluded that alkane variation in cuticular waxes was a useful source of taxonomic information.[476] Hallam's (1967) work on 316 species of *Eucalyptus* connected chemical studies of the wax with its physical appearance as seen with an electron microscope,[200] and demonstrated that the species of the Australian arid zone were a homogeneous group on the basis of wax characters. Other evidence suggests that these species form an unnatural assemblage. These findings about wax are helpful in that they agree with indications from cotyledon morphology, and so may help solve a taxonomic puzzle.

The attractions of wax alkanes as taxonomic characters include the ease of study, the possibility of relating chemistry to form of deposition, and the fact that, once formed, the material is not further metabolized. Suggestive surveys of the occurrence of wax alkanes, sometimes with contradictory results, have already been executed. For a final assessment, the factors affecting their variation must be more completely understood. Eglinton stresses the need for fuller biosynthetic knowledge of the wax alkanes.[143] Martin-Smith *et al.* assert that 'A systematic investigation into the possible influence of season, climate, geographical distribution and the kind and age of organs on the composition of plant surface waxes is essential before the method can be accepted without qualifications'.[324]

Similarly guarded statements are made about the taxonomic significance of lipids in general.[432] In the legumes most of the taxonomic correlations of lipid variation were revealed only by applying statistics[506] and it has been recommended that modern analytical methods should be more widely applied before taxonomic information is sought from variation patterns of legume lipids. Perhaps because of their structural simplicity and fundamental involvement in the life of plants, large discontinuities in the distribution of lipid types should be expected only where there are large differences in metabolism.

In view of the uncertain value of lipids in taxonomy, it is hardly surprising that they have scarcely been considered in schemes of phylogeny, apart from the statements of McNair and others discussed earlier, that molecular complexity and high unsaturation may indicate evolutionary advancement. Nichols has suggested a phylogeny of algae, based on lipid composition and metabolism in chloroplasts.[361] In an account of the seed oils of the Proteaceae, Vickery considers that the genus *Placospermum* may be a primitive group. The genus *Bellendera*, another candidate for primitive status, on more orthodox taxonomic criteria, did not appear particularly primitive in terms of fatty acid content.[490] Both these workers have produced interesting evolutionary assessments, but they rest on assumed primitiveness of certain lipid characters, i.e. low levels of unsaturation and chemical simplicity respectively. These are the familiar assumptions of fifty years ago which seem to indicate that the phylogenetic harvest from lipid studies will be sparse indeed. Nevertheless, comparison of classifications with such evolutionary schemes may sometimes be enlightening, as long as it is remembered that chemical assumptions are no more definitive than morphological ones.

7

Evidence from Carbohydrates

Carbohydrates comprise the bulk of the organic matter of plants. They have obvious storage and skeletal functions in addition to their ubiquitous involvements in the basic metabolism of all organisms. They are primary products of photosynthesis and therefore precursors of other organic materials. Owing to their wide distribution and fundamental importance they may not at first sight appear very promising material for the taxonomist eager for new characters. In the development of chemotaxonomy, carbohydrate studies have certainly been attempted less often than many other kinds of investigation, perhaps because their potential was, *a priori*, considered too low.

Early work on chemotaxonomic aspects of carbohydrates was mostly concerned with variation of starch grains. Reichert's classic paper on this subject should have encouraged interest in the possible use of carbohydrate evidence in systematics.[397] Characters of starch grains have since proved their value in several groups, notably the Gramineae,[242,451] but they are anatomical rather than truly chemical characters. Blackman discussed the use of carbohydrate data in phylogenetic studies,[56] but little critical work was done for many years.

In some ways the carbohydrates and their metabolism may be said to have provided very significant taxonomic evidence. The incidence of polysaccharide cell walls, of various types, is one of the best characters for separating major groups such as plants, animals and fungi. Some divisions of algae are partly characterized by the polysaccharide storage and cell wall polymers which they synthesize. Stoloff boldly classified red algae solely on the basis of polysaccharide type.[456]

Despite their general importance and occurrence, carbohydrates are extremely diverse. It is possible that in this diversity, of function as well as structure, careful research may yet reveal much of taxonomic value.

STRUCTURAL DIVERSITY OF CARBOHYDRATES

Only an outline of carbohydrate diversity can be included here and standard works on plant biochemistry should be consulted for complete classifications.

(i) Monosaccharides

These are the simple sugars, some of which occur in most living organisms. In plants the commonest members are four hexose (6-carbon) sugars (glucose, Fig. 7.1 (I), mannose (II), galactose and fructose (III) and three pentose (5-carbon) sugars (arabinose (IV), xylose (V), and ribose). Some 7-carbon sugars (heptuloses) are also found quite commonly. Glucose and fructose often occur as free sugars, but the others are normally polymerized, or found in combination with non-sugar molecules. Galactose, mannose and xylose occur in the polymers of gums and mucilages. Arabinose is found in 'hemicelluloses' and gums as **arabans**. Xylose occurs in seed 'hemicelluloses' and in the **xylans** of wood.

(ii) Oligosaccharides

Carbohydrates of two to ten polymerized monosaccharide units comprise this group. Oligosaccharides are thus distinguished rather arbitrarily from polysaccharides. Most have 2–4 sugar units, nearly always of the hexose type, linked together in various ways. Sucrose (glucose–fructose, (VI)) is the commonest plant disaccharide. Gentiobiose and trehalose are less common. Raffinose (VII) and stachyose (VIII) are the commonest tri- and tetra-saccharides respectively. Most other oligosaccharides are found only in glycosides. Some may be intermediates in the synthesis or degradation of polysaccharides. Others may have specific storage functions, and are found only in storage tissues.

(iii) Sugar derivatives

Reduction of the carbonyl group of a sugar produces a poly-hydroxy alcohol (**polyol**). Sugar alcohols are common in plants, particularly those derived from six and seven carbon sugars. Man-nitol (IX), found for example in gum exudates and brown algae, is formed by reduction of mannose or fructose. The cyclic sugar alcohols (**cyclitols**) can be represented by *myo*-inositol (X), wide-spread in plants both in the free state and as the hexaphosphate anhydride (phytic acid).

Oxidation of carbons one and/or six of a sugar molecule to a carboxyl group yields a sugar acid. If glucose is oxidized at carbon 6 the product is glucuronic acid (XI), a common constituent of gums and mucilages. Ascorbic acid (vitamin C) is another example.

Glycosides are compounds (often ethers) formed by sugars with non-sugar molecules (aglycones), and they are very diverse. Flavonoid glycosides are mentioned in Chapter 5. Although much of the taxonomic interest in glycosides is connected with the nature of the aglycone, some of the rarest sugars are found only in glycosides. Digitalose, for example, is known only in certain *Digitalis* glycosides. Glucose is the commonest glycosidic sugar. Rhamnose is a common sugar in glycosides which is rarely found free.

(iv) Polysaccharides

Polymers of more than 10 sugar units can arbitrarily be classified as polysaccharides, though many of the class have hundreds or even thousands of units. Both hexoses and pentoses form polysac-charides, sometimes occurring together in the same one. Several different monosaccharides may be linked in a polysaccharide, but they are generally known by a name derived from the dominant type, e.g. hexosans, mannans, fructans. Cellulose is the commonest wall polysaccharide, consisting of a straight chain of several thousand glucose units. Mannans and xylans also occur in cell walls (as 'hemicelluloses'), the last often in significant quantities in hard wood and grass 'straws'.

Primary walls of plant cells contain pectic substances. Pectins are complex and variable substances incorporating methyl esters of pectic acid (polygalacturonic acid), arabinose and rhamnose.

The most widespread food reserve polysaccharide is starch—a glucose polymer with a straight-chain component (amylose) and a branched component (amylopectin). Fructan storage polymers occur in some plants: inulin, which is especially common in the Compositae, is the best known example. Short-chain, water-soluble fructans are found as storage materials in certain grasses.

VARIATIONS AND FUNCTIONS

Taxonomists need to know if the biogenesis of particular carbohydrates is the same in all the plants which they study. Though carbohydrate biosynthesis has been exhaustively studied for many years, there are still problems to be solved, particularly in the mode of assembly of the larger polysaccharides. This process may involve different sugar nucleotides in different plants.[24] A proposed scheme for fructan metabolism in artichokes does not implicate sugar nucleotides.[141] The simple sugars and their derivatives are probably produced by several unrelated pathways. Variation and 'virtuosity' in carbohydrate metabolism should be expected in plants, though it is likely that many of the different pathways will be widespread.

Variation in carbohydrate content due to non-genetic factors is well known. Anticipation of gross quantitative and qualitative changes, associated with varying environmental and developmental conditions, has discouraged chemotaxonomic evaluations of carbohydrate evidence. Nutritional factors influencing growth will directly affect carbohydrate production and balance. Seasonal and diurnal variation is inevitable. Both quantitative and qualitative differences in plant tissues arise owing to their different functions, but may not be consistent. Non-taxonomic variation is well known even in secondary carbohydrates. In *Acacia* exudate gums, Anderson *et al.* have recorded developmental, seasonal and ecological variation.[15] In *Acacia senegal*, the gum exuded from the lower part of the stem differed considerably in chemical composition from that tapped from upper branches. Compounds present in small amounts may, in other circumstances, be synthesized on a large scale. Two ways to minimize this problem are, first, to develop extremely good methods of analysis which can detect materials present even in very low concentration, and second, to compare, as far as possible, samples from plants grown in standard conditions. For soluble carbohydrates, gas–liquid chromatography seems to invite the attention of taxonomists, because of its economy of material, high sensitivity, accuracy of identification and estimation, and speed of operation.[240]

Many kinds of carbohydrate have identifiable functions. Those of the skeletal and storage polysaccharides are obvious. The monosaccharides and simplest oligosaccharides are usually basic metabolic intermediaries or energy sources. Some of these are secreted by flowers and attract pollinating insects.[377] Larger oligosaccharides sometimes have a storage function. Gums and mucilages are presumed to have protective, wound-healing, anti-desiccatory or anchorage properties. The functions of sugar derivatives are diverse and not often clear. Some glycosides probably act as repellents of grazing animals. Linkage of the toxic aglycone to a sugar may increase its solubility. The sweet secretions of plants seem to have the opposite effect—that of attracting grazers by increasing palatability. As is often the case, the obvious effect may not occur in practice. Sugary gum exudates from *Acacia* attract ant populations, which act as repellents.[252] Similarly, the discharge from extrafloral nectaries in certain orchids, which consists of simple sugars, is consumed by ants.[253] Though the ants cannot usually kill harmful insect visitors, they have a valuable 'scare-crow' effect on these and other groups of potential grazers.

The xylans and mannans in cell walls are probably mainly skeletal in function, but they are by no means universally present. Differences might reasonably be expected to occur in all the secondary carbohydrates, which discharge less than fundamental functions in the plant. The problem is to distinguish the taxonomic variation from the developmentally and environmentally induced 'noise'.

SYSTEMATIC DISTRIBUTION OF CARBOHYDRATES

Little of taxonomic interest should be expected from the occurrence and distribution of common, free monosaccharides. Quantitative differences between different taxa have been reported,[51,253] but these may often be attributed to non-taxonomic variation. It is hardly a matter of taxonomic significance that one plant should be found to contain more glucose than another. Sedoheptulose (XII) was once thought to be restricted to the Crassulaceae, but its phosphate has now been detected much more widely, following its implication in photosynthesis.

Probably without exception, the unusual monosaccharides are found in combination, never naturally in the free state.

The rare, branched-chain pentose, apiose (XIII), occurs in the diglycoside apiin, with the flavone apigenin as the aglycone. Apiin is recorded from *Apium* and *Petroselinum* (Umbelliferae), *Vicia* (Leguminosae) and various genera of the Compositae. These occurrences do not seem taxonomically significant, at least at the family level, and are probably coincidental. Apiose also occurs in certain polysaccharides of *Posidonia* (Potamogetonaceae) and *Lemna* (Lemnaceae).[137] Hamamelose (XIV), a branched-chain hexose, is so far known only in *Hamamelis* (Hamamelidaceae), where it occurs in combination with a tannin, and in *Primula*. Rhamnose is a methyl

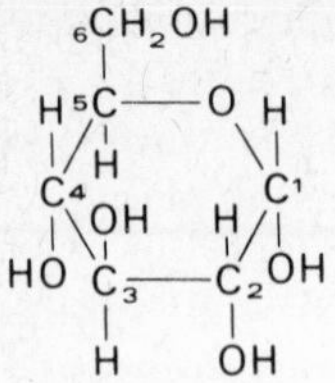

I Glucose

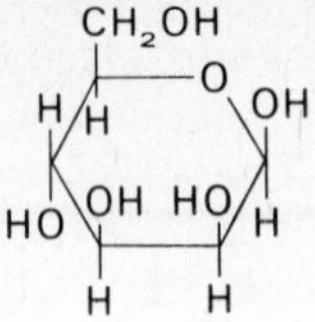

II Mannose

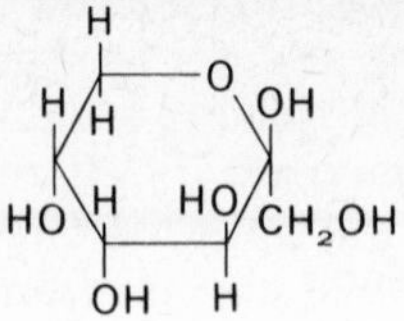

III Fructose

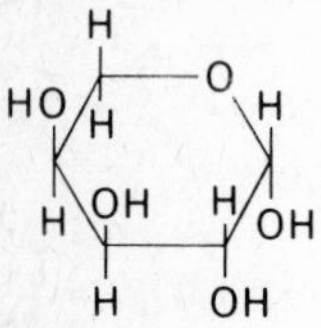

IV Arabinose

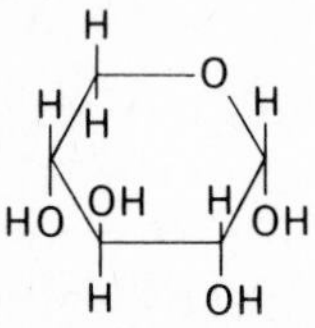

V Xylose

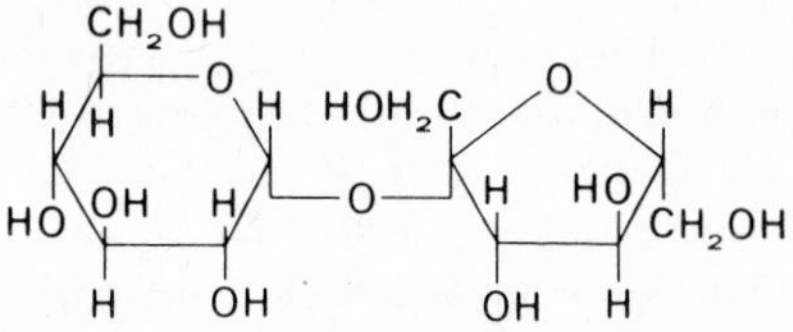

VI Sucrose

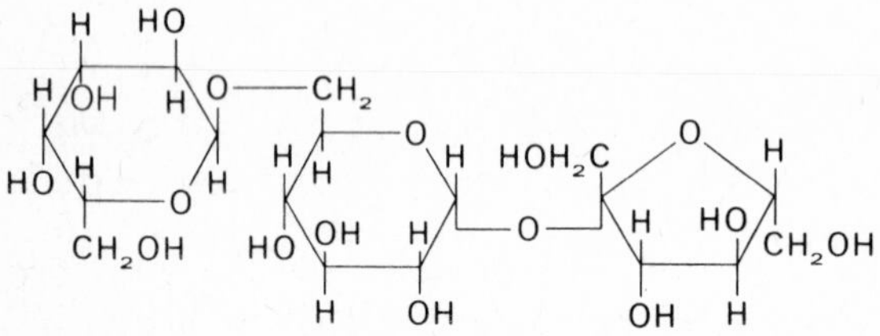

VII Raffinose

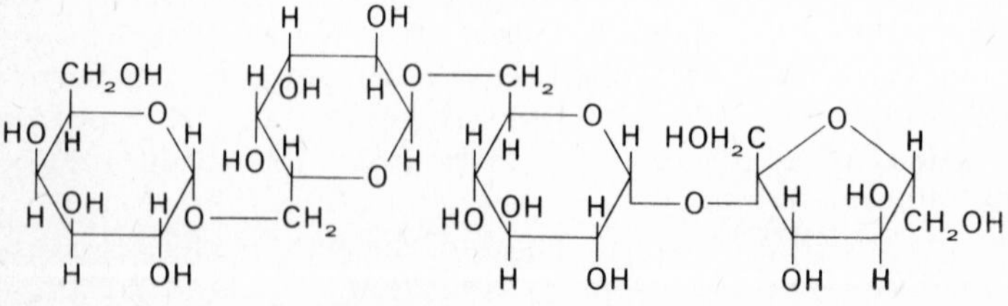

VIII Stachyose

Fig. 7.1 Structures of some carbohydrates.

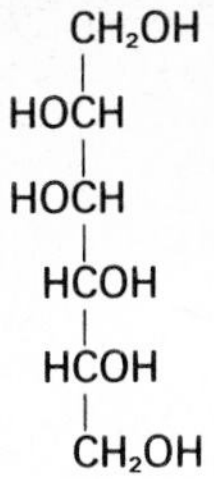

IX Mannitol

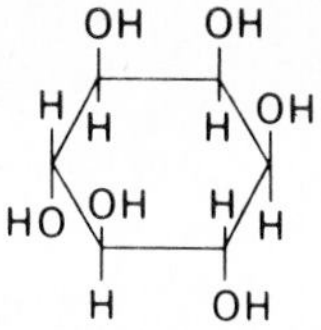

X *Myo*-inositol

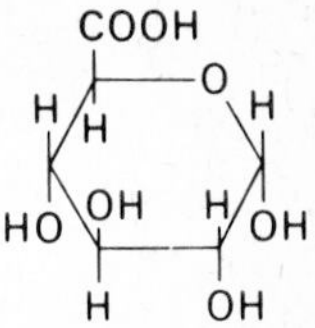

XI Glucuronic acid

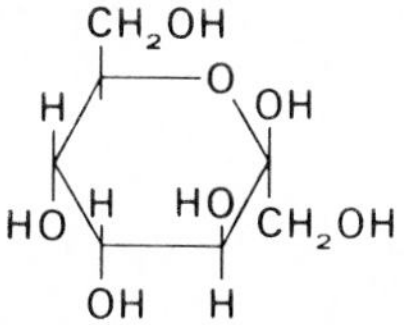

XII Sedoheptulose

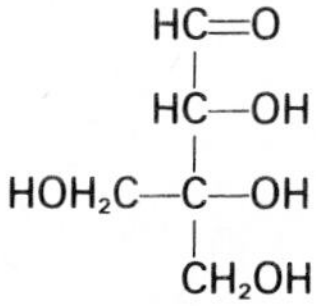

XIII Apiose

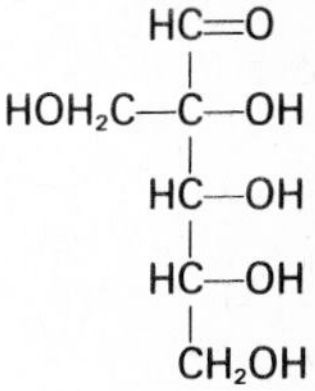

XIV Hamamelose

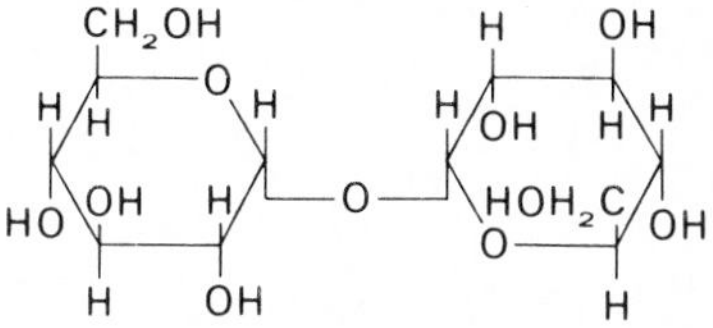

XV Trehalose

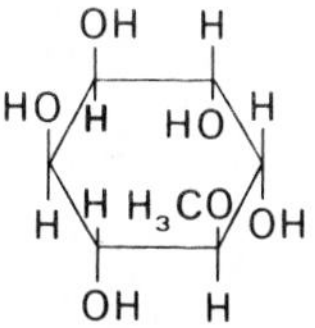

XVI Pinitol

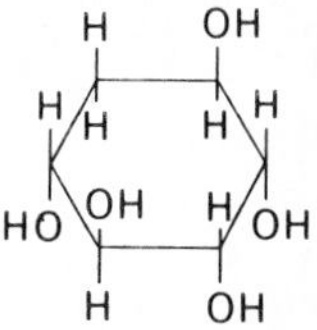

XVII Quercitol

Fig. 7.1 *continued*

pentose common in glycosides, but it occurs free in *Rhus* (Anacardiaceae). Other methyl pentoses are much rarer, and are not found in the free state. Quinovose occurs only in the glycoside quinovin (Rubiaceae and Convolvulaceae). Acofriose is known only from *Acokanthera friesiorum* (Apocynaceae).

Certain fungal sugars are restricted in distribution. They are found in the complex antibiotic glycosides produced by fungi (e.g. streptose in streptomycin) and nowhere else. Restricted sugars may be of some taxonomic value in certain small groups, but in general there appears to be little in monosaccharides to excite the interest of the systematist.

Not much has been done to expose the taxonomic value of studying oligosaccharide distribution. In the nineteen-thirties and nineteen-forties, French workers such as Colin, Belval and Cugnac worked on the possible significance of variation in the water-soluble fructans ('glucides') of grasses. In terms of a number of chemical criteria, including molecular weight and optical rotation before and after hydrolysis, they compared the fructan content of fruits and storage tissues in a range of grass genera.[42,442] Certain genera in the tribe Triticeae (*Hordeum, Triticum, Secale,* and *Aegilops*) possess indistinguishable fructans, which are referred to as **levosine**. Other triticoid genera, namely *Agropyron* and *Elymus,* have very similar fructans. *Festuca* and *Lolium* (tribe Festuceae) were found to have a fructan like **phlein**, from *Phleum, Phalaris* and *Ammophila* (Aveneae *sensu lato*). Though the affinities of *Bromus* would have been thought to lie more with Festuceae than Triticeae, the fructans of this genus resemble those of the latter tribe. *Festuca gigantea,* sometimes referred to *Bromus* in the past, had the phlein type of fructan, and so was considered to be a fescue, not a brome. Such a conclusion is supported by genetic evidence. Taxonomists are encouraged when independent lines of chemical and other evidence produce similar conclusions. Such correlations promote confidence in poorly established kinds of data, in this case fructan composition.[224] French work on fructans has continued.[18] In liverworts, the Jungermanniales have fructans as their storage carbohydrate, while the Marchantiales store starch.[389]

The commoner oligosaccharides are too widespread to be of much taxonomic value, though quantitative differences may be a manifestation of interesting biosynthetic variation. Trehalose (XV) is the major free sugar in species of *Selaginella* (Pteridophyta).[499] In the related genus *Lycopodium,* though trehalose is present, the major component is sucrose (VI). Short periods of photosynthesis in $^{14}CO_2$ showed clearly that the label was rapidly incorporated in trehalose by *Selaginella* but in sucrose by *Lycopodium*. The authors comment that this technique may be of value in assessing biochemical similarities or differences shown by compounds which display only quantitative variation between taxa.

The sugar alcohols have been studied from a taxonomic standpoint by Plouvier, who provides a useful classification of this group of carbohydrates.[383] Though he indicates the need for a much wider sampling, and though most of the compounds are widespread, Plouvier quotes some cases where the distributions of polyols and cyclitols seem to follow a taxonomic pattern. The cyclitol pinitol (XVI) is especially characteristic of the Caryophyllaceae (present in 83 of 85 species tested), although it is also found elsewhere. It is characteristic of *Magnolia* alone of genera in the Magnoliaceae, and does not occur in closely related families. Quercitol (XVII) is similarly widespread but is particularly common in the Menispermaceae. In the Fagaceae, it is absent from *Castanea* and *Fagus* but present in all 35 species of *Quercus* so far tested.

Sorbitol, a straight chain polyol widespread in plants, is exceptionally common in the Rosaceae. Plouvier considers that sorbitol distribution is in complete accordance with taxonomy in the Rosaceae, supporting, for example, the transference of *Ulmaria* to subfamily Rosoideae (usually lacking sorbitol) from the Spiraeoideae where all tested genera contain sorbitol.[382]

Glycoside distributions have been generally surveyed for possible relevance to taxonomy[371] but are usually considered in terms of the aglycone.[202] Harborne is impressed by the great variation in sugar components of glycosides and remarks on the small attention so far paid to it. The study of glycosides has so far been too patchy for their taxonomic value to be readily appreciated.

Certain glycosides have always interested taxonomists, because of their distributions and notable properties. The cardiac glycosides of *Digitalis* (Scrophulariaceae) are an obvious instance. Digitonin is a glycoside of galactose, glucose and xylose with the steroid digitogenin (a saponin) and is restricted to *Digitalis*. Other notorious glycosides release prussic acid on hydrolysis.[178] Whether or not these cyanogenic glycosides prove to be valuable in classification, at least they constitute a feature which is quickly determined. Picric acid paper is exposed to the fumes arising from crushed foliage. A brick-red coloration indicates the production of HCN by enzymic hydrolysis. About 60 diverse plant families contain cyanogenic glycosides.[221] The biosynthetic pathways for many or most of them may be similar,[465] so perhaps the presence of these glycosides is a very ancient character which was once universal. Jones critically reviews the possible reasons why it may be useful by rendering plants toxic to predators and parasites.[258] Some cyanogenic glycosides are widespread. Linamarin (acetone-cyanhydrin-β-glucoside) is recorded from *Phaseolus lunatus* (Leguminosae) and from *Manihot utilissima* (Euphorbiaceae). Amygdalin (D(−)-mandelonitrile-β-gentiobioside) by contrast appears only in certain groups of the Rosaceae. Gibbs[178] notes that no specimens from the Violaceae or Cucurbitaceae have yielded HCN in his tests.

Though a few suggestive distributions are hinted at in the literature, the general value of plant glycosides in taxonomy cannot be assessed until a systematic survey is made with a taxonomic instead of a pharmacological purpose.

Polysaccharides perhaps offer the greatest hope for taxonomic data from carbohydrates because of their complexity and diversity. At least in principle, they might carry some coded information if we knew how to read it, but they have so far not been much examined from a systematic point of view. This is partly because the isolation and fractionation procedures for polysaccharides often consist of several laborious stages, during any of which non-taxonomic variations can arise. Results from different laboratories may not always be comparable. Few plant groups have been studied comprehensively in terms of polysaccharide variation, and so the taxonomic gain has been scanty. Some groups have been studied in part only because their polysaccharides are commercially important. Investigations of cell wall polysaccharides of algae, and of timber or pulp plants fall into this economically inspired category. The poor coverage of the plant kingdom means that eventually many apparently restricted distributions of polymerized carbohydrate types will undoubtedly be shown to be spurious. It is possible to cite only a few examples of taxonomically meaningful polysaccharide surveys, because only a few have ever been made.

Celluloses seem to differ only in quantity and degree of polymerization in the various plant groups.[376] The xylans, mannans and arabino-galactans, occurring in the 'hemicellulose' fraction of cell walls, display a more promising diversity. In some algae they may replace cellulose almost completely. In the brown algae the cell walls seem to consist almost wholly of alginic acid, a β-1,4-linked mannuronogularan.[239]

The proportions of monosaccharide constituents which compose the hemicellulose fraction of cell walls (mainly mannose, glucose and xylose, with uronic acids) exhibit considerable variation. Hemicelluloses from varieties of the same species are found to be rather similar.[359] There is variation between different parts of the same plant. Gaillard compared linear and branched hemicellulose fractions of species of legumes and grasses.[175] She found conspicuous differences between the two families, especially in the branched hemicelluloses, in terms of proportions of monosaccharides (see Table 7.1) and structure. Branched polymers of the grasses contained a high percentage of xylose, whereas those of legumes had relatively more uronic acid, galactose and arabinose. In the grass preparation, it was found that the uronic acid was linked to xylose, whereas in the legume polymer it was attached to arabinose.

Table 7.1. Composition of the linear A and B, and the branched B hemicellulose polymers from some Gramineae and Leguminosae. (From Gaillard.[175])

	Trifolium pratense (red clover) (%)	Medicago sativa (lucerne) (%)	Glycine max (soya bean) (%)	Lolium perenne (rye-grass) (%)	Triticum vulgare (wheat) (%)	Zea mays (maize) (%)
Linear A						
Uronic acid	4.7	6.6	6.6	1.9	2.1	2.4
Galactose	—	—	—	—	—	—
Arabinose	—	—	—	12.9	5.7	5.3
Xylose	95.3	93.4	93.4	85.2	92.2	92.3
Glucose	—	—	—	—	—	—
Linear B						
Uronic acid	1.0	1.5	4.3	0.4	0.3	0.1
Galactose	—	—	—	—	—	—
Arabinose	10.8	8.3	8.3	16.5	11.1	10.9
Xylose	88.2	90.1	89.2	83.1	88.6	89.0
Glucose	(11.6)	(11.4)	(4.0)	(11.0)	(12.0)	(21.5)
Branched B						
Uronic acid	20.6	22.3	24.6	5.4	7.9	12.8
Galactose	34.5	31.1	34.3	7.7	9.8	8.7
Arabinose	27.6	34.2	24.0	23.8	26.5	24.4
Xylose	17.3	3.1	3.4	63.1	55.8	54.1
Glucose	—	9.3	6.9	—	—	—
Rhamnose	—	—	6.8	—	—	—

Among storage polysaccharides, some taxonomic claims have been made for the distribution of seed 'amyloids'. These compounds consist of a main chain of glucose with side-chains including xylose and galactose. A characteristic blue coloration is formed when amyloid is treated with I_2–KI and sodium sulphate. Structures of amyloid have been fully worked out only for *Tamarindus indica* (Leguminosae) and for *Annona muricata* (Annonaceae).[277,278] They were fundamentally similar. In a test involving over 2500 species, Kooiman detected amyloid in sixteen families of dicotyledons, but in none of the monocotyledons tested.[276] 'Amyloid families' cannot be said to be closely related (e.g. Acanthaceae and Leguminosae), but within families the distribution of amyloid sometimes follows taxonomic lines. In sub-family Caesalpinioideae (Leguminosae) though amyloid was found in many genera, all were in the tribes Cynometreae, Sclerobieae and Amherstieae. Only a few species in subfamily Lotoideae contained amyloid. *Paeonia* was the only amyloid-containing genus of 30 tested from the Ranunculaceae and it is noteworthy that some taxonomists would transfer *Paeonia* to a family of its own.

Polysaccharides of gum exudates have been studied by chemists mainly because of their commercial value (e.g. 'gum arabic'). Some of these studies have nevertheless been sufficiently comprehensive and careful to justify taxonomic scrutiny. Anderson and Dea have discussed chemotaxonomic aspects of variation in the wattle gums (*Acacia*, Leguminosae).[16] Their paper is a laudable attempt by two carbohydrate chemists to communicate specifically with plant taxonomists. The gums which they review are complex branched polymers of rhamnose, galactose and arabinose, with smaller quantities of uronic acids. Their study reveals that wattle gums are much more diverse than was formerly thought. The most comprehensive analyses have been on gums from the sections Gummiferae and Vulgares, and it is quite plain from the chemical results that the two taxa are distinct. Gum variation may not always be as discontinuous as in *Acacia*. Quite small differences were found between gums from species of the gymnosperm *Araucaria* (Araucariaceae).[17]

With present techniques the time taken for a complete analysis of a complex gum is about one year, and the method will probably not appeal to chemotaxonomists for that reason. However, Anderson and Dea point out that chemists will be analysing these gums in any case, and would therefore welcome taxonomic advice on which ones to choose for study.

CONCLUSION

Most of the taxonomic information from carbohydrate studies is fragmentary and sparse. The significance of distributions of many types of carbohydrate is still uncertain because they are often so involved in basic metabolism. Rare monosaccharides, known usually from glycosides, show the greatest discontinuities in distribution. They may well have arisen independently by chance, and in any case their taxonomic value is as restricted as their distribution. Polysaccharides may have more information to offer the taxonomist, if it can be decoded, but the laborious methods of analysis are an obstacle at present. More rapid progress in the application of carbohydrate evidence to taxonomy can be achieved only by co-operation between chemists and taxonomists.

8

Evidence from Alkaloids

It has long been known that certain plants and plant groups contain 'principles' which can exert marked physiological effects on the nervous systems of animals. According to the nature and advancement of the society, these plants have been variously regarded as a source of medicinal preparations, magical syrups or essences, or potent poisons. During the nineteenth century, chemists began to identify the compounds which possess these striking properties, pharmacologists studied the basis of their physiological action, while botanists searched diligently for more of the plants. It is not surprising that an investigation with such different aims and personnel led to difficulties in defining the nature of the substances being studied. In any case, the chemists soon showed that the structures of the active principles were very diverse.

Many of the materials were found to be basic, and so they became known as alkaloids. Chemists working on molecular structure classified them on the basis of the chemical nucleus (e.g. 'the pyridine alkaloids'). Pharmacologists were naturally more impressed by the effects on living animals and so classified the bases by reference to physiological responses (e.g. the 'curare alkaloids', the 'mydriatic alkaloids'). Botanists classified them by reference to the plant source (e.g. 'solanaceous alkaloids' from members of the Solanaceae). It is interesting that initial classification was deemed fundamental to further progress in all three fields of study.

No satisfactory definition of alkaloids exists even today, because they do not constitute a natural group of materials in terms of source, structure or properties. Alkaloids are organic, nitrogen-containing bases, usually with a heterocyclic ring of some kind. They are non-essential to the growth of the plant, and have effects on the central nervous system of animals. Almost every part of this definition has exceptions. Despite this it seems best to consider the alkaloids as a group, because heterogeneous as they are, they do not readily fit into any other category of compounds. Alkaloid definition has been considered by Hegnauer who concludes that for chemotaxonomic purposes a biogenetic classification of the compounds is most useful.[222,223] Biogenetic classifications reflect the manner (i.e. the pathways) in which alkaloids are synthesized rather than the final structure, properties or distribution of the molecule. Such groupings have been possible only since modern biochemical research, using radioisotopes, has revealed the main routes of synthesis. Many of the reactions leading to the formation of diverse heterocyclic structures are of the same type.[297] Problems with biogenetic classifications are that they are subject to rapid change with increasing knowledge, and that complex alkaloids may arise in part from more than one pathway. Whichever classification is adopted, some alkaloids can be placed in two or more categories. Taxonomists may assert that the obscurity of alkaloid classification has been a reason for the tardy recognition of their relevance to plant classification. Even modern works on alkaloids still use mixed classifications based partly on chemical, partly on botanical criteria. The system used in this chapter is based primarily on chemical structure, which alone is constant, secondly on biogenetic evidence, and finally on botanical distribution.

Three main categories of alkaloids must first be distinguished. **True alkaloids** have a nitrogen-containing heterocyclic nucleus derived from a biogenetic amine. The amine arises by decarboxylation of an amino acid. Examples of this type are the isoquinoline alkaloids (see below) which are formed by decarboxylation of phenylalanine. **Protoalkaloids** are similarly derived from amino acids, but lack a heterocyclic ring. Natural protoalkaloids are usually simple amines (e.g. ephedrine, Fig. 8.1, I; mescaline, II) with various additional groups. Protoalkaloids may sometimes be precursors of true alkaloids. **Pseudoalkaloids** seem to be biogenetically unrelated to amino acids and thus considerably different from the other two categories. They are included in some treatments of alkaloids because of their pharmacological significance, and because they contain nitrogen. Most of them are derived from terpenes (q.v.), from sterols, aliphatic acids, nicotinic acid or purines. Their distributions cannot meaningfully be compared with those of the

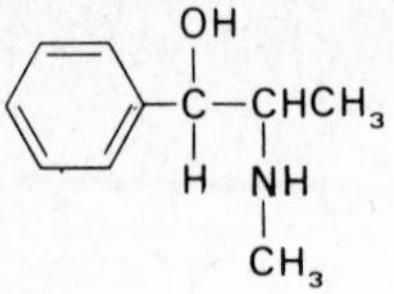

I Ephedrine

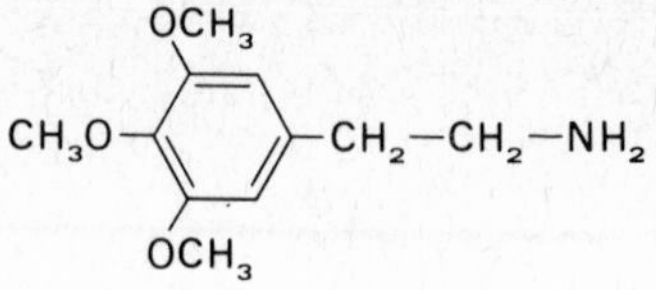

II Mescaline

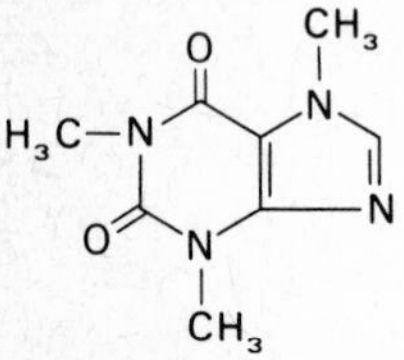

III Caffeine

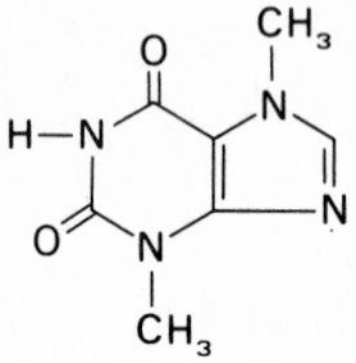

IV Theobromine

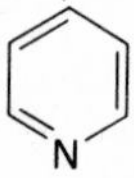

V Pyridine

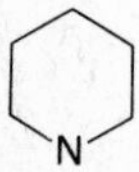

VI Piperidine

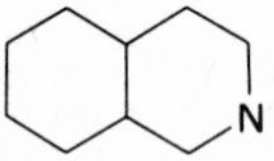

VII Isoquinoline

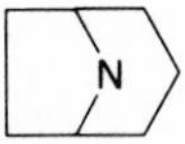

VIII Tropane

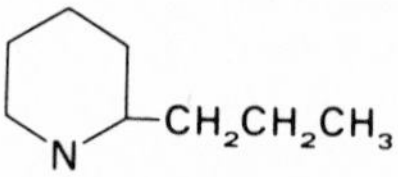

IX Coniine

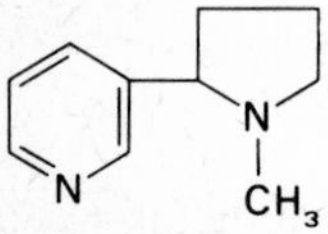

X Nicotine

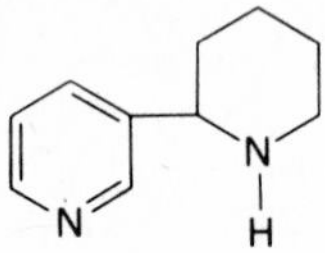

XI Anabasine

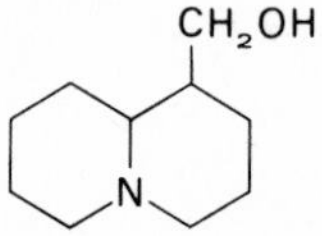

XII Lupinine

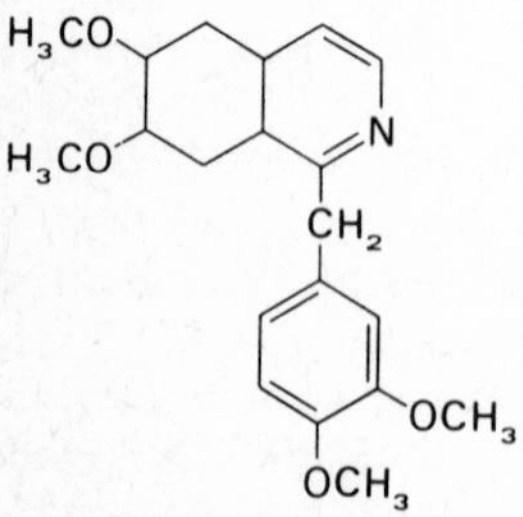

XIII Papaverine

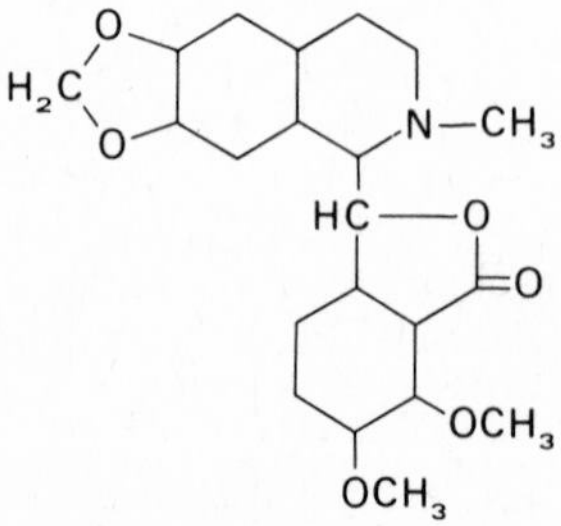

XIV Hydrastine

Fig. 8.1 Structure of alkaloids (and bases).

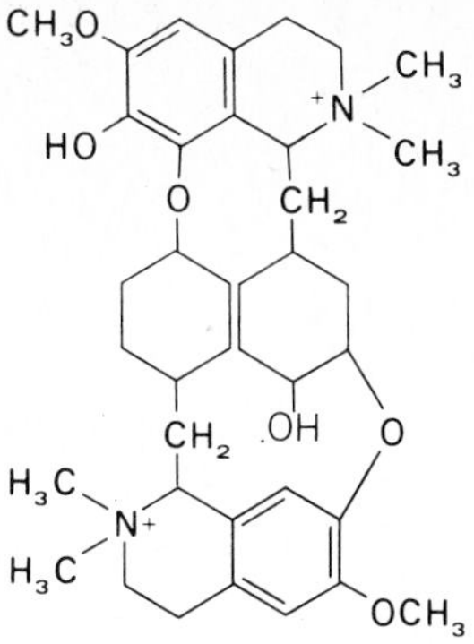

XV   Tubocurarine

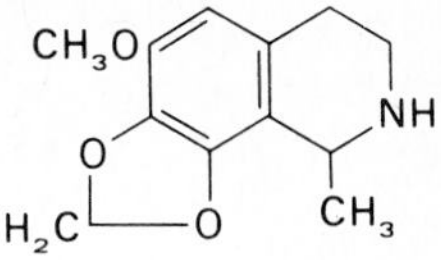

XVI   Anhalonin

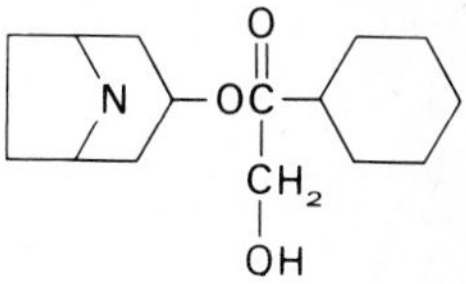

XVII   Atropine (D,L-hyoscyamine)

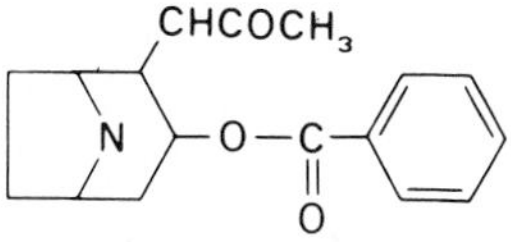

XVIII   Cocaine

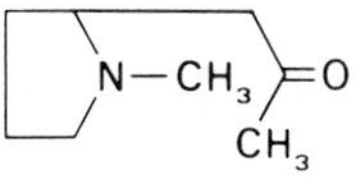

XIX   Hygrine

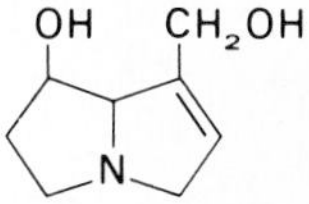

XX   Retronecine

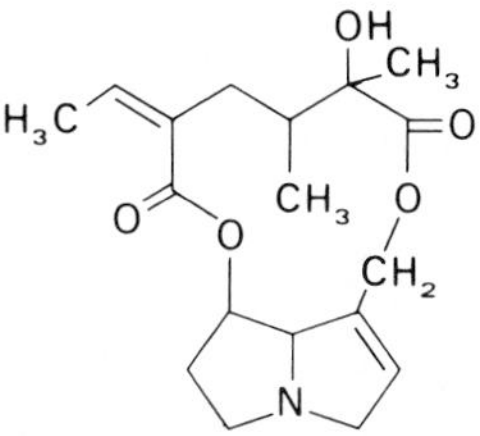

XXI   Senecionine

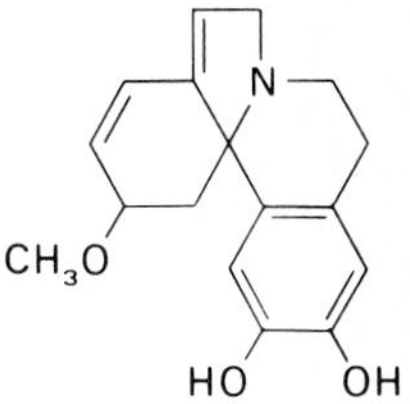

XXII   Erysopine

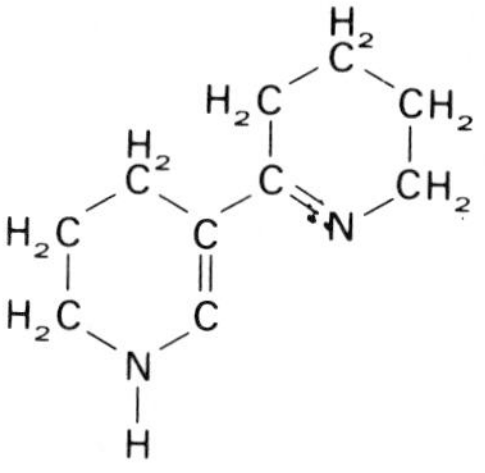

XXIII   Hystrine

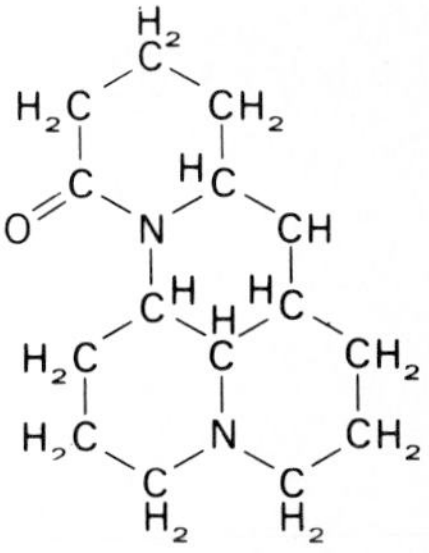

XXIV   Matrine

Fig. 8.1   *continued*

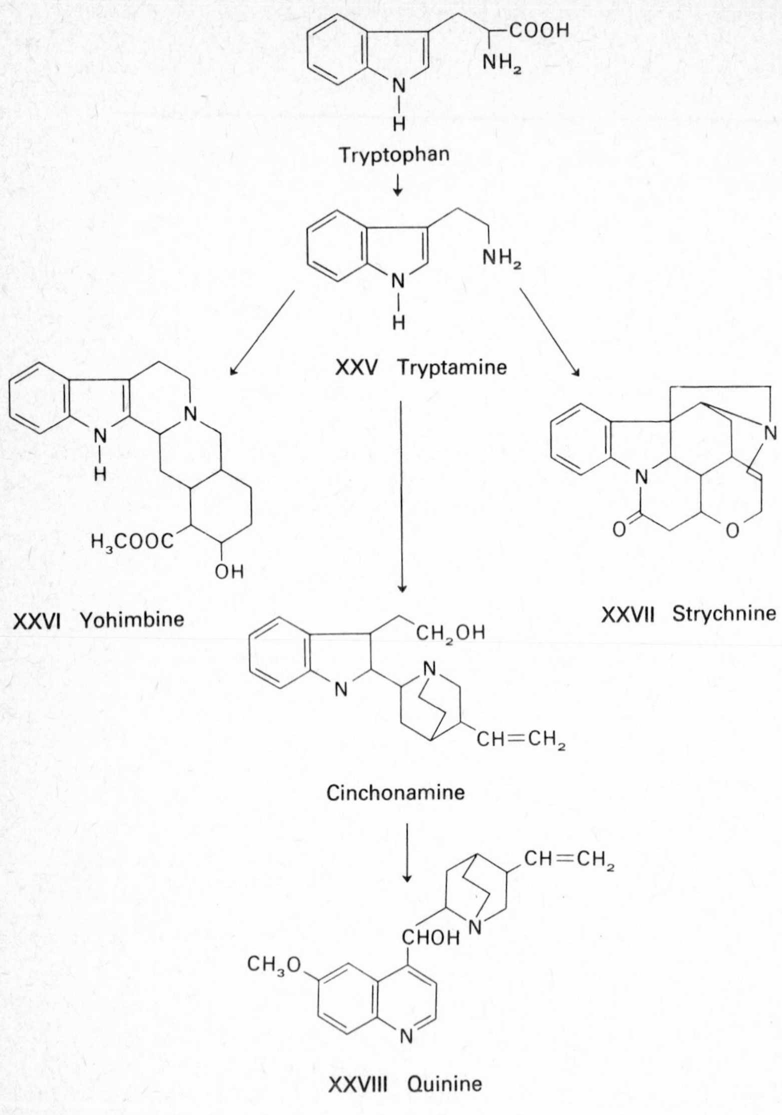

Tryptophan

XXV Tryptamine

XXVI Yohimbine

XXVII Strychnine

Cinchonamine

XXVIII Quinine

Fig. 8.1 *continued*

alkaloids derived from amino acids. In this discussion they are therefore excluded. Among well-known 'alkaloids' which are thereby omitted are caffeine (III) and theobromine (IV), which are methylated purines.

Alkaloids are precipitated readily by 'alkaloidal reagents' (e.g. Dragendorff's reagent—KBiI₄, or mercuric chloride), quickly separated by paper chromatography, and located by a range of test solutions. The techniques available are suitable for taxonomic use.

STRUCTURES OF ALKALOIDS

Even restricting the discussion to the protoalkaloids and true alkaloids does not permit more than a fraction of the structural diversity of the compounds to be indicated. For more complete treatment of alkaloid structure and biogenesis, standard works should be consulted.[227,320] Reviews of work on alkaloid biogenesis are frequent.[297,309,351,392] Information on the biological properties of alkaloids is best sought in textbooks of pharmacology, toxicology, and medical jurisprudence.

Most of the true alkaloids belong to groups which can be related structurally to parent bases such as pyridine (V), piperidine (VI), isoquinoline (VII) and tropane (VIII). Alkaloids of each type are not necessarily always synthesized in the same way, but most of them, and those related to other bases, seem to be derived from a quite restricted range of common amino acids.

Pyridine and piperidine alkaloids

The parent base pyridine occurs in some plants (e.g. *Haplopappus*), but lysine appears to be the precursor for most of these alkaloids. Coniine (IX), which is produced by *Conium maculatum* (Umbelliferae), was used to poison Socrates. Several related compounds (e.g. conhydrine, *N*-methyl coniine) accompany it, and they are collectively referred to the botanical category 'hemlock alkaloids'. It is suggested that this group of pyridine alkaloids may arise by condensation of four acetate units.[309]

Another group of alkaloids occurs in *Nicotiana* (Solanaceae) and some other genera. Of these the best known is nicotine (X).

Anabasine (XI) also occurs in tobacco, where it is formed from lysine and nicotinic acid. In the legume and chenopod species where anabasine also occurs, it can be synthesized from two molecules of lysine.[222] Presence of an alkaloid in two plants evidently does not guarantee that the same pathway is operating. Cromwell reviews evidence of variations in piperidine alkaloid biosynthesis.[103] It is quite likely that despite their structural similarities, the pyridine and piperidine rings may often arise in different ways. Label from lysine appeared rapidly in anabasine in *Nicotiana glauca*.[296] In *N. tabacum*, where anabasine is replaced by nicotine, no label appeared when plants were supplied with labelled lysine.

The lupin alkaloids such as lupinine (XII), sparteine and cytisine, characteristic of many species in the Leguminosae, are also derived from lysine. In chemical classifications they are termed the quinolizidine alkaloids.

Isoquinoline alkaloids

This large and diverse group of alkaloids includes many of commercial importance. The amino acids phenylalanine and tyrosine both seem to act as efficient precursors for the isoquinoline nucleus.[392] Many are quite complex molecules, not at all obviously related to isoquinoline itself. Benzyl derivatives include papaverine (XIII). Phthalide-isoquinoline alkaloids are exemplified by hydrastine (XIV) which is found in the Berberidaceae and Ranunculaceae. Other isoquinoline alkaloids are berberine, morphine, aporphine and protopine. Most of the curare alkaloids fall into the isoquinoline group. Curare is the name given to the complex alkaloidal extracts used by Amazonian Indians as arrow poisons. They cause rapid paralysis when introduced into the blood stream. Curarizing alkaloids of several different plants are included in the native preparations and it was a long time before the botanical sources were authenticated. Tubocurarine (XV), the principal alkaloid of bamboo-tube curare (so named from the Brazilian packing method), is a *bis*-benzylisoquinoline from *Chondrodendron tomentosum* (Menispermaceae).

Many of the hallucinogenic or stupefying principles from the Cactaceae have proved to be isoquinoline alkaloids. Anhalonin (XVI) is found in the dried crowns (mescal buttons) of the pellote cactus (*Lophophora williamsii*) which are chewed and then swallowed by the Indians of NW. Mexico and SW. United States. Mescaline (II) is a protoalkaloid from the same source.

Tropane alkaloids

Though they can be connected to the structure of the base tropane, these alkaloids seem to arise initially from ornithine. Some other alkaloids also originating from ornithine are also considered in this section.

Among the best known members of the group are the solanaceous alkaloids, which are very characteristic of the Solanaceae. Atropine and hyoscyamine (XVII) serve as examples. In *Erythroxylum* (Erythroxylaceae) are found the cocaine alkaloids which are of the same type (XVIII), but do not occur in the Solanaceae. Solanaceous alkaloids are not absolutely restricted to the Solanaceae. Hygrine (XIX) is also produced from ornithine, and occurs, often accompanied by derivatives, in most of the families synthesizing tropane alkaloids. Necine alkaloids (XX) also belong to the 'ornithine family', and from them can be derived the pyrrolizidene alkaloids such as senecionine (XXI).[81]

Indole alkaloids

Many alkaloids contain an indole ring, and might be considered as a recognizable group. They are synthesized in different ways, however. Sometimes the indole nucleus originates from phenylalanine, as in *Erythrina* alkaloids (Leguminosae) such as erysodine (XXII). In most cases (e.g. tryptamine (XXV), yohimbine (XXVI) and strychnine (XXVII)) the parent compound is tryptophan (see Fig. 8.1). Without experimental work it is not always possible to classify indole alkaloids into the appropriate biogenetic category, but when they occur together with alkaloids of known origin, these may be circumstantial evidence of their metabolic history.

The alkaloids related to the base quinoline are also formed from indole compounds. The best-known member of this group is quinine (XXVIII) from the bark of *Cinchona* species (Rubiaceae). In other families where quinine is synthesized, such as Annonaceae and Loganiaceae, the route of manufacture may be different from that in *Cinchona*.

VARIATION AND FUNCTION OF ALKALOIDS

The medical value of many alkaloids encouraged attempts to produce high-yielding strains of alkaloid plants, and stimulated work on the occurrence and variation of alkaloids in individuals and populations. Fluctuations characterizing secondary plant products must be fully recognized before their taxonomic value can be fully assessed.

Hegnauer carefully distinguishes 'plants which contain alkaloids' from 'alkaloidal plants'.[222] Many plants contain alkaloids in trace quantities, while others (alkaloidal plants) accumulate large amounts. Perhaps, like the situation reported for non-protein amino acids (Chapter 4), if enough plant material were extracted, some alkaloids would be found in most species. Narcotine was found in extracts of kilogram quantities of common fruits and vegetables, though at the time it was associated with the opium poppy.[417] Hegnauer asserts that there is a taxonomic significance in the accumulation of alkaloids, additional to and possibly more important than the mere presence of the synthetic pathway. Though that is a controversial point, it may often be the case that accumulation is possible only because of genotypic modifications which minimize damage arising from high concentrations of materials like nicotine. High-alkaloid selections of ergot (*Claviceps purpurea*) have a lower growth rate than strains which produce less alkaloid.[309]

Alkaloidal plants, as defined by Hegnauer, contain more than 0.01% of alkaloids. This is a practical limit which permits the use of small quantities of herbarium material as a source for analysis. Trace occurrences of alkaloids are excluded from consideration, and so are plants in which only a single alkaloid seems to be present. Usually the alkaloids of an alkaloidal plant belong to the same biogenetic category. By this definition, many of the Gentianaceae are not regarded as alkaloidal plants because they contain only gentianine. *Ricinus communis* is not an alkaloidal plant since it produces only ricinine. Neither of these two bases is derived from a biogenetic amine, however, so Hegnauer's definition appears to be a sound one.

The quantity and proportions of alkaloids in alkaloidal plants are to some extent under genetic control, but they are also greatly affected by fluctuations of the environment. Successful selection of high-yielding strains of alkaloidal species such as *Datura stramonium* (Solanaceae) implies that levels of alkaloid production are heritable. Induced polyploids produce more alkaloid than the original diploid.[412] Table 8.1 records some results in which it is clear that in hybrids of *Baptisia leucophaea* and *B. sphaerocarpa* (Leguminosae), alkaloid production differs considerably from the situation in the parents.[100] Control and proportions of different alkaloids have a trivial, easily upset genetic basis and proportional differences are

Table 8.1 Relative % of lupin alkaloids in seven hybrid plants and in the two parent species[a] of *Baptisia*. (From Cranmer and Turner.[100])

Parent *Baptisia* species	Cytisine	Methyl-cytisine	Ana-gyrine	13-Hydroxy-sparteine	Bapti-foline	Therm-opsine	Unknown
B. sphaerocarpa Nutt.[a]	9	74	6	—	1	11	—
B. leucophaea Nutt.[a]	77	Trace	23	—	—	Trace	—
B. sphaerocarpa × *B. leucophaea* hybrid plants							
1	3	13	38	5	—	41	Trace
2	3	21	39	3	—	34	Trace
3	2	31	42	3	—	22	Trace
4	1	6	90	2	—	1	—
5	2	96	2	Trace	—	Trace	—
6	2	36	36	4	—	20	2
7	2	15	70	1	—	12	—

[a] All the analyses with the exception of that for *B. sphaerocarpa* are for leaves and stems of young plants. The *B. sphaerocarpa* plants were flowering.

therefore unlikely to be reliable taxonomic characters. Nowacki also has studied genetic control of alkaloid synthesis and shown that it is disturbed in hybrids.[364]

Proportions of alkaloids seem constant in some species, but highly variable in others. The hyoscine : hyoscyamine ratio in *Atropa belladonna* (Solanaceae) is rather constant, whereas the morphine fraction of total opium alkaloids (*Papaver somniferum*) is inconsistent. Varying growth conditions arising from seasonal, climatic and soil differences have marked effects on alkaloid production. It is hardly surprising that compounds so closely connected with amino acid metabolism should exhibit such variations. The alkaloidal content of plants changes as they mature and age. Hyoscine is the dominant alkaloid of young belladonna leaves, but it declines as the leaves age to become a minor component of total alkaloids. Developmental and geographical variations occur in the lupin alkaloid content of leaves of *Baptisia leucophaea*. Methylcystine was present only in trace amounts in the young plants, but rose to comprise a fifth of the total alkaloids in old individuals.[334] Trace alkaloids in some specimens could not be detected in others, suggesting that careful sampling is necessary when alkaloids are to be assayed for taxonomic purposes. Anagyrine averaged 20% of total alkaloids in one Texas population, but only 11% of another.

Alkaloids are distributed throughout the tissues of alkaloidal plants, usually existing as salts in the vacuoles. They are often most concentrated in storage organs. Variation between species in the location of the alkaloids is partly due to the different sites of synthesis. Mothes gives a review of the general physiology of alkaloids in plants.[348] Synthesis in both leaves and roots has been detected.

Alkaloidal plants are not found in all plant groups. It is clear that while alkaloid production is not limited to the higher plants, the angiosperms are the best known sources. Others include certain fungi, pteridophytes and gymnosperms. Even a few animals produce alkaloids. In most instances, the alkaloidal substances of lower plants are pseudoalkaloids. Traces of nicotine occur in *Lycopodium* and *Equisetum* (Pteridophyta), ephedrine and some congeners are very characteristic of the Ephedraceae (Gymnospermae), while piperidine alkaloids derived from polyketo acids are recorded from Pinaceae. The highly poisonous principles of yew (*Taxus baccata*, Taxaceae) proved to be diterpene derivatives, and thus are not true alkaloids. Angiosperms have yielded by far the largest and most diverse range of alkaloids, over 5000 now being recorded, mainly from the dicotyledons. Hegnauer estimates that 15–20% of species of vascular plants are alkaloidal.[222]

There has long been speculation about the possible functions of alkaloids, since they are among the most remarkable secondary plant products. As noted earlier they are known to be non-essential for plant growth, though the structure of some resembles that of certain growth substances. Scions of alkaloidal plants (e.g. *Datura stramonium*) grown on non-alkaloidal stocks grew perfectly well without traces of their normal alkaloid content.[413] Tomato scions grew well in the presence of hyoscyamine produced from alkaloidal rootstocks. In other experiments, scions were damaged by high concentrations of nicotine when *Nicotiana* stocks were employed.[349]

It has often been asserted in the past that alkaloids have no particular function in many or most plants, despite their high concentrations. Luckner gives a recent statement of the view that any function of secondary products results from accidentally useful properties residing in excretory material, and that most of them are simply wastes.[309]

Other workers have ascribed a variety of possible functions to the alkaloids. As bases they may exchange with soil cations, so maintaining ionic balance, but this cannot be a general function since alkaloids are not universal. From the taxonomic standpoint, function may not necessarily be helpful in understanding the distribution of alkaloidal types, because their properties often have less to do with the heterocyclic nucleus than with the additional groups. Chemically similar alkaloids, in the same category, may have quite different biological properties and hence potentially different functions. Such alkaloids would comprise different, i.e. non-homologous, characters, and could not be compared for purposes of classification. Without time-consuming experiments it is impossible to decide if identical alkaloids are produced by the same pathway, except perhaps in closely related taxa. Difficulties relating to the homology of alkaloid characters mean that unless a general function can be assigned to all the alkaloids of a plant, i.e. to the 'alkaloidal' phenomenon, the taxonomic usefulness of the compounds must be dubious. Happily, the complexity of the alkaloid complement of alkaloidal plants is such that it makes fortuitious resemblances between taxa less likely.

The observation that alkaloids seem to be physiologically redundant was explained at first by the simple, if unimaginative, suggestion that they are waste products. Too toxic to be detoxification products, like those well known in animals, they are stored in the vacuoles and cause damage if they escape.[309] If they are waste products, it is curious that they are synthesized so rapidly by some plants, but not others. It is not obvious which metabolic process generates waste alkaloids in such large quantities, nor why this process is found only in certain plants.

The nitrogenous content of alkaloids has suggested to some that they are a source of stored, soluble nitrogen. Certainly they accumulate in storage organs, but they are often concentrated in leaves and stems as well, which are not the best protected sites for storage. In some plants, endosperm alkaloids disappear during germination, but they constitute so small a fraction of total nitrogen that they cannot be significant. In artificially starved plants, alkaloid content remains high, suggesting that alkaloidal nitrogen is not available in time of need.

Alkaloids may have a protective or defence function, by repelling predators and pests. Their poisonous or unpalatable properties in this event would be no more accidental than the result of any other mutation. Luckner doubts that this explanation can be general, since not all plants produce alkaloids, and those which do have not so far out-survived those which do not.[309] But this only draws attention to the fact that some plants are defended in other ways. He points out that only in extreme conditions of altitude or desert can selection be seen to have favoured alkaloidal species. Furthermore, he suggests that the highly poisonous nature of some alkaloids may blind us to

Fig. 8.2   *Senecio jacobaea*, resistant to grazing by cattle, in a Scottish pasture.

the fact that they are ineffective against some non-human predators: belladonna can be consumed with impunity by certain rabbits and pigs.

These statements support rather than refute the thesis that alkaloids are defence products. Alkaloidal plants will have been selected only during a time when they inhabited marginal habitats, such as deserts. Subsequently they may have been so successful that they invaded mesic environments. The alkaloidal character would persist until it became disadvantageous. Evolution is demonstrable only in ecologically marginal circumstances, just like those cited by Luckner. Occurrence of successful non-alkaloidal plants merely demonstrates that other protective devices are possible, such as persistent basal meristems, woolly indumenta, or other toxic chemicals (e.g. amino acids, cyanogenetic glycosides, *q.v.*).

Thorns are the classic defence mechanism in plants, and they also are common in arid areas where grazing pressure is high. Alkaloids selected for defence purposes will be related to the tastes and susceptibilities of the predators present at the time of selection.

Atropa belladonna presumably developed its tropane poisons in an environment where rabbits and pigs were no threat to its survival.

Further evidence of the power of alkaloids as defence mechanisms is not hard to find. *Senecio jacobaea*, the ragwort (Compositae), is a striking example of a plant which can survive in pasture because of its unpalatability to stock (Fig. 8.2). Most of the thousand or so species of *Senecio* and the related genus *Erechtites* contain necine-type alkaloids. Species of *Echinops* (Compositae), presumably evolving their defence metabolism at a different time, in a different biotic environment, and with a different genetic background, are characterized by isoquinoline alkaloids. Alkaloid concentration is a commonly used index of palatability in forage plants.[172]

Secondary substances are not commonly produced by animals, which generally have powers of defence altogether greater than those of individual plants. Many animals can run away from predators. Where animal secondary substances are produced, however, they can often be connected with defence. Toads produce a defensive secretion which includes alkaloids and cardioactive glycosides. Some animals sequester toxins from the plants on which they feed. Though the *Senecio* alkaloids are avoided by cattle, they are accumulated by the caterpillar of the cinnabar moth (*Tyria jacobaea*) and act in the larva and the adult as a deterrent to bird-predators. Both stages in the life cycle are characterized by striking pigmentation and patterning which advertises the unpleasant taste.[410]

Finally, the observation that relatively few monocotyledons are alkaloidal might reflect their possible origin from primitive aquatic angiosperms. In the aquatic habitat, grazing by herbivores is so negligible that selection pressure for defensive alkaloids would be unusual, and may have developed independently in several monocotyledonous groups after they secondarily colonized the land. Alkaloids are not produced by algae. Most aquatic angiosperms which produce alkaloids have floating, not submerged, leaves (e.g. Nymphaeaceae). It is possible, if alkaloids are solely excretory, that their absence from many water plants is related to the ease of disposal of water-soluble wastes in the aquatic habitat.

If the alkaloids function primarily as a means of defence, related plants might be expected to synthesize similar types. This need not always be the case, since different alkaloids could sometimes serve the purpose equally well. Large families should be expected to include plants synthesizing different kinds of alkaloids. Unrelated plants might rely on the same alkaloid for defence purposes, but would probably produce it by a different pathway, manifested by differences in accompanying minor alkaloids and protoalkaloids. Alkaloids of different biogenetic categories might be expected to co-occur in plant groups which have reacted to more than one phase of selection for defence mechanisms. Some species may have evolved particular alkaloidal defence systems, which characterize their descendants (possibly now amounting to a whole genus or family). Others may have developed systems relying on cyanogenetic or cardiac glycosides or toxic amino acids. It seems odd that so many secondary plant substances should have powerful physiological effects if they are merely storage or waste materials. It is hardly likely that plants are so inefficient that they are obliged to squander energy on production and accumulation of large amounts of useless secondary by-products. Natural selection exercises a pitiless scrutiny on waste. *A priori*, therefore, we should conclude that only a small fraction of the alkaloids produced (the fraction found in non-alkaloidal plants?) is metabolically inevitable. Perhaps Hegnauer is correct in thinking that alkaloid accumulation is taxonomically meaningful. Perhaps, also, the defence systems of plants should be considered in relation to the time and place in which they are thought to have evolved.

ALKALOID DISTRIBUTION AND TAXONOMY

Alkaloids are not universally accumulated by plants. Some families are especially rich in alkaloidal species, such as the Berberidaceae, Leguminosae, Ranunculaceae and Solanaceae. These families are sufficiently different to show that mere accumulation of alkaloids does not imply a taxonomic relationship at the family level.

Alkaloids characterizing species of a particular taxon are frequently of the same chemical or biogenetic group, suggesting that related plants share the same pathways of alkaloid synthesis. If this is so, there is some reason to consider alkaloid content as a source of taxonomic evidence. Thus the Papaveraceae contain isoquinoline alkaloids, always including protopine. Many legumes synthesize the lupin alkaloids, while the Solanaceae have their characteristic tropane derivatives. On the other hand, some families are more versatile in their alkaloid metabolism. The Gramineae and the Compositae produce many different kinds of alkaloid.[223] The Rutaceae synthesize alkaloids of nine different types.[387]

Specialization of alkaloid production is sometimes shown by the very narrow distribution of certain molecules. Morphine is the extreme example, being found only in the opium poppy (*Papaver somniferum*). Coniine (IX) is restricted to a few umbellifers. Indole alkaloids of the strychnine group (Fig. 8.1) occur only in a few *Strychnos* species (Loganiaceae) which are the sources of the arrow poisons of calabash curare (Guyana). Though tropane alkaloids are usually associated with solanaceous plants, the cocaines also fall into this category. Cocaine is known from two species of *Erythroxylum*.

Mears and Mabry give several interesting examples of alkaloid restriction and possible taxonomic value in the Leguminosae.[334] Dipiperidyl lupin alkaloids such as hystrine (XXIII) occur only in three genera (see Table 8.2). *Genista* and *Adenocarpus* (Genisteae) have long been considered close relatives, but *Ammodendron* is normally placed in the Sophoreae, though it lacks the matrine alkaloids (XXIV) which characterize that tribe. Perhaps this replacement of one alkaloid type by another is an indication that *Ammodendron* should be transferred to the Genisteae. Other characters of the genus should be re-examined.

Table 8.2. Distribution of the ammodendrine-hystrine alkaloids in the Leguminosae. (From Mears and Mabry.[334])

Genera	Hystrine	Sphaero-carpine	Adeno-carpine	Iso-orensine	Santi-aguine
Genista	+	+			
Ammodendron		+			
Adenocarpus			+	+	+
Adenocarpus species					
A. anagyrus			+		+
A. foliolosus			+		+
A. mannii			+	+	+
A. grandifolius			+	+	+
A. intermedius			+	+	+

Supposed restricted occurrences of alkaloids are liable to change when further analyses are made. Previously it was thought that alkaloids were absent from the monocotyledons. Further study of alkaloid distribution should be encouraged, particularly in groups of unknown pharmacological significance. The need for new and better drugs still determines the main directions of alkaloid research, which tends to concentrate for economic reasons on taxa which are already known to be good sources. Such concentration does nothing to expose spuriously narrow distributions. There has been much interest in the eserine alkaloids used as ordeal poisons in

W. Africa. Though they are thought to be restricted to two species of *Physostigma*, there are early reports of eserine from another legume genus *Dioclea* which need confirmation.

Some alkaloids are much more scattered in distribution, occurring in plants which are thought to be only distantly related on other criteria. These alkaloids may not be synthesized in the same way in the different species, and cannot be considered to have general taxonomic significance. Nicotine (X) is present in quantity only in *Nicotiana, Duboisia* and *Salpiglossis* (Solanaceae) and in *Zinnia* and *Eclipta* (Compositae). Conceivably there is a different synthetic pathway in each of these two families. Nicotine in trace amounts is found in a number of unrelated plant groups such as *Equisetum* (Pteridophyta), *Sedum* (Crassulaceae), *Mucuna* (Leguminosae), *Asclepias* (Asclepiadaceae), *Herpestis* (Scrophulariaceae) and others. These trace occurrences are probably coincidental and lack taxonomic significance. The isoquinoline alkaloid berberine has an equally random distribution in many species of at least eight families, not all of which are obviously related.

There are numerous striking examples of the agreement between alkaloid accumulation and taxonomy.[222,223,334,387] Manske's work[319] on the alkaloids of Fumariaceae and Papaveraceae is often quoted. Both families accumulate isoquinoline alkaloids, and always contain protopine. Manske therefore considered them to be very closely related. Most of the alkaloids are not found in both families, even though all contain the isoquinoline nucleus. It is not possible to decide whether to keep the two families separate or to lump them together solely on the alkaloid data. The chemical evidence can only contribute to a final decision, which must be based on all available information.

The lupin (quinolizidine) alkaloids seem to be especially characteristic of the tribes Sophoreae, Genisteae and Podalyrieae of subfamily Lotoideae of the Leguminosae. Some are very restricted, but the lupinine, cytisine and sparteine types are so widespread that the tribes producing the lupin alkaloids may have originated from a common ancestral stock.[100] Variants of the lupin alkaloids characterize smaller groups within the tribes. The matrine bases referred to earlier are restricted to *Sophora* and related genera.

The general evaluation of alkaloid accumulation as a taxonomic character must await fuller knowledge of alkaloid distribution and biosynthesis. Sufficiently suggestive distributions have been established for taxonomists to enter this field, particularly now that the survival value of alkaloid characters is more clearly appreciated.

9

Taxonomic Evidence
from Terpenoids and Steroids

Natural terpenoid and steroidal materials resemble the alkaloids in
being very diverse and in lacking an obvious demarcation from
other kinds of compound. Sometimes they are treated with
alkaloids, sometimes regarded as glycosides or plant pigments, or
even as sugars, according to the definitions favoured. Often the
terpenoids are thought of in a narrow sense, as the components of
plant essential oils. This is unsatisfactory because not only is it
difficult to define essential oils, but not all their constituents are
terpenoid.

Modern work on biosynthetic pathways fortunately enables us to
recognize a large biogenetic group of diverse compounds all having
mevalonic acid as a precursor.[185] This group includes nearly all the
miscellaneous compounds of terpenoid or steroid affinity, and so
encourages the plant taxonomist to regard the category as a more
acceptable 'chemical taxon' than hitherto. Principal types of terpenoids and steroids are briefly reviewed below.

Most of the members can be considered as modified or
polymerized isoprene residues (I) (Fig. 9.1). The isoprene unit(s)
may have different additional groups, may vary in level of unsaturation, and have open or closed rings. They can be linked together in
several ways (e.g., II). Great variation in structure is hence possible
despite common ancestry from mevalonic acid. Though terpenoids
and steroids have this biogenetic uniformity, a functional unity in

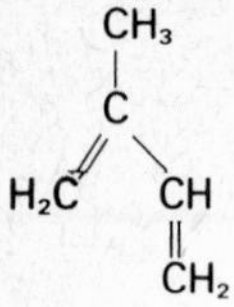

I Isoprene

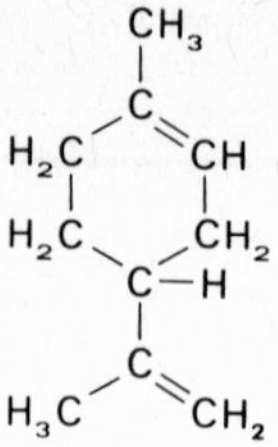

II Dipentane

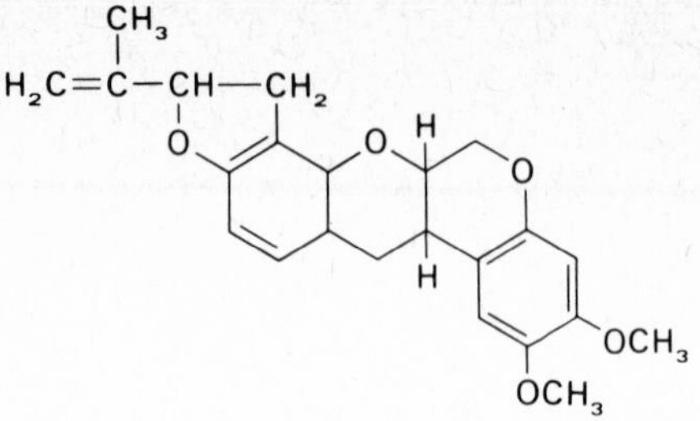

III Rotenone

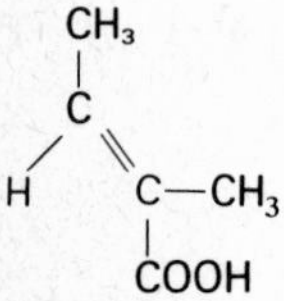

IV Tiglic acid

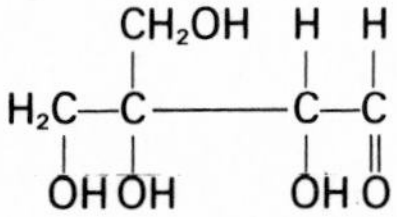

V Apiose

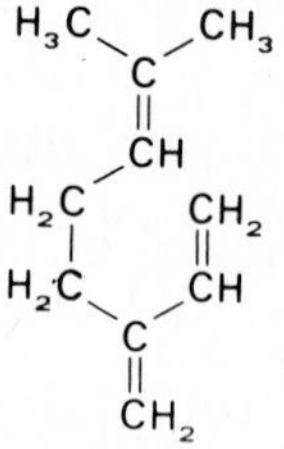

VI Myrcene

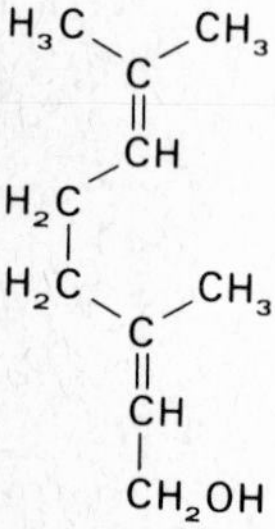

VII Geraniol

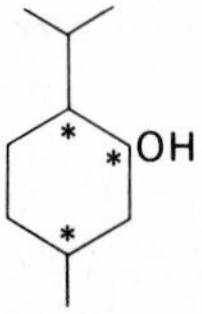

VIII Menthol

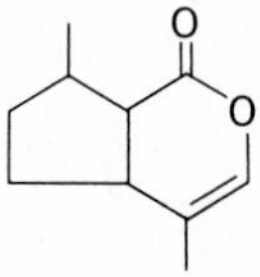

IX Nepetalactone

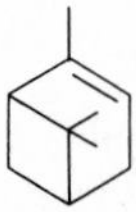

X α-Pinene

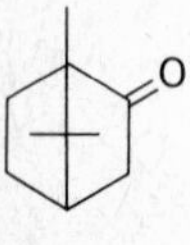

XI Camphor

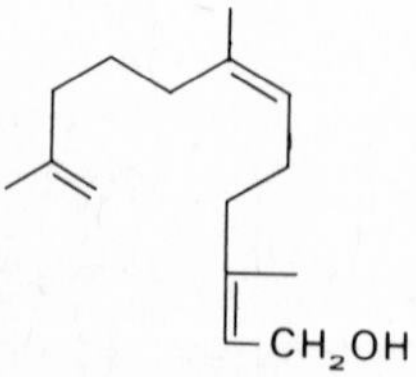

XII Farnesol

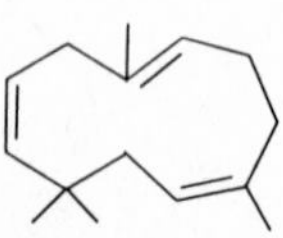

XIII Humulene

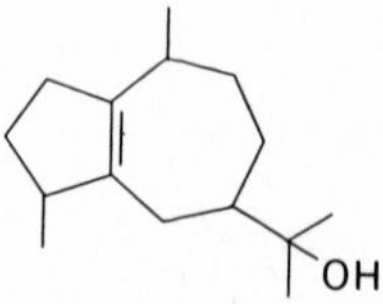

XIV Guaiol

Fig. 9.1 Terpenoid formulae. (* = asymmetrical carbon atom)

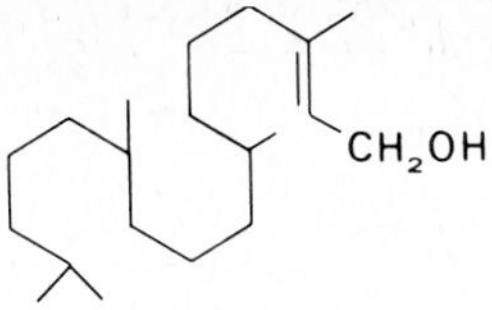

XV   Phytol 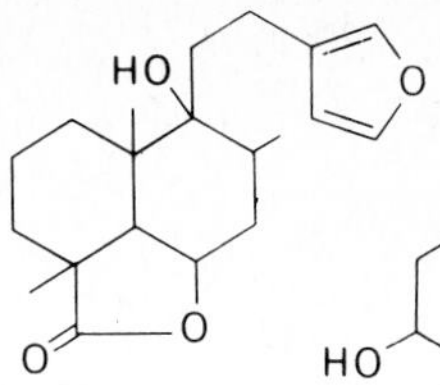   XVI   Marrubin 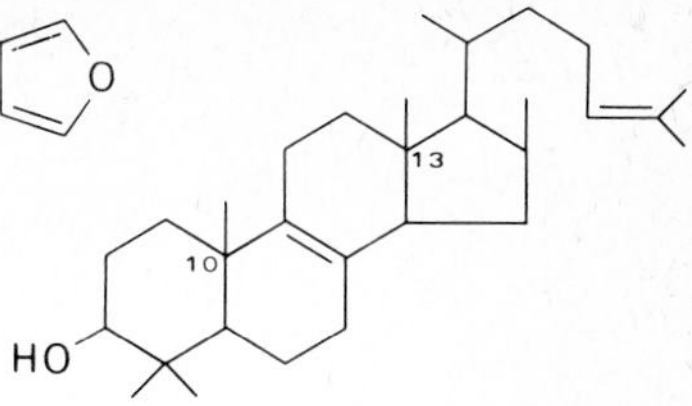   XVII   Lanosterol

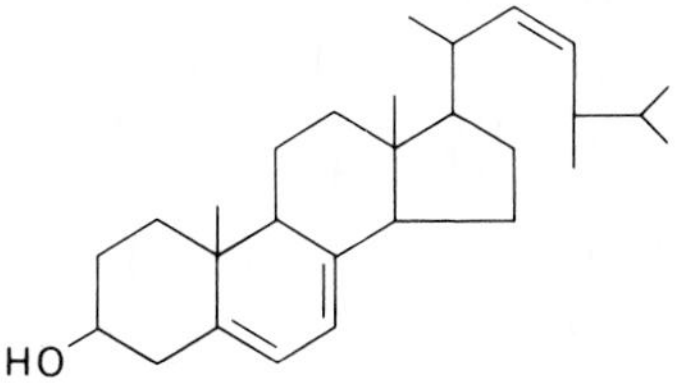

XVIII   Ergosterol 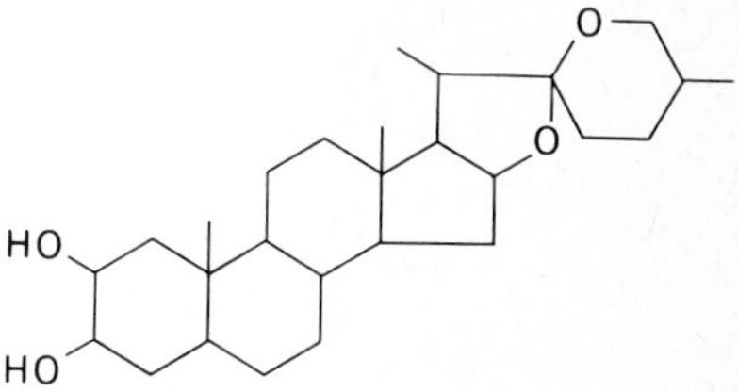   XIX   Digitogenin

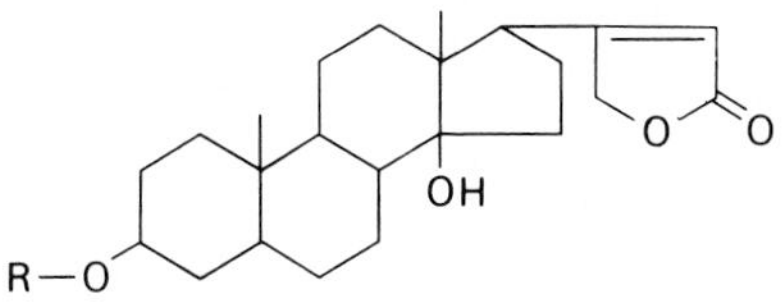

XX   Cardiac glycoside nucleus
(R = an oligosaccharide)

(XX)
O
digitoxose
digitoxose
acetyl-digitoxose
glucose

XXI   Aligosaccharide of
digilanide (=digitoxigenin)

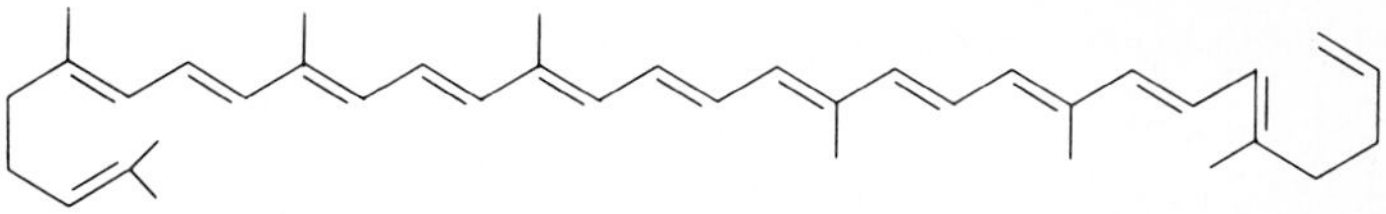

XXII   Lycopene

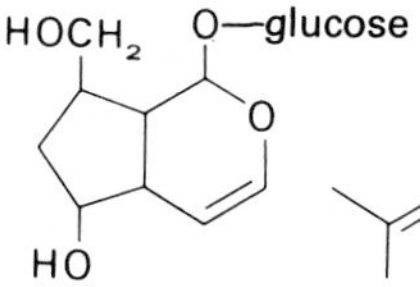

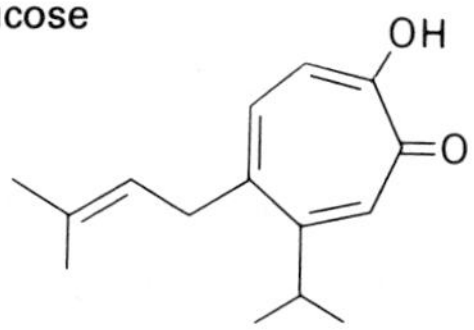

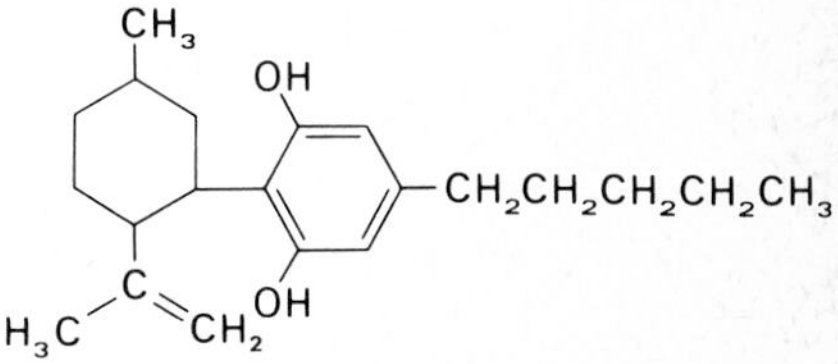

XXIII   Aucubin   XXIV   Nootkatin   XXV   Cannabidiol

Fig. 9.1 *continued*

the group is not implied. As in the case of alkaloids, the properties of the molecules are determined more by the additional groups than by the carbon skeleton.

Compounds which have just an odd isoprenoid side-chain are not included in the terpenoid category. The basic stucture of true terpenoid molecules must consist solely of one isoprenoid skeleton or of a polymer made up of several such units. Many interesting compounds, which may prove to have taxonomic significance, are thereby excluded. One such is rotenone (III), the active principle of derris insecticides, which is perhaps better regarded as a flavonoid.

Even with these restrictions, the terpenoids are an enormous group, and the mevalonic acid pathway from which they arise is so widespread that it is likely to be an extremely ancient character. It has been suggested that it was selected for in primitive plant groups as a useful means of disposing of excess acetate, i.e. that terpenoids in general are waste products. Whatever their ancestry, terpenoids and steroids have come to have very clear cut functions in plants, one of their derivatives being chlorophyll itself.

STRUCTURAL DIVERSITY OF TERPENOIDS AND STEROIDS

Table 9.1 lists the terpenoids discussed subsequently. *'Terpenoid'* refers to all isoprenoid compounds collectively, and is not synonymous with *terpene*, which refers only to isoprenoid hydrocarbons. It will be noted from Table 9.1 that the basis of the chemists' classification is the number of isoprene residues which can be detected in a terpenoid molecule. Single residues characterize the hemiterpenoids, which are nevertheless extremely diverse. They may be exemplified by tiglic acid (IV), and apiose (V) which can also be regarded as a sugar (see Chapter 7).

Over a hundred monoterpenoids (with 10 carbon atoms) are known, mainly as components of essential oils. They are best known from higher plants but are also synthesized by fungi and bryophytes. Many have clearly recognizable functions as growth inhibitors, insecticidal principles or as chemical attractants. This category of plant scents may be exemplified by myrcene (VI), and by geraniol (with an open chain) (VII). Monocyclic monoterpenoids have only one isoprene ring intact, and include a number of important substances. Limonene, for example, is the major component of *Citrus* oils (Rutaceae). Other examples are menthol (VIII), pulegone and nepetalactone (IX), the names being related to the names of the

Table 9.1   A classification of plant terpenoids.

Terpenoid category and general formula	Plant product	Principal chemical types
Hemiterpenoids (C_5H_8)	Essential oils	Hydrocarbons, alcohols, aldehydes, acids, esters, ethers
Monoterpenoids ($C_{10}H_{16}$)	Essential oils	Hydrocarbons, alcohols, aldehydes, ketones, esters
Sesquiterpenoids ($C_{15}H_{24}$)	Essential oils, resins	Hydrocarbons, alcohols, ketones
Diterpenoids ($C_{20}H_{32}$)	Resins, bitter extractives	Hydrocarbons, alcohols, acids, ethers

Triterpenoids ($C_{30}H_{48}$)
  Pentacyclic types:
    sterols
    sterolins
    saponins
    cardiac glycosides
	Resins, latex, corks, cutins	Hydrocarbons, alcohols, acids, glycosides

Tetraterpenoids ($C_{40}H_{64}$)	Pigments	Hydrocarbons (carotenes), xanthophylls
Polyterpenoids (($C_5H_8)_n$)	Latex	Rubber, balata, gutta
Modified terpenoids Modified (($C_5H_8)_n$)	Diverse	Diverse, incl. gibberellins, tocopherols, quinones, pyrethrins, tropones

plant sources. Bicyclic monoterpenoids, having both isoprene rings intact, include α-pinene (X), a constituent of *Pinus* turpentine, and the ketone camphor (XI).

The 15-carbon derivatives are also common in essential oils, and are called sesquiterpenoids. Farnesol (XII) is widely distributed, and its pyrophosphate is an important intermediate in terpenoid metabolism. Monocyclic sesquiterpenoids are typified by zingiberene (from ginger) and humulene (XIII - from hops). Bicyclic types include guaiol (XIV) and the lactone santonin.

The diterpenoids (20-carbon atoms) have a high boiling point and are rarely found in essential oils, which are characteristically volatile. The diterpenoids occur mainly in resins such as rosin, the residue remaining after steam distillation of pine resin has driven off the turpentine fraction. Fewer diterpenoids are known mainly because of the extra difficulty of isolating them. Phytol (XV) is an acyclic example which forms part of the chlorophyll molecule; marrubin (XVI) is a cyclic member.

Terpenoids with five isoprene residues do not seem to occur naturally, but the triterpenoids (C_{30} compounds) are common, widespread and diverse, in resins, cutins and corks, and also dispersed as glycosides. The correlation of structure, distribution and plant classification have been well reviewed.[26,75,284] Most of the group are acyclic (e.g. squalene), but lanosterol (XVII) is a tetracyclic type (not really a sterol!) and there are many pentacyclic examples. These last are common in plant cutins, where they may exercise a waterproofing function.

True steroids (e.g. ergosterol, XVIII) resemble lanosterol but all have only two methyl groups on the ring system, at carbons 10 and 13. They are important for reasons developed later, and are mostly alcohols (sterols) or esters, especially associated with particulate fractions of plant cells.

Sterolins and saponins are glycosides of terpenoid and steroid alcohols. Sterolins are insoluble in water and non-toxic, whereas the water-soluble saponins frequently have physiological effects on animals. They foam in solution—hence the name saponin (Latin: *sapo*, soap)—can haemolyse red blood cells, and are often toxic to fish in very low concentrations. For this last reason, saponin-containing plants are used in many parts of the world to daze fish, which rise to the surface and are caught. Some steroidal saponins have become important since they were recognized as a good starting point for the synthesis of artificial steroid hormones. The aglycones are termed sapogenins (e.g. digitogenin (XIX) from foxgloves), and are usually attached to an oligosaccharide.

Cardiac glycosides are easily defined by their stimulating effect on the heart. They are diterpenes which resemble steroidal saponins in structure, and in their production of foaming aqueous solutions. All have an unsaturated lactone ring attached to carbon 17 (see basic nucleus XX) and involve rather unusual sugar moieties. Their toxic qualities reside in the aglycone and have been widely exploited in arrow and ordeal poisons. The cardiotonic effect is shown only by the glycoside. Seeds, leaves and roots of *Digitalis* (Scrophulariaceae) are the chief commerical source of cardiac glycosides. Digilanide is an example (XXI).

Terpenoid and steroid alkaloids (classified as pseudoalkaloids in Chapter 8) are well known. Aconitine has been called the 'Queen Mother of Poisons'.

Carotenoids consist of two diterpene phytol-like units, and are the most familiar tetraterpenoids. They are yellow-red, fat-soluble pigments comprising hydrocarbons (carotenes) and oxygenated derivatives (xanthophylls). A few are colourless. Lycopene (XXII) is a major pigment of tomato fruits.

Though the 'bitter principles' of plants are not chemically homogeneous, many of them are terpenoid. Both saponins and cardiac glycosides have bitter tastes. Bitterness cannot be associated with any functional group, though many bitter-tasting terpenoids have lactone groupings. The bitterest substance known is the diterpenoid amarogentin. Asperuloside and aucubin (XXIII) belong to this group.[35] Paradoxically, the related substance steviol is the basis of stevioside, which is the sweetest substance known.

Polyterpenoids have indefinite, large numbers of isoprene residues. They include familiar substances such as rubber, gutta and sporopollenin. Though only a few plants produce commercially significant quantities of rubber, it is known to occur in the latex of over 2000 species of dicotyledons, mainly in tropical genera. Rubber is absent from monocotyledons, gymnosperms and lower plants. No plant has been found to produce both gutta and rubber: the necessary genes seem to be mutually exclusive.

'Mixed terpenoids' appear to have lost or gained carbon atoms, but still to have a fundamentally terpenoid structure, though the carbons are not in exact multiples of five. In this group are the gibberellin substances and the tocopherols, which act as antioxidants in seed oils. The pyrethrins are not only valuable insecticides,[87] but are interestingly confined to the composite genus *Chrysanthemum*. Active principles of marijuana can be included here. They have a non-terpenoid second ring, e.g. cannabidiol (XXV) from *Cannabis sativa*.

Tropones, which often have a terpenoid affinity, and are related to the base tropolone, seem to be a particular feature of the Cupressaceae, e.g. nootkatin (XXIV). They have a fungicidal action, recalling that of certain wood phenolics, but in this case the property may be related to their powerful chelating qualities. The pseudo-alkaloid colchicine has been regarded as a terpenoid tropone, but its affinities are uncertain, and its presence in a few genera of Liliaceae does not diminish interest in the curious tropone content of Cupressaceae.

Methods for extracting and analysing terpenoids vary as much as the compounds themselves. Many terpenoids can be extracted from plant material in organic solvents, and freed from contaminating lipids by saponification of the latter. Separation of this crude terpenoid extract is possible by steam distillation and various rapid chromatographic methods, well suited to the taxonomist, Quick spot tests are available for comparing essential oils.

BIOGENESIS AND VARIATION OF TERPENOIDS

All terpenoids can be derived from an isoprene unit in the form of isopentenyl phosphate, which serves as a nucleus for the condensation of further 5-carbon units. Isoprene itself has only comparatively recently been detected in plants[394] as a volatile effluent. The recognition of mevalonic acid as an efficient precursor for cholesterol and other terpenoid categories[466] was the major break-through in studies of terpenoid biosynthesis. After isopentenyl phosphate, farnesyl phosphate (see XII) is formed, and from it the sesquiterpenoids, squalene and triterpenoids are now known to arise. The pathway appears to be almost universal, and encourages the taxonomist to regard its products as indicating the operation of related genetic systems.

Variations in terpenoid content seem to be considerable in certain plants, but high degrees of constancy have also been reported. It has been suggested that some categories of terpenoid (e.g. those in resins) are not further metabolized when once they have been formed.

Variations in terpenoid content are at least in some instances under genetic control. Murray recorded the genetic basis for variations in the essential oil composition in *Mentha*.[354,355] Results of this work revealed typical Mendelian ratios. Terpenoid production is greatly disturbed in albino mutants of maize and tomato.[59] Carotenoid content dropped to 1% of normal, suggesting that the genes determining chlorophyll deficiency may be connected in some way with those concerned in carotenoid synthesis.

Chemical races, which presumably have underlying genetic differences, have been demonstrated with reference to turpentines in *Pinus*,[342] and in *Eucalyptus* essential oils.[373] Essential oils of *Myoporum deserti* (Myoporaceae), which are highly toxic to grazing stock, have been used to define nine chemical races.[461] Unfortunately these races could not be detected on any other criteria, and the authors conclude that the usefulness of terpenoids in taxonomy should be viewed with caution. In other plants, essential oils may be much more constant.[497]

Some genotypic variations in terpenoid content may not reflect very substantial genetic differences. Birch comments on work of Bonner which showed that a single gene determined rubber or lupeol production in two species of *Cryptostegia* (Periplocaceae).[52] Their F_1 hybrid produced rubber only, and there was simple Mendelian segregation for these characters in the F_2.

Environmental changes such as mineral status of substrate, and temperature fluctuation have well-established effects on terpenoid levels.[59] Commercial production of essential oils (e.g. oil of peppermint) is economic only in certain places, indicating an environmental effect. Oil composition varies from year to year.[308] Mirov's work (*op. cit.*) on *Pinus* turpentines involved careful sampling of plants from different locations and habitats in different seasons. Some variation was found. If terpenoids are to be used reliably as taxonomic characters it is vital to have basic knowledge of how they are affected by environmental factors. Zavarin *et al.* carried out a model survey of the environmentally determined variation in pine-needle oils, as a preliminary to a taxonomic interpretation.[512]

Fluck has reviewed evidence that changes in essential oils may arise from changes in the environmental conditions for plant growth.[162] Diurnal variation occurs in the quantity of oil extractable from foliage, presumably related to the greater volatilization of oils during the day. *Mentha* oil was the same when derived from plants grown in different pH conditions in sand culture experiments. Some of the reported effects are contradictory. Increased soil nitrogen generally increases the amount of essential oils produced, but it has also been reported to have no effect. *Artemisia* bitters are less concentrated in plants from higher altitudes, while in *Gentiana* the reverse is true. Water and temperature have complex interacting effects related to vapour pressure and the amount of leaching that is taking place.

Most of the reported changes in terpenoid content are quantitative: the proportions of different constituents remain more or less constant in tissues at the same developmental stage. Developmental variation is considerable, and taxonomists must be alert to it. The menthofuran and unsaturated ketones which dominate the oil of young peppermint leaves are replaced by menthyl esters as the leaf ages.

Biotic effects also must be expected by taxonomists, although the result of grazing or human cropping seems to be quantitative only. Second and third crops taken from peppermint are poorer in essential oils than the first.[162] In an exceptional case, tapping seems to encourage latex production in *Hevea brasiliensis*. Rubber content of the laticifer seems to reach a maximum, whereupon biosynthesis is 'switched on' again only by tapping. Tapping is so stimulatory that cultivated *Hevea* plants can be tapped every day for many years.

FUNCTIONAL SIGNIFICANCE OF TERPENOID CHARACTERS

Except for the tetraterpenoid carotenoids, with their obvious pigment properties, the functional significance of terpenoids has often been regarded as obscure. Even the carotenoids may not always be functional. As light-trapping or attractant pigments they may be effective in foliage, flowers and fruits, but it is hard to explain their role in the carrot root. Bonner assigned no function to lower terpenoids, except to suggest that they might be aberrant precursors of carotenoids.[59] Significantly, he commented on the high volatility and aromatic properties of many of the group, and cited the old report of Kostytschev and Went of the daily loss of 30 g of volatile terpenoids from a single juniper plant.[279] Possible reserve functions were dismissed by Bonner on the grounds that the terpenoids are often found in special ducts or glands where further metabolism is unlikely to occur. Suitable catabolic enzymes are usually not known. Rubber, for example, is not mobilized when rubber plants are artificially starved, and it can be broken down only by micro-organisms. Bonner suggests no natural function for rubber.[60]

Though secondary plant substances have traditionally been regarded as wastes, and the terpenoids are no exception in this case,[422] the argument is unusually difficult to sustain. The oil glands of peppermint fill up while the leaf is still very young and unexpanded.[308] Synthesis does not take place in mature leaves. It is hard to explain why this is so if the essential oils are genuine excreted by-products of metabolism. It is equally difficult to understand why a *Hevea* plant generates more 'waste' rubber only when its existing stock of 'waste' is removed.

The paper of Fraenkel marks a turning point in evaluation of secondary plant substances, including terpenoids, and .wider thought has now been applied to the problem of assigning functions to them.[171] As in the case of the alkaloids and phenolics, the problem of function arose because only the internal physiological arena of the plant was being considered as the *locus operandi*.

Some clear physiological functions are now well-established for certain terpenoids apart from the carotenoids already discussed. Dormin is a sesquiterpene growth substance regulating dormancy in buds, and also affecting leaf abscission. The diterpene gibberellin stimulates cambial activity and promotes cell expansion. Sirenin is a sesquiterpene which attracts male gametes to the oogonia in the fungus *Allomyces*. Though these substances are important, and probably represent only a fraction of the terpenoid phytohormones which will eventually be discovered, it seems unreasonable to assume that all other kinds of terpenoid are either their precursors or their degraded products. The converse is more likely. Goodwin wisely points out that there are too many terpenoids already known to expect every one to have a specific purpose.[184] A collective function is more likely, as previously described for the alkaloids (Chapter 8).

Functions for terpenoids must reconcile their ubiquity and diversity, their frequent volatile properties, their sometimes deadly effects and their often superficial sites of accumulation. All these observations suggest that terpenoids, like alkaloids, are principally involved in what might be called the ecological warfare of plants. They may perhaps attract useful insects and discourage predators and competitors. If this is so, terpenoid diversity can be related to the diversity of problems posed by the environment of a plant, the manifold pressures of selection, and the long period of time through which plants, their terpenoids and their environments have evolved.

The evidence for such functions, which bears heavily on the value of terpenoid characters in taxonomy, is briefly reviewed below. It is now of such magnitude that only a little can be mentioned here: for more detail, ecological texts should be consulted.[208,447]

Antifungal properties have been demonstrated for ipomeamarone in *Ipomoea batatas* (sweet potato), and the compound is synthesized in quantity when the plant is attacked by *Ceratostomella*. The amount of ipomeamarone produced is related to the degree of disease resistance shown by the host variety being tested.[484] This shows a phytoalexin activity of a sesquiterpene. Rishitin is an antifungal terpenoid produced by *Solanum tuberosum* when attacked by *Phytophthora infestans*.[487]

Allelopathic effects can often be related to terpenoids which plants release into their environments.[501] These compounds have functions similar to those of the water-soluble phenolic exudates mentioned in Chapter 5, but they escape from the plant, not by rain or fog drip, but by volatilization. They prevent the growth of competing vegetation near established plants by inhibiting germination and seedling ecesis. More cases of allelopathic interactions are constantly being demonstrated, and they are probably of wide occurrence. In the soft chaparral of California, Muller has shown that the fragrance of the community is due to the allelopathic terpenoids cineole and camphor (XI) released by the dominant shrubs *Salvia leucophylla* (Labiatae) and *Artemisia californica* (Compositae).[352] Both compounds are readily absorbed by soil colloids and experiments show that they inhibit germination and seedling growth, so bringing about the characteristic absence of annual herbs and grasses in the vicinity of the dominant shrubs. Parallel situations in Mediterranean garrigue are indicated for *Erica* and *Rosmarinus*.[122-124] Volatile terpenoids would not be so effective in cooler, wetter climates, like that of Britain, but not all allelopathics are aerial. Decaying roots of couch grass (*Agropyron*) release an essential oil which may inhibit growth of cultivated species.

After a time plant species should evolve immunity to allelopathic chemicals released by their competitors. Such evolution is suggested by a comparison of the luxuriant ground cover underneath eucalypts in their native Australia, with the meagre flora below the same species when introduced into America.[501] Weeds and crops might be expected to show similar chemical interactions, and this has already been demonstrated by several workers.[323]

Plant–animal interactions are in many cases also thought to be based on terpenoid recognition signals. Insects are very rarely found among peppermint plants, suggesting that monoterpenes may determine palatability in some species.[184] Pollinating insects may be attracted to some plants by terpenoid scents, while in *Pinus strobus* the wound-plugging system consists of resin crystallization induced by visiting insects.[423] Animal pests have sometimes evolved in response to the terpenoid output of host plants, perhaps outweighing its original chemical usefulness. Resinous bark exudates frequently attract insects.[290] Elm bark beetles are stimulated to feed by a pentacyclic triterpene in the bark of the susceptible host *Ulmus americana.*[20]

Bitter-tasting terpenoids are common in plants and serve as grazing deterrents. Some have more drastic physiological effects such as diuresis or vomiting, or fatal disturbances of the nervous and vascular systems. Most remarkable among the latter are the cardiac glycosides and steroidal alkaloids. Different plants would be expected to react to selection pressure for grazing deterrents in different ways, presumably fixing mutants for those repellent products which cost them least energy. Different taxa should therefore display different terpenoids, suggesting that there may be a taxonomic significance to plant groupings founded on cucurbitacins, asperulosides or related saponins. Terpenoid repellents would also relate to the nature of the grazing threat, and would not necessarily deter every kind of herbivore. It is noteworthy that cardiac glycosides are especially dangerous only to higher vertebrates.[399] Though hallucinogens such as cannabidiol (XXV) may have arisen as repellents originally, they now encourage depredations by Man.

Insects are unable to synthesize the steroid nucleus *de novo*, and rely on ingested plant steroids from which to manufacture their hormones. Steroids are ideal messenger molecules because of their size, rigidity, stereochemical diversity and capacity for cyclization, and can carry information unambiguously to receptors. Plants which are attacked by insects, partly for their steroids, therefore have a *prima facie* opportunity to develop a steroidal weaponry. Only recently has it become obvious how they may have seized it.

Williams gives a lucid account of the discovery of natural ecdysone, the steroid hormone mainly responsible for control of insect growth and differentiation.[503] It was established that ecdysones were sterols resembling cholesterol partly on the basis of 0.33 mg of β-ecdysone, laboriously isolated from a ton of silkworms. Interest was expressed in using synthetic ecdysone as insecticides to disrupt normal development of insect pests in the larval and pupal stages, but in 1968 Nakanishi announced that certain plants already produced phytoecdysones.[356] They included β-ecdysone, and were present in far greater concentration than in insects. Many were much more active than the natural insect products, causing gross malformations of larvae in very low concentrations. Most of the phytoecdysone plants are ferns and gymnosperms (Taxaceae and Podocarpaceae). Ecdysone activity has been noted in 54 species in 18 families in the Japanese flora.[246]

It is slightly puzzling that β-ecdysone, the commonest phytoecdysone, should be non-toxic when orally administered, as it would be in natural feeding. Staal (cited by Williams) seems to have solved this problem by showing that β-ecdysone is a powerful feeding deterrent even in concentrations as low as 1 part per million.[503] Synthesis of β-ecdysone may have been initially selected for as an unpalatability factor. In certain solvents, some of which are found in plants, phytoecdysones can penetrate the unbroken skin of insects and promote fatal abnormalities in development. It seems improbable that the hormonal properties of the chemical deterrent are not exploited. If they are, it is of taxonomic interest that two relatively primitive groups of land plants should possess one of the most elaborate chemical anti-insect systems.

TERPENOIDS AND STEROIDS AS TAXONOMIC CHARACTERS

Most of the classes of terpenoids reviewed above have been investigated for their taxonomic potential. Though distributional data are still far from complete for most compounds and most plant groups, it can be stated with confidence that, in some cases at least, terpenoid evidence has contributed helpfully to taxonomy. Only a limited selection of the many reports can be cited, since there are too many kinds of terpenoid for each one to receive a mention. Many examples other than those quoted can be found in journals of biochemistry and plant systematics.

The carotenoids are a prominent group which have received much attention but those from vegetative organs of plants appear to have little taxonomic usefulness. They are uniform in a wide range of plant groups. Goodwin also discusses the possible taxonomic use of the distribution of carotenoids in flowers and fruits.[183] In a few cases only there appears to be a homogeneous and unique pattern in small taxa. Table 9.2 shows that the rose species examined have a qualitatively similar pattern and contain rubixanthin. This carotenoid is rather characteristic of rose-hips and also of the legume genus *Astragalus*.[357] Similar cases of characteristic carotenoids are known in *Taxus* (rhodoxanthin) and *Capsicum* (capsorubin), but in general the distribution of fruit carotenoids is aptly described by Goodwin as 'capricious'.

Table 9.2   Carotenoid distribution in *Rosa* spp. (After Goodwin, T. W. (1956), *Biochem. J.*, **62**, 346.)

| Pigment | % of total pigments | | |
	Rosa canina	*R. moyesii*	*R. rubrifolia*
Phytoene	Trace	4.5	2.5
Phytofluene	0.3	3.0	2.7
β-carotene	16.5	14.5	28.5
ζ-carotene	0.2	3.5	Trace
γ-carotene	1.4	—	Trace
Prolycopenes	0.5	12.5	—
Lycopene	6.0	21.0	16.5
Mutatochrome	—	2.0	—
Cryptoxanthin	1.8	11.0	4.0
Zeaxanthin	6.0	4.5	2.5
Rubixanthin	42.0	14.0	41.0

In a few genera, petal carotenoids have been thought of as tax-onomic value. Valadon and Mummery comment on their applications in Compositae.[486] Harborne notes that the variation which they show in the genera of the legume tribe Genisteae should be welcomed as a possible source of new evidence for classification in this refractory group.[207] It remains to be seen if the polymerized carotenoid sporopollenin[431] will be found to vary in a taxonomically comprehensible fashion. If it does, a new dimension might be added to palaeobotanical research.

Considering attention has been paid to the taxonomic distribution of bitter-tasting compounds, since they are so obvious and because they are possibly so important in evolution. Bate-Smith and Swain[35] review the possible value to taxonomy of the monoterpenoid cyclopentanoid lactones known as **iridoids**. Of these, asperuloside is particularly common in the Rubiaceae, while aucubin is frequently found in the Cornaceae and in Scrophulariaceae, Orobanchaceae and some closely related families. On hydrolysis they eventually yield a black precipitate, which may cause the darkening of specimens of many parasitic and semi-parasitic plants in the Scrophulariaceae during herbarium processing. Several taxonomic changes have been made or suggested on the basis of iridoid distribution. *Buddleia*, which contains aucubin, has been transferred from Loganiaceae to Buddleiaceae, with a position near the Scrophulariaceae, in the twelfth edition of Engler's *Syllabus*. In the same work, morphological evidence is adduced to support the removal of Garryaceae from the apetalous orders to the vicinity of the Cornaceae. It is interesting that both should now be known to produce aucubin. Hegnauer has suggested that a minor modification of Takhtajian's system of classification would bring all iridoid-containing orders into one group, with a possible common origin. Bate-Smith and Swain (*op. cit.*) suggest modifying the Englerian system by removing Rubiaceae from Gentianales, so forming four iridoid groups, each of which can be distinguished also on other botanical evidence.

Sesquiterpene lactones are another group of bitter-tasting, toxic principles. Distributional studies reveal that they are rare except in the Compositae.[229] Lactucin and lactucopikrin are the typical bitter principles of the Compositae. The level of oxidation of sesquiterpene lactones is sometimes specific to single tribes, subtribes or even single genera in this family. Table 9.3 shows how different sesquiterpene lactones are distributed in the thirteen tribes of the Compositae. Though absences of a compound may prove to be more apparent than real, when wider sampling is made, Herout and Šorm[229] think it likely that absences (e.g. in the Astereae) are either genuine or reflect very rare occurrences only. It is striking that most of the Cynareae lack all lactone types except for germacronalides. Evidently they lack the rich enzyme complement which can transform farnesyl pyrophosphate into a wide range of lactones, which must characterize, for example, Heliantheae. However, if *Ambrosia* and its relatives (*Iva, Franseria* and *Xanthium*) are removed from Heliantheae (as some taxonomists propose) it is interesting to note (Table 9.4) that the residue now resembles the Helenieae in its lactone distribution. Most of the biochemical diversity in lactone production in Heliantheae is seen to reside in the relatives of

Table 9.3 Frequency of occurrence of sesquiterpene lactones in the family Compositae. (After Herout and Šorm.[229])

Tribe	Number of plant species investigated	Number of lactones of different types per tribe[a]					
		Germacra-nolides	Santa-nolides	Eremophila-nolides	Guaia-nolides	Ambrosa-nolides	C-skeleton changed
Vernonieae	2	2	3	—	—	—	—
Eupatorieae	4	2	—	—	2	1	—
Astereae	—	—	—	—	—	—	—
Inuleae	8	3 (4)	8 (11)	—	5	1	3 (4)
Heliantheae	31	1	5 (9)	—	2 (4)	16 (28)	10 (14)
Helenieae	32	12	1	—	1	34 (61)	3 (4)
Anthemideae	45		13 (39)	—	14 (23)	—	1
Senecioneae	4	—	—	6	—	—	3 (4)
Calenduleae	—	—	—	—	—	—	—
Arctotideae	—	—	—	—	—	—	—
Cynareae	20	10 (19)	—	—	6 (7)	—	—
Mutisieae	9	—	—	—	—	—	—
Cichorieae	9	—	1	—	3 (12)	—	—

[a] Figures in brackets refer to the numbers of species per tribe which contain a particular lactone type.

Table 9.4 Frequency of occurrence of lactones in the tribe Heliantheae. (After Herout and Šorm.[229])

	Number of plants investigated	Germacra-nolides	Santa-nolides
Tribe:			
Heliantheae	6	1	—
Family:			
Ambrosiaceae	25	2 (3)	5 (9)

	Guaia-nolides	Ambrosa-nolides	Carbon skeleton changed
Tribe:			
Heliantheae	—	5 (6)	2
Family:			
Ambrosiaceae	2 (4)	11 (22)	8 (12)

For the meaning of figures in brackets see footnote, Table 9.3.

Ambrosia. Perhaps, therefore, these genera should indeed be recognized as a separate tribe or even a separate family.

A remarkable feature of sesquiterpene lactone distribution is the restriction of those known as eremophilanolides to the tribe Senecioneae. The occurrence of peculiar alkaloids in this tribe was noted earlier. Eremophilane sesquiterpenoids were used as taxonomic characters in work on European *Petasites* species.[363] *P. hybridus* and *P. albus* contained compounds differing in the position (either carbon 6 or 9) at which they were oxidized, indicating enzyme differences. The natural hybrid of these species, *P.* × *rechingeri*, contained both series of parental molecules. It was thought that a Carpathian species (*P. kablikianus*) was also a hybrid of the same parents, but its eremophilane terpenoids are oxidized at both possible positions, unlike the situation in *P.* × *rechingeri*. It is therefore very unlikely to be a simple hybrid, and most probably is a species of independent origin. A similar double oxidation has since been shown to occur in *P. paradoxus*, which Novotny *et al.*[363] regarded as an Alpine vicariad of *P. kablikianus.*

Eremophilane-type compounds have also been recorded in *Adenostyles alliariae*, confirming the genus as a member of Senecioneae, rather than of Eupatorieae, where it was previously classified.[214]

In general, sesquiterpene lactone distribution fits closely with established taxonomy. When minor discrepancies occur, the chemical evidence is sufficiently well-established to justify careful scrutiny of the existing classification. Chemical races, varying in lactone content, are known in *Achillea*,[448] *Petasites*[363] and *Ambrosia*.[312] Qualitative variation in different tissues of the same species is also recorded, but provided these phenomena are given due consideration, sesquiterpene lactones are likely to be a valuable source of taxonomic evidence in Compositae. Their usefulness on the micro-evolutionary level is discussed in a subsequent chapter.

Other bitter compounds which have been considered from a taxonomic standpoint include the cardiac glycosides. They are characteristically common in certain unrelated families (e.g. Apocynaceae, Ranunculaceae and Liliaceae). The distribution of the steroid alkaloids in the tribe Veratreae of Liliaceae supports the generic classification established on morphological grounds.[286] The veratrum alkaloids are found only in Veratreae. Cucurbitacins (triterpenoid glycosides) have been considered as taxonomic characters in the Cucurbitaceae.[149]

Perhaps the most noted example of the use of terpenoids in plant taxonomy is the classical work of Mirov in California, on the gum turpentines of *Pinus*. They consist chiefly of cyclic terpenes with a few aliphatic hydrocarbons. Mirov's many publications on the taxonomic and evolutionary significance of the *Pinus* turpentines culminated in his book.[342] The work is based on a careful investigation of the factors affecting turpentine composition within and between species, and is a model for later workers to emulate. Mirov has detected chemical varieties in certain species, notably *Pinus ponderosa*, but finds that other species are chemically rather constant. More clearly than many chemotaxonomists, he recognizes that phylogenetic interpretations based on comparative chemistry of modern species give as obscure a picture of the past history of a plant group as does any other field of comparative phenetics. When considered together with more traditional evidence, his turpentine data clarify a number of situations.

One example concerns the relationship of *Pinus ponderosa* and *P. jeffreyi*. The latter is a relict Californian species with no terpenes in its turpentine. *N*-heptane and a few aliphatic aldehydes are the main constituents. *P. jeffreyi* has been considered to be a variety of *P. ponderosa*, with which it shares certain morphological attributes, and can exchange genes. Mirov discovered that *P. ponderosa* turpentines were quite distinct, containing α- and β-pipene and limonene. The turpentine of the Jeffrey pine shows strong resemblances to those of

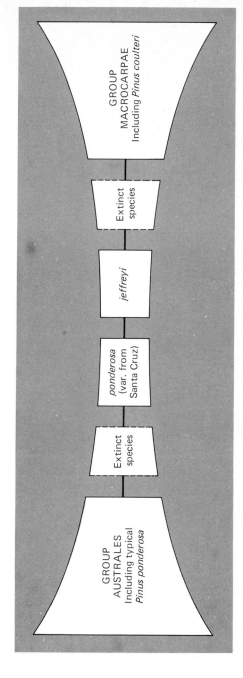

Fig. 9.2 Mirov's interpretation of the taxonomic position of the Californian relict pine, *Pinus jeffreyi*, based partly on turpentine evidence. (Modified from Mirov (1958) in Thiman, K. V. (ed.), *Physiology of Forest Trees*. Ronald Press, New York.)

pines in the rather distant group Macrocarpae, not to the Australes group to which *P. ponderosa* belongs. *P. jeffreyi* produces fertile F$_1$ hybrids in natural crossing with *P. coulteri* (Macrocarpae group).[404] This genetic evidence is a further indication that *P. jeffreyi* may have been wrongly placed in Australes. Figure 9.2 represents Mirov's theory of the relationships of *P. ponderosa* and *P. jeffreyi* taking into account the genetic and chemical knowledge.

Even the physical characteristics of turpentines, arising from their terpenoid composition, enable possible relationships of the pines to be detected. Figure 9.3 shows an example where density has been plotted against index of refraction.

Turpentine characters have now been investigated for most of the known species of *Pinus*. Few differences have been noted between

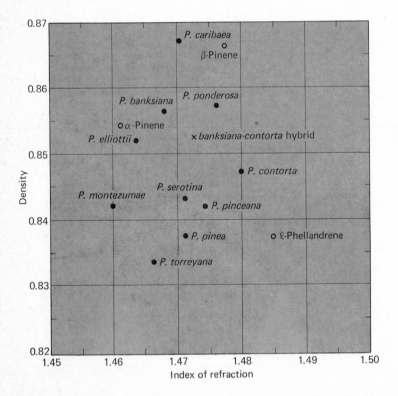

Fig. 9.3 Physical characteristics of turpentines from some different *Pinus* spp. (After Mirov.[342]) Values for some pure components are included. Note the intermediacy of the *banksiana-contorta* artificial hybrid relative to its parents.

the sub-genera Haploxylon and Diploxylon, most terpenoid compounds being common to both. This situation contrasts with another reported by Lindstedt and Misiorny where the phenolics of the two sub-genera are found to be distinct.[306] Perhaps chemical data of different kinds will show discrepancies as often as varied sorts of anatomical or morphological evidence.

Mirov's work opens up the fascinating possibility of detecting phytogeographical connexions between the pine floras of different continents. It is clear from turpentine compositions that the pines of Eastern North America have much in common with those of SW. Europe and the Mediterranean area. Both have simple turpentines consisting mainly of α- and β-pinenes. Perhaps this shows support for existing palaeobotanical views that the European pines migrated from North America via Greenland. A similar connexion, via the Bering land bridge, between Western North American pines and their SE. Asian counterparts, is also supported by the turpentine evidence. These pines have much Δ^3-carene in their turpentines. Two aberrant European pines which are rich in Δ^3-carene (*P. peuce* and *P. sylvestris*) are considered to be of Asiatic, not North American origin. Perhaps the new evidence accumulating for the times when continental blocks fragmented and drifted apart, together with Mirov's results, will one day be used to make a re-appraisal of the past migrations of the pines.

It may be concluded that some but by no means all kinds of terpenoids seem to be remarkably useful in adding to our knowledge of certain plant groups. Other examples will be mentioned subsequently in relation to particular taxonomic situations. Terpenoids and steroids are so widespread, so diverse and now so obviously important in plant adaptation and success that it is unthinkable that they will not be found to have considerable taxonomic potential.

IO

Taxonomic Usefulness of Protein Comparisons

Despite growing recognition of the true functional significance and taxonomic value of many secondary substances, it is probable that comparisons between the proteins of different taxa will eventually comprise the bulk of all work involving chemical assay for systematic purposes. Already the literature on this topic is enormous, and together with studies on the distribution of phenolic compounds investigation of proteins is the most popular approach to plant chemotaxonomy.

There are several reasons for the pre-eminence of proteins in chemotaxonomy. Modern recognition of DNA as the genetic material which determines protein structure via messenger RNA confirms the close coupling between the genetic 'blueprint' of an organism and its proteins which has been suspected for a long time. We now know that proteins represent a third copy of the sequence of genetic information in which the language of the genetic code is translated from nucleotide bases into sequences of amino acids. Comparisons of proteins, if possible of the amino acid sequences themselves, therefore make possible a new measurement of the similarity of the organisms compared. Zuckerkandl and Pauling refer to proteins as 'tertiary semantides'—a useful way of indicating their role as carriers of third-hand information.[514]

Apart from their connection with the physical basis of the genotype, there are other striking features of proteins which increase their taxonomic value still further. Firstly they are large, complex molecules, mainly with well-defined functions in metabolism, and *a priori* it might be expected that they would show little qualitative variation in response to changing environmental factors. Secondly, proteins are universally distributed so that there is no theoretical limit to the bounds of taxonomic comparison, provided that the proteins compared are known to be homologous. In principle, protein investigations might be made in taxonomic comparisons of plants in different divisions, classes, orders, families, genera, species or varieties. The use of, for example, different kinds of saponin as taxonomic characters is restricted by the limit of saponin distribution.

A third attractive feature of proteins is that they are often present in quantity (though less often in plants than in animals) and that many of them are relatively simple to extract and handle, provided that they are protected from extremes of temperature and pH. Enough protein may be available from an individual to permit that individual to be compared with another one. This fine level of analysis is not always possible with secondary substances, where extract from several or many individuals may have to be bulked to provide a working sample.

Finally, taxonomists are drawn to study proteins because of the availability of numerous cheap, simple, and rapid methods of analysis and comparison. The importance of proteins in nutrition and metabolism encourages continued progress in techniques.

It has been pointed out that the genetic code of an organism is a statement of its evolutionary history, minimally obscured by the environment, which modern methods now enable us to read.[514] Similarities between genetic sequences betray community of descent, convergent evolution being uniquely improbable. The translations of this compelling story represented by protein structure will appeal to all systematists as a source of phylogenetic information, in addition to acting as taxonomic evidence. Protein comparisons may compensate to some degree for the disappointingly sparse fossil records left by plants of the past. The use of proteins as phylogenetic indicator molecules is discussed in Chapter 15. In the present chapter proteins are considered in taxonomic terms—how they may help to confirm or reject existing classifications. It is already clear that they can help to evaluate similarities between very different kinds of plant, in contrast to the narrow areas of genetic affinity to which the technique of biosystematics is necessarily confined.

Taxonomy is a practical subject, and it is interesting to note that proteins are valuable from the practical standpoint. Not only may

protein data contribute to improvement of general-purpose classification, they also constitute features which may be of predictive value
in a practical sense. Protein evidence can be sufficiently reliable for
plant breeders to predict the presence of correlated gene complexes
determining desirable characteristics. Protein analysis permits
investigators to score a few seeds of potentially useful varieties of
crop plants for signs of valuable properties in the mature crop (e.g.
baking quality in wheat flour) without necessarily going through the
labour of growing every variety.

CHEMISTRY AND ANALYSIS OF PROTEINS

Proteins are polymers of the twenty-odd 'protein' amino acids
listed in Chapter 4, which are linked together in various sequences
and numbers by peptide bonds:

$$NH_2—CHCOOH + NH_2CHCOOH \rightarrow NH_2CHCO—NHCHCOOH$$

amino acid 1   amino acid 2   peptide

The peptide bond (—CO—NH—) forms by the elimination of a
molecule of water. When water is added again across the bond
(hydrolysis) the amino acids are released. Obviously there is a vast
number of possible combinations of amino acids, and this is reflected
in the enormous variation now known to occur in protein molecules.

Protein chemists have followed the suggestion that the structure
of protein molecules be considered at three levels.[305] The **primary
structure** is the amino acid chain, consisting of a spine of peptide
bonds with twenty-odd different side chains in a sequence unique to
each particular protein. The **secondary structure** is the form in
which the peptide chain is held by hydrogen bonds. The two
commonest secondary structures are the pleated sheet and the
α-helix (Fig. 10.1). The **tertiary structure** refers to the way in which
the parts of the coiled or pleated peptide chain are related to each
other in three dimensions, by further pleating or folding. Forces
maintaining the tertiary structure include hydrogen bonds, covalent
bonds (e.g. disulphide bridges in the cystine molecule), van der
Waal's forces and ionic attraction. Few protein structures have been
fully worked out to the three dimensional level. Figure 10.2 shows
the structure determined for horse heart cytochrome c, to which
plant cytochromes c are substantially similar.

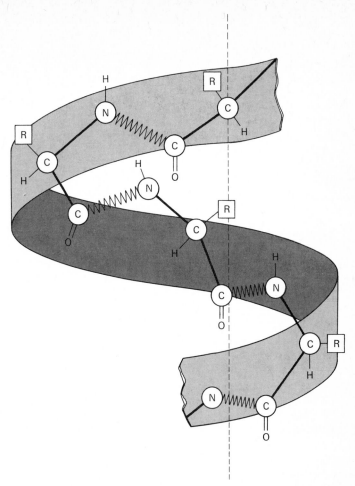

Fig. 10.1   A portion of a peptide α-helix, showing 3.6 amino acid units per turn.
R = amino acid side chain.

C〜〜〜N = peptide bond.

(Modified from Dickerson and Geis.[130])

The genetic code determines the sequence of amino acids (i.e. the primary structure) which limits the variation possible in the secondary and tertiary structures, and so controls the properties of the

Table 10.1 The base triplet code. Codon assignments for RNA which relate to particular amino acids (U = uracil: G = guanine; C = cytosine; A = adenine)

Amino acid	Triplets	Amino acid	Triplets	Amino acid	Triplets
Glycine	GGU GGC GGA GGG	Threonine	ACU ACC ACA ACG	Arginine	CGU CGC CGA CGG AGA AGG
Alanine	GCU GCC GCA GCG	Cysteine	UGU UGC	Histidine	CAU CAC UUU
Leucine	CUU CUC CUA CUG	Methionine	AUG	Phenylalanine	UUC
		Aspartic acid	GAU GAC		
Isoleucine	AUU AUC AUA	Asparagine	AAU AAC	Tyrosine	UAU UAC
Serine	UCU UCC UCA UCG AGU AGC	Glutamic acid	GAA GAG	Tryptophan	UGG
		Glutamine	CAA CAG	Proline	CCU CCC CCA CCG
		Lysine	AAA AAG		

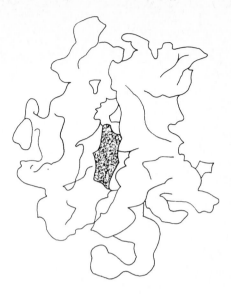

Fig. 10.2 Diagram of 3-D structure of horse heart cytochrome *c*, based on the Dickerson model. Haem prosthetic group is stippled. The resolution depicted is 4 Ångströms. (After R. E. Dickerson and I. Geis, *The Structure and Action of Proteins*, W. A. Benjamin Co., Menlo Park, California. Copyright 1969 by Dickerson and Geis.)

molecule as a whole. Table 10.1 shows the amino acid code expressed in nucleotide triplets (codons) of messenger RNA. The code is degenerate, i.e. presence of a particular amino acid at a particular location in a peptide sequence does not unambiguously indicate the presence of a particular codon. Several triplets code for the same amino acid, e.g. CUU, CUC, CUA and CUG all code for leucine.

The properties of proteins are diverse, enabling the use of different analytical techniques for their investigation. Amino acids are amphoteric, containing a basic amino group and an acidic carboxyl group. Many contain more than one such group, not involved in the peptide linkage, which are hence free to ionize in different pH conditions. Proteins will therefore have a net positive or negative charge, which will vary with the pH of the medium. These electrical properties can be used to separate different proteins, which usually have different net charges, by the techniques called **electrophoresis** (Fig. 10.3). Variants of this method are very often used in protein separations for taxonomic purposes.

Disc electrophoresis

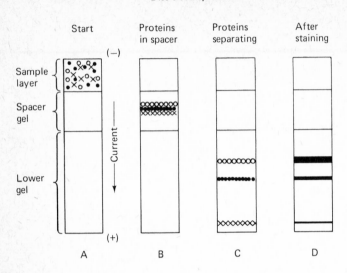

Fig. 10.3 The separation of a protein mixture into narrow bands within acrylamide gel columns by discontinuous ('disc') electrophoresis. The test sample is placed on the top of the column containing two gels differing in pore diameter (A). The spacer or upper gel has a large pore size and facilitates the initial sorting of proteins into a closely layered stack of discs (B). The lower or separating gel allows these protein fractions to spread out into bands (C). These separated protein bands can be observed by applying specific stains (D). Flatbed separations through gel of uniform consistency are possible with acrylamide, starch or agar gels. (From Fairbrothers.[155])

Sequence analysis of proteins rests upon the ability of certain reagents and enzymes to break peptide bonds selectively, i.e. only those between particular amino acid residues. The enzyme trypsin, for example, selectively cleaves the lysine–arginine bond, so producing 'tryptic peptides'. These peptide units may then be separated by chromatography and electrophoresis in the technique known as **'fingerprinting'** (Fig. 10.4). The pattern of peptides (or 'fingerprint') can be used as a source of taxonomic evidence. Similar proteins, indicating similar plants, are assumed to have lysine–arginine bonds in similar positions and so to produce peptide patterns which are similar. If the peptides are separated in a pure form (usually by a chromatographic procedure) they can be selectively hydrolysed from either the free amino group end or the free carboxyl group end by various reagents. As each terminal amino

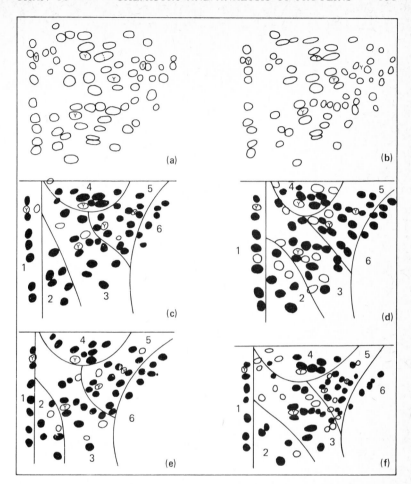

Fig. 10.4   Fingerprint patterns of various species of the Vicieae. (**a**) *Vicia faba* cv. Sharps Conquerer; (**b**) *V. faba* cv. Masterpiece Green Longpod; (**c**) *V. dumetorum;* (**d**) *Lathyrus sylvestris;* (**e**) *Vicia angustifolia* and *Lathyrus sylvestris;* (**f**) *Lens esculenta.* Sample spotted in the top left corner, electrophoresis from left to right and chromatography in the other direction. Y = yellow. (From Jackson *et al.,* 1967. *New Phytol.,* **66**, 47–56, Blackwell Scientific Publications Ltd.)

acid is hydrolysed free it can be identified by chromatography, and so the sequences of the different peptides can be established. Peptides prepared with other reagents are similarly treated and the full sequence of the protein determined by comparison of the overlapping portions of the peptide sequences obtained. Pure protein must be available for sequence analysis, because even small proportions of other kinds of protein molecule in the preparation would vitiate the technique.

Protein molecules vary considerably in size, and this can be used as a criterion for their fractionation. The pattern of fractionation may be potentially useful in taxonomy. **Ultracentrifugation** of proteins is a separation technique directly related to the size of their molecules. This method has been used to study proteins of the Leguminosae.[115] Two proteins, called legumin and vicilin, were recognizably distinct in terms of size in most of the genera tested, and the proportions of the two types varied from genus to genus. Ultracentrifugation however gives too coarse a resolution of protein fractions to be generally useful in taxonomy. The two sedimentation fractions are, in any case, not homologous in all legume genera.[272]

Molecular size determines the rate of migration of proteins in gels, but the application of this method, called molecular sieving, is mainly in the preparation of proteins and it has not been taken up by taxonomists.

Size and shape of protein molecules, which are features of the tertiary structure, can be assessed and compared to some degree by immunological techniques. Determinant groups on the outside of the molecule can elicit antibody formation when injected into experimental animals. Antisera so formed can recognize the materials injected when subsequently combined with them *in vitro*. The degree, speed and clarity of this molecular recognition system have been widely used to reveal protein variation by plant chemotaxonomists. The long history of this serological approach to chemotaxonomy, its specialized terminology and voluminous literature warrant separate treatment, and it is reviewed in the next chapter.

It should be noted that all the techniques mentioned above are 'biochemical short-cuts' with the exception of sequence analysis. With that exception, they rely on the use of some kind of pattern of separated proteins or protein sub-units as a basis of taxonomic comparison. The patterns comprise the taxonomic evidence. Molecular structures are compared only at second or third hand. Mainly because the short-cuts are cheap and rapid, they have been readily adopted by taxonomists who have now applied them to enormous numbers of protein extracts from different plants. Though sequence comparison is the ultimate form of protein evidence it has hitherto been little used by taxonomists because of its cost, slowness and complexity. The automatic protein sequenators now available may prove as useful in taxonomy as they are infelicitously named.

This brief treatment of protein structure and analysis can be expanded by reference to modern biochemical texts.[130]

Extraction and purification methods for proteins are numerous and the details are beyond the scope of this chapter. The methods are nevertheless relevant to the usefulness of proteins in taxonomy, mainly in terms of how simple and rapid they are. Expressed sap was used as the protein source for the classical research by Gell, Hawkes and Wright on the application of proteins in the taxonomy of potato species (*Solanum*).[177] Seed and fruit proteins are extracted by grinding plant material to flour or slurry, and then applying suitable solvents to the preparation. Proteins have been classified on solubility criteria and though the proteins in the various solubility groups may or may not be fundamentally different, this classification is the most generally useful one to have emerged so far.[366] Different plant groups have different proportions of albumins, glutelins and other types, so that there is a small taxonomic gain even from the technical process of extraction. Grains of grasses contain much prolamine and glutelin protein, while legume seeds are rich in globulins. Blagove-schchenski has used solubility criteria in a consideration of the evolution of legume subfamilies.[57]

SOURCES OF VARIATION IN PROTEINS

An individual organism exhibits variation in its protein complement which may arise from several sources. Much genetic information is used only during certain stages of the process of growth and development, and it might be expected that such stages would be characterized by the proteins coded for by the genes switched on at that time. Later stages would involve other proteins. This is the source of developmental variation in the protein complement. As an individual matures, its proteins change. Developmental variation of this kind was shown by the experiments of Brown and his co-workers on root-tips,[408] and in many other systems subsequently. An enzyme may exhibit different electrophoretic variants (isoenzymes) at different stages of differentiation.[96,195] Many of the proteins coded for in the genetic material, therefore, are fleetingly produced in small quantities only. Such variations will confuse the investigating taxonomist if they are not allowed for or avoided.

Allied to developmental variation is the organ-specificity of proteins. Though all proteins are highly characteristic of an organism, and accurately reflect some piece of genetic information, they are not all found in every part of it. Certain proteins with fundamental roles, e.g. respiratory enzymes and skeletal proteins, will be found, albeit in varying concentrations, in all living tissues of the plant. Others are more local in occurrence. In an interesting investigation relating the protein differences between different parts of various legumes to taxonomic specificity, it was found that the protein differences between leaves, stems, hypocotyls and cotyledons of an individual were as large as the differences between taxa.[271] It was notable that the proteins from stems, leaves and hypocotyls showed much smaller differences between species than did those from cotyledons. Clearly it is essential to base taxonomic interpretations on comparisons of proteins from homologous organs. There can be

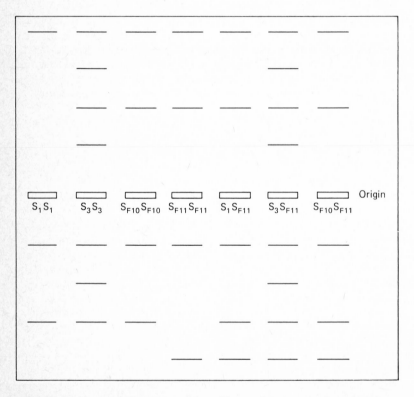

Fig. 10.5 Electrophoretic patterns of peroxidase activity in style extracts of seven different incompatibility genotypes in *Nicotiana*. S_1, S_3, etc. represent different alleles at the incompatibility locus. (From Pandey.[369])

no valid taxonomic conclusion from a comparison of the leaf proteins of one species with the seed proteins of another.

Protein variation also occurs between plants in different populations of the same species. Notable in this connexion is the polymorphism of many enzymes, when studied on a population basis. Plants have the capacity to produce several or many isoenzymes, and it seems likely that these have different selective advantages in different environments. As an example where isoenzyme variation appears meaningful, the work of Pandey may be mentioned.[369] Figure 10.5 represents the different electrophoretic patterns shown by the peroxidase enzyme in the styles of *Nicotiana* (Solanaceae) plants of seven incompatibility genotypes. Different incompatibility genotypes evidently produce different peroxidase isoenzymes. The functional significance of the situation may be clearer when we know more about the ways stylar proteins are implicated in the recognition of pollen. At least in some cases the recognition phenomenon which underlies compatibility involves the release of proteins from the pollen grain.[273] Where abundant pollen supplies have encouraged taxonomic investigations of pollen proteins, high levels of variation have been detected.[372,420]

The work of Allard and his colleagues also implies that interpopulation variation in isoenzymes may have an ecological significance, and that it results from selection.[5] Eventually, such relatively minor variants of protein structure may aid taxonomy at the infra-specific level.

At the level of species and genus, at which many practical problems arise, considerable differences in protein complements have been recorded. These form evidence upon which taxonomic systems may be founded, tested or demolished. Some species seem comparatively similar in their proteins, and so might be considered to be closely related, while others are more different and so theoretically more distantly related. The facts of the situation in each case depend largely on the kinds of protein being compared. Protein variation is closely correlated with protein function and cannot be discussed separately. Furthermore, the involvement of the environment in determining the pattern of protein variation in a taxon is intimately linked with the function which the proteins discharge.

It is commonly stated that protein characters are, by their complexity and close relationship with the genetic material, immune, either partially or wholly, to environmental modification. In one sense this is true. The proteins characteristic of an organism do not appear to be altered by growing the plants in different environments, except for quantitative changes and changes in the proportions of isoenzymes. Though the proteins of an individual may be indifferent to environmental changes, the environment is the greatest single factor controlling variation in the protein complements of populations, species and higher categories. It acts through the agency of selection. Protein characters are probably exceptionally sensitive to selection pressure.

The kind of selection pressure brought to bear on a protein will depend on its function. In plants the chief functions of proteins are as catalytic, storage and structural molecules. The size and number of variations exhibited in response to selection pressure should theoretically depend on how precise the function of a particular molecular type may be. This expectation is borne out by the observation that certain functional types of protein vary a good deal more than others. Proteins characterized by different levels of variability will be taxonomically valuable at particular points in the hierarchy of categories. Variable protein types should be of interest at infra-specific to generic levels, while more conservative proteins might be used with profit at family or order level, or even above that.

Before reviewing briefly the variability of different kinds of protein, it may be helpful to exemplify what general kinds of change may occur in protein molecules as a result of selection pressure. There may be, for example, some increased selective advantage for rapid hydrolysis in a storage protein of a certain species. This desirable property might be achieved by fixation of a mutant form which exposed as many peptide bonds as possible to the activity of proteolytic enzymes. In the same protein it might be useful to have maximum numbers of molecules per unit volume of storage tissue, and hence compact outside dimensions, and efficient packing shape might also be at a premium. To a degree this could conflict with the demand for accessible peptide bonds (i.e. minimal folding), and a compromise molecule might evolve. Competition between the compromise molecules of different genotypes might well be intense, so generating considerable differences in the storage protein of related taxa or of conspecific plants from different habitats. The general reactivity, intra-cellular disposition and packing quality of a protein would be greatly affected by the number and position of its hydrophilic and hydrophobic groups. These might be sensitive to selection pressure for better packing qualities, up to the point where further change would impair the chemical functioning of the molecule.

VARIABILITY AND EVOLUTION OF PROTEINS

The ways in which proteins can vary, with the production of multiple forms of themselves, have been classified by Epstein and Schechter[150] (Table 10.2). Such variants are the first step in the origin of new, i.e. non-homologous, proteins.

Table 10.2 Origins of multiple forms of proteins. (From Epstein and Schechter.[150])

I. Evolutionarily unrelated: 'convergent' evolution
II. Evolutionarily related
    A. Genetically unrelated: 'divergent' evolution of duplicated genes
    B. Genetically related
        a. Covalent differences
            1. Introduction during translation
            2. Introduction after translation
                (i) Deamination
                (ii) Attachment of carbohydrate
                (iii) Phosphorylation, sulphation
                (iv) α- and ε-NH_2 acetyls, formyls, Schiff's bases
                (v) Oxidation of sulphydryl groups
                (vi) Oxidation and reduction of prosthetic group
                (vii) Cleavage of peptide chain
        b. Mixed multimers
        c. Non-covalent differences
            1. Aggregation
            2. Binding of small molecules
            3. 'Stable' conformational variants

Many investigations have established that there is a wide spectrum of level of variability in different kinds of protein. At one end of the range are the ubiquitous proteins carrying out vital functions in photosynthesis and respiration. Cytochrome c is best known of the latter. Sequence data show that it varies little even when species from the plant and animal kingdoms are compared. Of the 100-odd amino acid residues in cytochrome c, about 35 are invariant. They always occur in particular places in the peptide chain. Presumably they constitute the functional 'heart' of the molecule, which is altered by mutation only with disastrous results. The conservatism of this molecule arises from the fact that almost any mutation effecting a change at almost any amino acid position in the sequence results in a less efficient protein, which is rapidly extinguished by the force of natural selection. When the mutation affects one of the 34 invariant positions, it is lethal because the molecule becomes completely non-functional.

Boulter and his co-workers have carried out a number of sequence analyses of plant cytochromes c, from a range of taxa, and it seems that only 15–20 residues may differ among higher plants.[65] This protein will clearly be of scant value in the investigation of taxonomic problems at the specific and generic levels. Boulter *et al.* employ the data in phylogenetic placings of families (see Chapter 15).

The other end of the scale of protein variability is probably represented by storage proteins. Here the chief function of the molecule is as an amino acid or nitrogen reserve. Ease of packing and hydrolysis are probably major requirements governing the way storage proteins have evolved. Though selection is likely to be quite as intense on the genotype of these molecules, involved as they are in the critical phases of ecesis and seedling competition, a larger number of possible structural variations probably exist which do not reduce efficiency. Potentially valuable protein characters might therefore be expected for use at and below the generic level.

Genus- or species-specific characters may occur in the proteins accompanying the differentiation of specific anatomical or morphological characters. The problem is that such molecules are ephemeral and in low concentration. 'Recognition proteins' in pollen constitute a chemically based system of classification of plants, by plants, for plants! It may eventually be possible for taxonomists to exploit it, if the protein variations are large enough for us to perceive them.

Between the conservative and mutable ends of the spectrum of protein variability there should exist homologous proteins which exhibit all intermediate levels of constancy, and which might therefore be useful at appropriate hierarchical levels. Cytochrome c exemplified the type of protein which is now relatively indifferent to selection pressures, having reached a stable peak of efficiency in the major groups. Other proteins show progressively greater degrees of specificity to lower categories, greater variability, and a more rapid response to selective forces. They are the proteins which are likely to be of most interest to the taxonomist, who must discover how useful they are in practice.

Pending a scientific evaluation of all classes of proteins as taxonomic guides, most workers have employed storage proteins from seeds, fruits and perennating organs. The proteins have the practical merit of being easy to extract, are in reasonably high concentration, and they characterize an easily recognizable, stable phase of development—so minimizing ontogenetic variation. It is a happy coincidence that most taxonomic studies have shown these accessible proteins to vary considerably at and below the levels of genus and species. Examples of the use of storage protein variation in taxonomy are mentioned in the next section. Here it is relevant to recall again the work of Kloz in which cotyledon proteins were found to differ more between a range of legumes than did the proteins from vegetative organs of the same taxa.[271] In the cotyledon extracts, the globulin (storage) fraction differed more between taxa than did the albumin (enzymic) fraction.

It has been suggested that the greater differences noted between storage proteins of different species merely arise from an accumulation of mutations, most of which have no deleterious effect on the structure of the molecules. This assumes that storage molecules have structures which are not tightly correlated with precise functions. As indicated earlier, it is more likely that strong selection pressures are exerted during the germination and establishment phases, and consequently that storage proteins are selected variants of moderately well-defined structures. Smith (unpub.) has shown how long-separated roadside populations of soft brome-grass (*Bromus hordeaceus* L.), sampled from different continents, differ comparatively little in certain seed globulins. There was no sign of a random accumulation of mutations through the long periods during which these annual grasses had been isolated. In some places, sand dune populations only metres away from roadside plants exhibited serological and electrophoretic differences in their globulin fraction. Together with the results of Allard *et al.* (*op. cit.*), this suggests that grass seed proteins do not display random variation.

As with any other character, other kinds of taxonomic evidence must be considered together with protein data. Proteins which are found to be conservative in a particular plant group might, if considered on their own, mask rapid evolution in other important features, even in other proteins. Several or many proteins should ideally be included in a taxonomic project, with the use of all possible biochemical 'short-cuts' to save time and labour.

It is too early to indicate which kinds of protein are best suited to taxonomic investigation at different hierarchical levels. We are only now beginning to consider the evolution of proteins in terms of function and environmental pressures—i.e. in a biological rather than a chemical context. Woolhouse provides an interesting account of the possible role of light intensity and/or temperature as sources of selection pressure in the continuing evolution of the CO_2-fixing enzyme carboxy-dismutase.[507] Where the CO_2-fixing capacity of the

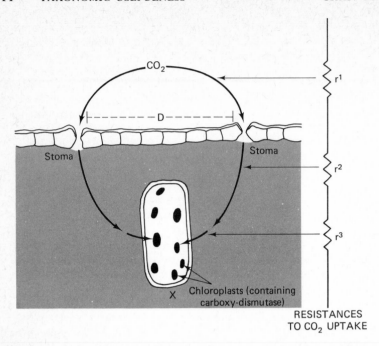

Fig. 10.6 Part of T.S. of a leaf (diagrammatic) showing some factors involved in CO_2-fixation by a palisade mesophyll cell. Many plants show increased leaf area (achieved via lateral cell expansion) when grown in low light intensity (e.g. shade ecotypes) increasing distance D. Diffusional resistances to CO_2 uptake are thereby increased and the effect of reduced r^3 is minimal. In sun ecotypes r^1 and r^2 are minimized, so making reduction of r^3 significant, and potentially of selective advantage. (After Woolhouse.[507])

enzyme is the largest component in mesophyll resistance to carbon dioxide uptake (e.g. when light intensity is not limiting and there are many stomata per unit leaf area), Woolhouse predicts that carboxy-dismutase will be under heavy selection pressure (see Fig. 10.6). Shade plants, with broad leaves and fewer stomata per unit area, have a greater diffusional resistance to CO_2. Changes in the CO_2-fixing ability of the enzyme would then have very small selective value. Shade ecotypes of *Solidago virgaurea* (Compositae) developed lower carboxy-dismutase activity than sun ecotypes, when grown in the same conditions.[55] Although this tends to support the view of Woolhouse, the evidence is not yet critical. The enzyme may be varying in quantity rather than quality, in the two ecotypes, and selection for thermal stability of the protein may be more important than its CO_2 fixation properties. Natural selection of proteins with different levels of heat sensitivity seems to have occurred among esterases,[370] and in phosphatases of cacti.[424] However the carboxy-dismutase situation may turn out, further biological investigations relating protein distribution to taxonomy and ecology must be started. Carboxy-dismutase is so important to our future food supply that taxonomic investigations of its variation and distribution in major crop taxa may be rewarding.

A great deal is known about protein structure and properties and, in the case of many enzymes, we often have an intimate knowledge of their precise functions and how these are discharged. We have a growing awareness of protein variation within and between individuals, populations, species and higher taxa. Before the taxonomic significance of the variation can be fully estimated, much more work must be done to relate it to factors of the environment and the biology of the individual plant.

PROTEINS IN TAXONOMIC INVESTIGATIONS

A range of examples may be cited which illustrate the applications of major analytical techniques in taxonomic work. Serological examples are deferred until Chapter 11. Although the most spectacular form of analysis is amino acid sequencing, the work of Boulter and his colleagues[62,65] relates to phylogeny rather than to taxonomy, and is accordingly discussed in Chapter 15. The only major taxonomic advances made so far with the sequence method are in the bacteria, and are dealt with in Chapter 13.

Electrophoresis is the most popular analytical technique with chemotaxonomists, and very considerable volumes of work relating to its taxonomic applications have now been published. Proteins are usually separated in a starch, acrylamide or agar gel, and then stained.

Desborough and Peloquin separated the soluble tuber proteins of species of *Solanum* by disc electrophoresis.[127] In this technique (see Fig. 10.3) the proteins are applied in the extract to a column of acrylamide gel in a tube; when the current is switched on they separate along the tube in moving 'discs' of protein, at a speed determined by their net electrical charge at the pH of the gel. Table 10.3 shows the occurrence of the most frequent bands. The authors were unable to demonstrate geographical correlation of the band patterns from the different species, nor did they show that

Table 10.3 Desborough and Peloquin's results[127] from electrophoresing proteins of *Solanum* species in acid gels. Not all 14 major bands consistently
occurred in all species. Species-specific patterns are shown if the consistently
present (100%) bands are considered alone. In *S. acaule* and group Stenotomum
of *S. tuberosum* only single bands are always present in the protein pattern.

Solanum species	100% Bands	80–99% Bands
S. bulbocastanum	47	810
S. cardiophyllum subspp. *ehrenbergii*	8910	12
S. jamesii	4678	—
S. pinnatisectum	46781213	11
S. chacoense	491214	81011
S. acaule	10	45789
S. demissum	4679	10
S. verrucosum	46789	—
S. megistacrolobum	4578	—
S. fendleri	8912	—
S. stoloniferum	891012	5714
S. polyadenium	2457891012	—
S.tuberosum		
Group Andigena	491011	58
Group Phureja	5812	39
Group Stenotomum	5	6910
S. canasense	489	—
S. sparsipilum	3710	8

supposedly similar species had similar band patterns. Considerable
variation occurred within some species. *Solanum acaule* produced
nine protein bands when all eleven tested samples are considered
together, but only one of these (band 10) was invariably present.
Mixtures of some tuber extracts were made, and the electrophoretic
separations of these showed that the numbered protein bands were
homologous between the species. Many of the minor, infrequent
bands which were seen may indicate different proteins with accidentally similar electrophoretic mobilities. In respect of the consistently
present bands, each of the 16 species tested had a species-specific
pattern, which is of potential taxonomic value.

Work on the proteins of the wheat group has shown a close
correlation between storage protein characters and genome
constitution.[256] Figure 10.7 represents the electrophoretic patterns
characterizing the named species, all of which were of established
genome constitution. In this case the proteins were separated in a
bed of acrylamide gel. It can be seen that the amphiploid wheats
Triticum aestivum (AABBDD) and *T. dicoccum* (AABB) possess
almost all the proteins of the A genome as shown in the diploid
species *T. monococcum* (AA). They also share proteins of the B
genome. which is of uncertain origin. The D genome of the
hexaploid wheats is usually thought to have come from *Aegilops*

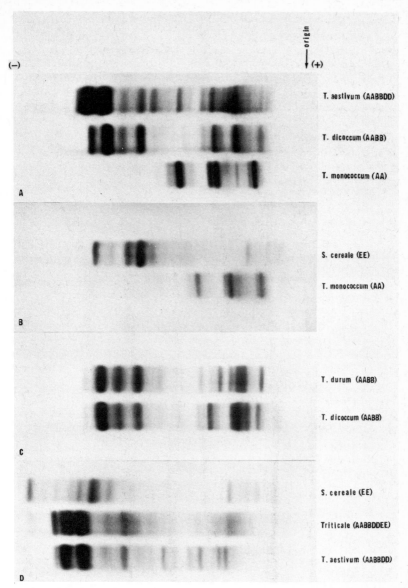

Fig. 10.7 Flat-bed acrylamide gels showing separation of seed proteins of *Triticum* species, *Secale cereale* and the intergeneric hybrid *Triticale*. AA, BB, etc. represent genomes. There is considerable correlation of protein pattern and genome constitution. (From Johnson and Hall.[256])

squarrosa, mainly on morphological and cytogenetic evidence. By use of disc electrophoresis (Fig. 10.8) Johnson has demonstrated the high probability of the ancestry of *T. aestivum* from *Ae. squarrosa* (DD) and *T. dicoccum*, by mixing their proteins artificially.[255] The mixture has the same electrophoretic properties as extracts from *T. aestivum*. Certainly there seems to be a future for grass storage proteins as taxonomic characters.

The results of Johnson and his colleagues are perhaps the most promising to have appeared so far from electrophoretic separations

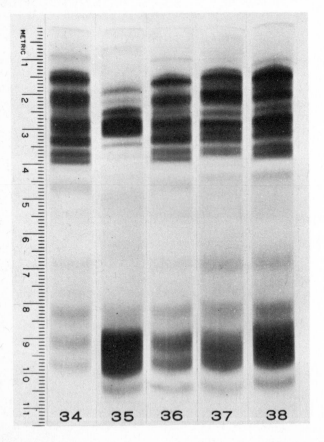

Fig. 10.8   Protein separations in disc gels illustrating simulation of the *Triticum aestivum* pattern (36) by mixing extracts of *T. dicoccum* (34) and *Aegilops squarrosa* (35). Gels 37 and 38 are separated proteins of *T. aestivum* ssp. *spelta* and *T. aestivum* ssp. *compactum*. (After Johnson.[255])

undertaken for quasi-taxonomic purposes. Correlation with the well-established genomic properties of the material is the cornerstone of the conclusions. In situations where less detailed or objective evidence is available for cross-checking, the contribution of electrophoretic studies is usually less clear. Demonstrations of electrophoretic differences between proteins of seeds of different legume species[67] do little more than display a new facet of natural variation. Some tribes seemed to have a characteristic pattern while in others the protein spectra varied considerably. It is difficult to be sure that bands with similar electrophoretic properties are in fact homologous proteins, and hard to say which may be manifestations of an intraspecific polymorphism. It has been concluded that, in most cases, electrophoretic data alone are inadequate as a measure of protein variation for taxonomic purposes.[64] Electrophoresis seems to have been very successful when combined with serological methods, for example in *Magnolia*[380] and in *Brassica*.[488] In more limited contexts, electrophoretic evidence alone may be of practical taxonomic benefit. The electrophoretic pattern of cereal storage proteins displays varietal differences which may be useful in predictions of baking quality and other flour properties.[146] The fingerprinting technique has been applied to globulins from species of five genera of the legume tribe Vicieae.[249] Some of the fingerprints appear in Fig. 10.4. The conclusions were that tryptic peptides of *Vicia* and *Lathyrus* were similar, supporting the close relationship of these genera implied in most existing classifications. *Lens* and *Pisum* preparations showed differences from the *Vicia–Lathyrus* pattern while *Cicer* was rather distinct. The assumption that homologous proteins, if similar, will fragment at the same points of the molecule, producing homologous peptides, seems well-founded from this chemical confirmation of taxonomic relationships which are generally accepted. The assumption has not been borne out by certain animal studies, for instance on myoglobins,[455] where the fingerprinted peptides failed to produce patterns consonant with taxonomic data from anatomy, serology and palaeontology. Fingerprinting may therefore be particularly well-suited to the plant chemotaxonomist, though the interpretation of the patterns is not easy. Jackson *et al.*[249] divided up the fingerprint into homologous areas (see Fig. 10.4) and compared these between taxa, to reduce the complexity. With impure protein preparations the patterns would have been even more complicated. A restriction on the technique is the establishment of the limits of protein homology. Jackson *et al.* found the fingerprints of globulins from species in the tribe Phaseoleae to be so different from those of Vicieae that it was impossible to say which spots were homologous. Further work on fingerprinting must establish the extent to which 'cryptic non-homology' of peptides frustrates valid taxonomic conclusions. A parallel in morphology might be the accidental comparison of characters from the lowest leaflet of one species with those from the stipule in another.

Taxonomic use of secondary compounds is usually based on scoring the presence or absence, and hence the general distribution, of a particular compound, whereas with proteins it is more usual that the pattern of fractionation of a complex mixture of several or many molecular species is the source of information. Proteins are rarely identified even partly in chemotaxonomic studies. There are a few exceptions to this. Blagoveschchenski's work on solubility categories has already been mentioned in another connexion.[57] In general it is only where the protein has some striking property, enabling quick recognition, that distributions of particular protein types have been deliberately attempted. Two examples can be mentioned.

The phytohaemagglutinins (PHAs) are unusual plant pseudo-globulins which can agglutinate erythrocytes and stimulate mitosis in animal cells. They are especially characteristic of the Leguminosae, though they are known from several other higher plant families, as well as from certain fungi and lichens. It is natural that PHAs should attract taxonomic interest because they are of considerable forensic importance. Though their functions in the plant are obscure it is tempting to speculate that, since they can be used to agglutinate, and hence identify, blood of different kinds, they may have a repellent function. It is difficult, however, to understand how they might penetrate the vascular system of most herbivores.

The PHAs of the Leguminosae have an uneven distribution in the family.[474] Non-specific PHAs are found in all three subfamilies, but those which specifically agglutinate particular animal blood groups are absent from the Mimosoideae. The type called anti H lectins are very common in the subfamily Lotoideae, and seem to confirm the agreed close relationships of *Virgilia, Cytisus, Ulex, Genista* and *Laburnum.* They further suggest that *Lotus* also may belong to that group of genera.

Production of specific PHAs is widespread in Lotoideae and appears to be under genetic control. Genetic determination of such remarkable specificity implies some functional value for the PHAs but there is little evidence for a role as antibacterial antibodies[419] or carriers of carbohydrate.[148]

Both functions seem rather too important to attribute to such narrowly distributed molecules, and in any case varietal differences are known which seem to rule out a fundamental significance. Some populations of the wild bean (*Phaseolus aborigineus*) include both PHA-positive and PHA-negative plants: others are completely PHA-positive.[80] It was concluded that there was no natural selection pressure, and therefore no function, for phytohaemagglutinins.

Bohlool and Schmidt[58a] have produced evidence suggesting that lectins may be the basis of specificity in the *Rhizobium*–legume root nodule interaction. Clarke *et al.*[93a] implicate them broadly as cell–cell recognition agents.

Enzymes constitute a second category of easily recognized proteins. Their specificity to substrates can often be demonstrated by quick staining procedures *in vivo* or *in vitro*, and exploited as the criterion of identification. Equally specific enzymes from different plants are presumably homologous proteins which it is valid to compare. Theoretically there will be wide areas of homology since many enzymically catalysed reactions are ubiquitous. Thurman gives a valuable review of the taxonomic potential of comparative enzymology in a discussion of legume enzymes.[472] All the standard techniques of protein analysis are applicable to enzymes in addition to the study and comparison of their catalytic powers.

Thurman *et al.* compared electrophoretic mobilities of glutamic and formic dehydrogenases from 103 legume species, detecting activity by the reduction of a tetrazolium salt to insoluble red formazans.[473] They found that heterogeneous taxa (such as the tribe Genisteae) had greater enzyme variation than more precisely delimited tribes such as Vicieae and Trifolieae. No taxonomic changes were indicated by this work. Characteristic isoenzymes of glutamic dehydrogenase occur in species of *Vicia, Pisum, Lens* and *Lathyrus,* with a different isoenzyme pattern in *Cicer.*[472] This agrees with fingerprint evidence (Jackson *et al., op. cit.*) of a position for *Cicer* somewhat apart from other genera of Vicieae.

Isoenzyme polymorphism may complicate the taxonomic use of comparative enzymology if sampling of natural populations is inadequate. An isoenzyme pattern based on a single collection of a species may be taxonomically meaningless, and every band in an electrophoretic pattern could be an isoenzyme of something. Considerable intraspecific polymorphism has been reported in the isoenzyme patterns of leucine amino-peptidase, β-galactosidease and indophenol oxidase in natural populations of three species of *Baptisia* (Leguminosae).[428] It was rightly concluded that there could be no systematic conclusion from individual isoenzyme patterns. Phylogenetic schemes for *Datura* (Solanoaceae) have been based on peroxidase isoenzyme patterns, but it appears that only single samples of the ten species were chosen for study.[96] It is unlikely in the extreme that peroxidase isoenzymes are constant within species.[369] The work on *Datura* might usefully be extended therefore.

A last difficulty with isoenzymes in taxonomy is that biochemists have not so far been able to define them very satisfactorily. They are said to be multiple forms of enzymes existing in one plant, differing in electrophoretic mobility and substrate specificity. It is clear that different plants in a population, in a species or a genus may have different combinations of isoenzymes. How different do the characteristics of two isoenzymes have to be before they are more reasonably regarded as different, i.e. non-homologous, enzymes? Without detailed sequence analysis it must surely be a matter of opinion. The taxonomy of isoenzymes may have to be worked out before they can be used to check the taxonomy of plants.

II

Serology and Taxonomy

The phenonenon of immunity was first recognized in connection with the long-lasting resistance of human beings to infections by disease-causing bacteria from whose attack they had previously suffered. The blood serum of infected patients was found to have developed the remarkable and persistent power to destroy or render harmless the invading bacterial cells. Antibodies were postulated to arise in the immune serum (**antiserum**) following the introduction of foreign cells or particles (**antigens**).

Kraus showed in 1897 that soluble material, such as foreign blood serum, could also be antigenic, and that a precipitation reaction between antibodies and antigens could be demonstrated *in vitro*.[281] This 'precipitin reaction' was a sign that an antiserum 'recognized' the antigens supplied to it *in vitro* as the same as or similar to those with which the animal had previously been infected or immunized. It was clear that there was considerable specificity involved in immunological reactions, because, for instance, the immunity developed to smallpox conferred no protection against measles. Antigens were precipitated or otherwise attacked only by the corresponding antibodies.

Immune blood sera can therefore be used as reagents to identify antigens similar to or identical with those involved in the production of the immunity. The study of the origins and properties of antisera is known as **serology**. Serology developed for many years in isolation from the growing discipline of biochemistry, and as a result acquired a specialized terminology which has delayed its integration with biochemistry and molecular biology almost to the present. In many ways, serology can be regarded as the molecular biology of the nineteenth and early twentieth centuries.

Enormous advances in serology have been made during the last seventy years, particularly in our understanding of what antibodies are, how they are formed, and how they react with antigens. Much of the detail of the antigen–antibody recognition process remains to be elucidated, but we now have enough knowledge to predict with confidence what is happening in a given immune response.

How does serology relate to taxonomy? It was quickly appreciated by taxonomists at the turn of the century that specific antigen–antibody reactions provided a unique method of molecular recognition, especially useful since the demonstration that they would occur *in vitro*. If molecules were characteristic of species, and were the ultimate key to relationships, as the contemporary phytochemists were saying, then surely serology was the ideal way to expose the degree to which different species resembled each other.

Nuttall wrote a classic paper employing the method for the comparison of blood from different primates.[365] The results showed a clear relationship between human blood and that of higher primates. Antiserum to human blood serum (i.e. using human serum as an antigen) reacted only with primate sera, and not with sera from lower animals. From the outset, serology was visualized as a technique offering insight into the evolutionary relationships (i.e. the phylogeny) of the group of organisms being studied, rather than an aid to classification *per se*. Even today, serological data are used primarily to shed light on phylogeny, rather than as phenetic evidence for taxonomy. Reasons for this are complex and varied. The phenetic evidence in even a simple series of serological tests is so considerable as to daunt all but a competent taxonomist, but the phyletic import is usually obvious and can easily be expressed. Early serologists believed that serology revealed a facet of variation which somehow reflected natural relationships more accurately than other, more orthodox, characters. In Chapter 2 it was noted that the proponents of new techniques often suffer from this conviction. Partly because of the ancient association of blood with lineage and descent, 'blood relationships' as revealed by serology seemed to be a natural measure of affinity, rather as DNA comparisons may seem seventy years later. Serology was further associated with phylogenetic investigation by the discovery that all antibodies and many antigens were proteins, often specific to the organism producing them. Proteins have long been recognized as important carriers of evolutionary information (see Chapter 10). Most of the techniques for protein comparison can be applied together with the serological method, often with rewarding results.

After the work of Nuttall and others, serological methods were applied more widely. It was soon found that plant proteins elicited antibody formation when injected into vertebrate animals. Kowarski, Bertarelli and Magnus were notable first plant serologists.[50,280,316] They compared proteins from various grass and legume species, showing similarities and differences in good accord with modern taxonomic ideas despite the crudity of their technique. Magnus found that the specificity of his antisera depended on how many injections he administered to the test animal.[316] Antigens extracted from distantly related species would eventually produce a reaction with an antiserum when numerous injections had been given. The findings of Magnus have been confirmed many times.[299,326]

Serotaxonomy has always been popular in Germany, and Göhlke at Königsberg founded a celebrated 'school' of plant serology in about 1914. Later workers were Mez and Ziegenspeck. Numerous publications on plant relationships appeared, culminating in the 'Stammbaum' of 1926, illustrated in Chapter 2.[337] It was a family tree for the whole plant kingdom based largely on serological results. Serotaxonomy in the 1920's and 1930's was enlivened by disputations between Königsberg and the 'school' of Gilg and Schurhoff in Berlin.[180] They disagreed so violently on principles, methods and interpretation that it is not surprising that they obtained conflicting results. The defunct methods and results of these early workers are well reviewed by Chester,[90] whose papers coincided with a temporary decline of serology in Germany. After 20 years of vitriolic controversy between Königsberg and Berlin, the curse of the scientific world fell upon both their houses.

The hysterical application of serology to systematics had not been supported by an investigation of the fundamental systems being employed. No contribution to immunological theory was made by serotaxonomists, and they do not appear to have been aware of the advance in immunology gradually achieved in schools of medicine. Only Wells and Osborne made attempts to study the antigenic properties of plant proteins for their own sake, rather than as a short-cut to an 'evolutionary' scheme. They demonstrated[496] that seed storage proteins of grasses were markedly different in different taxa. Osborne had previously believed that storage proteins were essentially similar in a wide range of plants. A 'wheat group' and a 'corn group' in grasses were later distinguished, on the basis of seed proteins, using two different serological techniques.[304]

Other early workers made significant contributions to the application of serology to systematics. Rives showed a strong correlation of serological similarity and grafting affinity in vines.[405] Recognizing that serological data should correlate with genetic traits, if they were valid at all, Nelson and Birkeland compared wheat strains of known genetic relationship by means of serology.[358] The serological data correlated well with the known phylogeny of the wheat varieties. Working in the shadow of the Berlin-Königsberg controversy, Moritz compared the serological properties of seed proteins in rye, in wheat, and in their hybrid. The parental proteins were readily distinguishable, and the extract of the hybrid contained both parental sets.[344] Here was strong evidence of a link between serological characters and inheritance.

The school of serology at Rutgers University, New Jersey, made important contributions to the theory and technical progress of serotaxonomy, under the guidance of the zoologist Boyden. They developed the technique of measuring the turbidity of the precipitate in antigen–antiserum reactions in liquid media, by use of the Libby photronreflectrometer to produce 'Boyden curves' (see Fig. 11.5). Quantification of the reaction was an important step forward.[69]

From about 1945 serological reactions were studied in gels, and the additional resolution given by this technique immediately became popular with serologists. Pioneers of the gel diffusion methods for antigen–antibody combination were Oudin and Elek.[145,368] Ouchterlony developed the methods and made careful interpretations of the diffusion reactions.[367] Prior electrophoresis of the antigens followed by diffusion of antiserum in the gel (immunoelectrophoresis) was developed by Grabar and Williams.[187]

The principles of serology are today better established than ever, following experimental investigations of antiserum production, the nature of antigenicity and the mechanism of antigen–antibody reactions. Interpretation of the results is accordingly far less laborious and controversial. Taxonomic applications continue to show ever-wider correlations of serological characters with other evidence. In the taxonomy of viruses the method is paramount. As a cheap biochemical short-cut, it has much to offer.[90,268,346]

SEROLOGICAL PRINCIPLES

The basis of the antigen–antibody reaction is a complementarity of surface sites on antibodies with others on the antigens. The

antibody combining sites number 2–5 per molecule, and by linking with several of the antigen surface sites (**antigenic determinants**) may form a complex lattice. *In vitro* the lattice can comprise a visible precipitate (**precipitin reaction**). Small units such as bacterial cells or virus particles may be clumped together by the reaction (**agglutination reaction**). Motile bacteria may be immobilized by the binding of their flagella during the reaction between antibodies and flagellar antigens.

Many materials have been found to be antigenic, including nucleic acids, proteins and polysaccharides. Their determinant groups can be modified by the addition of low molecular weight compounds such as dinitrofluorobenzene or arsanilic acid. These are known as **haptens**. Though antigenic alone, they are recognized by precipitation only when attached to a large carrier molecule, such as a protein. Lipids are probably not antigenic except in combination with proteins.

Antibodies formed even to pure antigens are highly heterogeneous and do not all react in the same way. Some react with all antigenic determinants on the injected material, others with some of them, or perhaps only one. Therefore the antigen–antibody reaction is inevitably complex, and antisera will differ in their properties according to the type and duration of the injection programme and to the reaction of the individual animal.

Antisera consequently have distinctive properties and it is sometimes possible, by varying the injection programmes, to incorporate certain qualities into the antiserum. In terms of a taxonomic survey it should not be expected that two antisera produced independently by injection of the same plant extract, or of similar extracts from replicate samples of the plant material, will give exactly similar results. The results should be compatible nevertheless, and the investigator soon finds out the performance of an antiserum and can use it in the best way. Several antisera should be raised for comparison.

A complex of proteins called **complement** is involved in every antigen–antibody reaction. It is bound by antigen–antibody complexes, and hence is used up during the reaction. By supplying known quantities of complement, and measuring how much remains after the reaction, it is possible to measure the extent of immune reactions which never form visible precipitates (**complement fixation reaction**).

Agglutination, complement fixation and precipitin reactions all rely on *in vitro* use of antisera. *In vivo* tests are possible using intact immunized animals or their tissues. Guinea-pigs previously sensitized by a single injection of antigen may die, or show signs of distress (anaphylactic shock) when the same or similar antigens are administered subsequently. Strips of sensitized intestinal or uterine muscle, mounted in physiological saline, contract when the antigen is added to the bathing medium (Schultze–Dale reaction). These tests are no longer widely used by taxonomists. Most of the tax-onomic enquiries involving serological methods have relied upon the precipitin reaction, and it is that alone which is discussed below.

Further details of serological principles should be sought in text-books of immunology.[260]

SEROLOGICAL TECHNIQUES

Figure 11.1 shows a plan which might be used to investigate a hypothetical genus by serological means. An advantage of the method is that it provides an assessment of the protein similarities of all tested species to the proteins of the species which were injected. Antiserum to extracts of second or third species may be used to check the first assessment from other taxonomic positions. It is rather like taking bearings on distant objects from two or more viewing points. The investigator chooses viewing points as far apart as possible. There are as many possible viewing points as taxa in the investigation.

Preparation of antigens

Proteins are the most widely used antigens in serotaxonomy. They are ubiquitous, carry useful taxonomic information, and are quite easy to handle. Plant proteins are less easily extracted than those of animals, and are rarely so concentrated. Storage proteins have been found to have ideal features for taxonomic purposes (see Chapter 10) and are highly antigenic. Pollen proteins are also suitable.

Plants which have no rich source of stored protein, or which do not produce much pollen, may not be amenable to serological study. Grasses and legumes have been much studied since both have large protein reserves and are in any case economically important.

The antigen extraction methods which are suitable in a particular case depend on the nature of the tissue and of the proteins.

Soft tissues may be extracted by grinding to a slurry in an appropriate protein solvent (e.g. dilute saline for globulins). Expres-sed sap may be suitable.[177] Hard seeds and fruits can be ground to flour which is then extracted by irrigation with appropriate

(A) <u>Plan of group to be studied</u>

GENUS A●□	GENUS B□	GENUS C□	GENUS D●□
Section I●			
Species 1*	Species 1†		Species 1●*
2*			2●*
3*			3●*
4*	2†		4●*
5†			5●*
6*			6●*
7*	3*	Species 1*	7●†
8*			8●†
			9●†
Section II●	4*	2*	10●†
Species 1†			11●†
2†	5*		12□†
3†			13□†
4†	6†		14□†
Section III□			15□†
Species 1†	7†		

KEY: ⌐‾‾¬ alternative classification; ● annual; □ perennial; * diploid; † tetraploid.

(B) <u>Serological Investigation (Comprehensive)</u>

All available species should be used as antigen sources. Antisera might initially be raised to the following species, supposing materials were available:

GENUS	SECTION	SPECIES
A	I	1, 2, 4
	II	1, 2
	III	1
B	–	1, 3, 4, 5, 7
C	–	1, 2
D	–	1, 12

Fig. 11.1 A plan for the serological investigation of a hypothetical group of three related genera A, B, and C. Antisera should encompass as wide a diversity of taxa, especially those of uncertain position, as resources permit. Taxa with aberrant geographical distribution may also repay attention. The more distantly related genus D should be used in an attempt to gain serological perspective.

solvents.[441] Concentration of protein extracts can be adjusted to suitable levels by dilution or by dialysis against high molecular weight resins. Proteins are heat labile and are readily attacked by micro-organisms. Therefore the antigen solutions should be refrigerated, with suitable bacteriostatic agents added (e.g. 0.1% sodium azide), or frozen solid.

Preparation of antisera

Purified or mixed antigens may be injected into a range of test animals, of which the rabbit is the most popular. Rabbits reconcile cheapness, availability, control of pedigree and size quite satisfactorily.

Rather small quantities of protein are required for the immunization, although the more that is available the better. 50–100 mg of protein are usually sufficient, but all depends on the antigenicity of the injected material, and how many separate molecular types are present in it.

It is still uncertain as to how antibodies are formed. Plasma cells and lymphocytes are principally involved. Spleen and bone marrow tissue form antibodies and the lymph nodes are especially active. Good immunization programmes make use of as many antibody-producing sites as possible.

Aqueous antigen solutions produce only an ephemeral antibody response when injected. Antigen is excreted or digested, and the dose has to be increased to compensate for that. Alum-precipitated protein particles can be injected as a suspension, and are less readily metabolized by the animal. Particles are quickly incorporated in phagocytic cells. Use of **adjuvants** also prolongs the active life of injected antigen. Freund's complete adjuvant is a mixture of mineral oil, dead mycobacteria and an emulsifier. Antigen solution is emulsified together with the adjuvant, and injected intramuscularly. The depot of emulsion releases antigen slowly so providing a constant stimulus to antibody-forming tissue. Cells migrate to the site of the bacterial-surface antigens, ensuring good contact of antibody-forming tissue and antigen. Some of the injected material will reach lymph nodes near the site of injection, while some will be circulated to the bone marrow.

Many different injection regimes have been found suitable. After a few weeks the antiserum is usually strong enough for use. It is tested against serial dilutions of antigen to find out how sensitive it is. High-titre antisera are those which react to very low antigen concentrations. When antisera are judged ready for use, a large blood sample can be taken from the animal, which can then be rested and perhaps given a second immunization later. Antiserum is best stored frozen as small aliquots, containing a preservative.

Combination of antigen and antibody

The antigen–antibody complex forms a precipitate. The amount and nature of the precipitate and the ease with which it forms are serological observations of potential taxonomic value.

If the reaction takes place in liquid, the turbidity of the precipitate can be measured. There is an optimal point of antigen–antibody proportions which yields the greatest precipitate. To identify it, a range of antigen–antibody ratios is tested and the turbidity plotted for each. This produces the Boyden curve (Fig. 11.5). At extreme antibody excess and antigen excess, the precipitate does not form. In fact, precipitates may disappear after formation if the antigen–antibody proportions are sufficiently changed—the reaction is reversible. The area under the reaction curve of the *homologous species* extract (the extract used to raise the antiserum) should theoretically be greater than that for any heterologous system. If expressed as 100, the heterologous reactions can be quoted as percentages of the homologous reaction.

Table 11.1 shows how a number of grass antigens reacted to an antiserum of *Bromus inermis* and of *Eragrostis curvula*.[156] The

Table 11.1 Turbidity measurements of precipitin reactions using rabbit antisera to *Bromus inermis* and to *Eragrostis curvula,* with a range of antigen extracts of different grass fruits.

| Antigen extracts | Antisera | |
	Bromus inermis	*Eragrostis curvula*
Bromus inermis	100	0
Lolium perenne	25	0
Festuca rubra	12.5	0
Dactylis glomerata	12.5	0
Poa pratensis	6.2	—
Briza maxima	1.5	0
Melica mutica	12.5	6.2
Spartina cynosuroides	0	12.5
Tridens flavus	0	50
Distichlis spicata	0	100
Eragrostis curvula	0	100

The lowest antigen concentration at which a visible precipitate would appear after 40 minutes was established for each antigen extract. The turbidity of this precipitate was measured and is here represented as a percentage of the homologous reaction, which is expressed as 100.

SIMPLE DIFFUSION

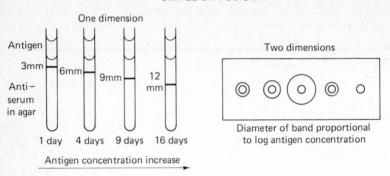

DOUBLE DIFFUSION

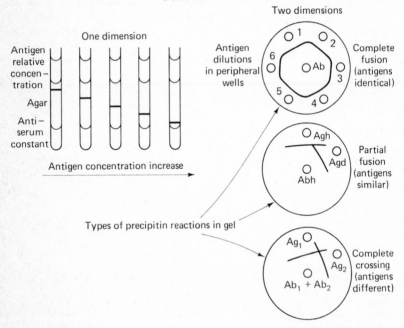

Fig. 11.2 Simple and double diffusion in gels. In simple diffusion the antiserum is incorporated in the gel. In double diffusion both reagents diffuse. Position of precipitin bands varies with the antigen concentration. (After Kabat.[260])

relationships of the heterologous species to the homologous species are presumed to be in the same order as the percentages of their reactions to its antiserum.

A criticism of the turbidometric measurement of liquid precipitation has been that the same percentage of precipitation shown by two species might not arise from the same antigen–antibody reactions. The single figure of 70%, for instance, might be made up in a number of different ways. To avoid this potential difficulty precipitin tests can be carried out in gels. Figure 11.2 illustrates different methods (simple and double diffusion) by which antigens and antibodies may be reacted in gels. The merits of gel diffusion include the physical separation of antigen–antibody systems, according to diffusion rate (i.e. molecular size) and the fact that an infinity of antigen–antibody ratios is inevitably tested. Related antigen–antibody reactions, for extracts of different species, can be studied side-by-side in the same gel, and the similarity or otherwise of their antigens is indicated by the degree of physical fusion of their precipitin lines. The number of lines can be counted. Figure 11.11 shows a double diffusion plate where some extracts are antigenically similar (fusion of all or most lines) and some are different. All these phenomena, together with the simple presence or absence of reaction, give taxonomic information.[106]

Figure 11.3 illustrates the principle of electrophoretic separation of the antigens in a gel, before the antiserum is added. This technique of immuno-electrophoresis (IEP) fractionates the antigens on the criteria of molecular size, electrical charge and finally serological affinity. It has proved to be an economical and powerful method for producing chemotaxonomic evidence.

The numbers and shapes of precipitin arcs, their clarity and strength and how fast or tardily they develop are the classical serotaxonomic characters in both diffusion and IEP analyses. Figure 11.9 illustrates a number of IEP spectra of extracts of different species of *Bromus*.

A final variant of all these techniques is to pre-absorb some of the antibodies out of the antiserum. This often reduces the labour of interpretation, and certainly makes the spectra simpler to the eye. If species X antiserum is mixed with extract of related species Y, all the reaction common to the two species will be removed. By centrifuging off the precipitate, the absorbed antiserum is made ready for further reactions. If numerous antigen–antibody systems persist in the absorbed antiserum, then Y is clearly not closely related to X, in serological terms. Antiserum X–Y can then be used to study the extracts of other species and may reveal several or many

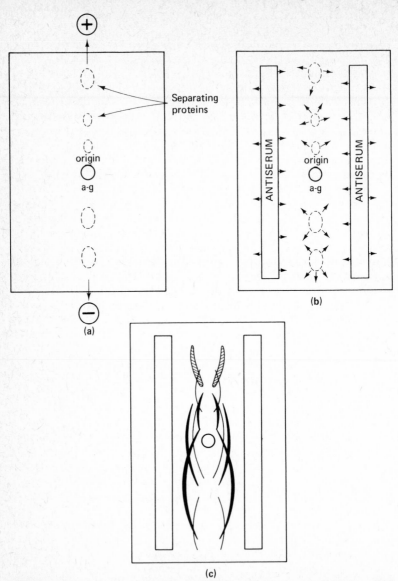

Fig. 11.3 Principles of immuno-electrophoresis. (**a**) Plan of a flatbed gel in which antigenic proteins in solution (a–g) are separating towards cathode or anode, according to their net electrical charge. (**b**) After electrophoretic separation, troughs are cut parallel to the axis of fractionation and charged with antiserum. Antibodies and antigens diffuse towards each other. (**c**) After a time, the antibodies and antigens meet. Precipitation occurs along an arc of optimal antigen–antibody proportions.

of them to be non-reactive. This means that they may be related to species Y (see Fig. 11.4).

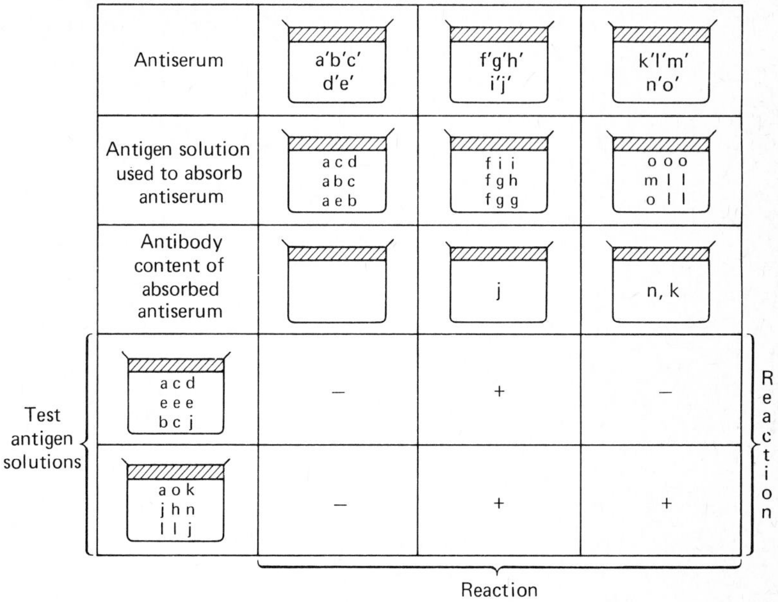

Antiserum	a'b'c' d'e'	f'g'h' i'j'	k'l'm' n'o'
Antigen solution used to absorb antiserum	a c d a b c a e b	f i i f g h f g g	o o o m l l o l l
Antibody content of absorbed antiserum		j	n, k

Test antigen solutions					Reaction
	a c d e e e b c j	−	+	−	
	a o k j h n l l j	−	+	+	

Reaction

Fig. 11.4 Pre-absorption of antisera. a', b', c', etc. are *antibodies* to *antigenic determinants* a, b, c, etc. acd, llj, etc. are protein antigens in antigen extracts. +/− indicate positive and negative reactions using the absorbed antisera with test antigen solutions. (After Jensen.[254])

Shape and size of proteins are probably very important features (see Chapter 10), often reflecting selection pressures. Surface structures will determine their packing qualities and many of their other properties. Serology offers a quick method of assessing proteins for just such differences. Like fingerprinting and chromatography, the data appear largely in terms of a pattern, and to the biochemical eye these may appear complex and hard to interpret. Perhaps these techniques are so popular with taxonomists partly because they are, paradoxically, so readily interpreted. Possibly 'taxonomic intuition' is a highly developed capacity for natural principal components analysis.

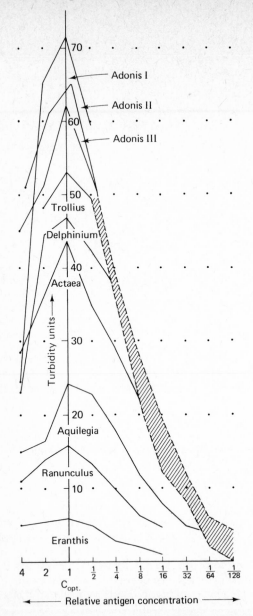

Fig. 11.5 Boyden precipitin curves of *Adonis vernalis* antiserum reacted with antigen extracts of *Adonis vernalis* (homologous reaction *Adonis* I), *A. autumnalis* (*Adonis* II), *Adonis aestivalis* (*Adonis* III), *Trollius europaeus*, *Delphinium consolida*, *Actaea spicata*, *Aquilegia vulgaris*, *Ranunculus acris*, *Eranthis hyemalis*. (After Jensen.[254])

APPLICATIONS OF SEROLOGY IN PLANT TAXONOMY

Serotaxonomy has so long a history that there is almost an embarrassment of riches from which to choose examples to illustrate the possibilities. Much early work has to be ignored since it can be shown that the experimentation was insufficiently critical in the light of modern immunological knowledge. Some of the better early studies have already been mentioned in connection with the correlations of serological and other lines of evidence. However too little of the chemistry and biology of proteins was known to the pioneers for them to produce consistent results. Though Dunbar demonstrated organ-specificity of proteins,[138] Mez at Königsberg seems to have assumed that the proteins of an organism were distributed uniformly within it. On the other hand, Moritz gave a most elegant demonstration of the serological intermediacy of the rye–wheat hybrid between its parents,[344] which was subsequently confirmed in full using modern immuno-electrophoretic methods.[199] The study of hybrids attracted the serological pioneers because it provided an opportunity to validate their method at the same time as investigating an interesting biological situation. In 1914, it was shown that *Trifolium hybridum,* the putative hybrid of *T. pratense* and *T. repens,* was serologically more similar to its supposed parents than either was to the other.[510] Moritz and vom Berg discussed serology of plant hybrids at length, and showed for the first time that plant proteins behave as Mendelian characters.[347] Correlations between serological variation and genetic relationships are often reported.[483]

Serological enquiries are sometimes undertaken with a view to gaining evidence of phylogenetic relationship, or to check a system of classification based on other taxonomic characters. A conflict in the evidence from other sources may be resolved by resort to a serological approach. Serological data may help to decide which of two possible taxonomic choices is the better.

Jensen has continued the tradition of serotaxonomic research at Kiel, Germany, and more recently at Cologne. His principal interests have been in the Ranunculaceae, paricularly the relationships *and* classification of the genera. In a survey of 20 ranunculacean genera he compared the proteins of mature seeds by serological methods.[254] The antigens were injected intraperitoneally into rabbits, producing antisera to ten genera. A number of techniques of analysis were used, including turbidometry of precipitation reactions in liquid (Boyden procedure), immuno-diffusion and absorption.

Figure 11.5 illustrates the Boyden curves obtained by Jensen for antigens of seven genera reacting in liquid medium with antiserum to *Adonis vernalis.* Turbidity of reaction is plotted against relative antigen concentration. Optimal precipitation occurred at position1. It can be seen that *Adonis vernalis* produces the strongest reaction. This would be expected since it is the *homologous species. Adonis autumnalis* and *A. aestivalis* antigens gave stronger reactions with the *A. vernalis* antiserum than antigens from any other genus. The remaining genera may be ranked in the following order of serological similarity to *Adonis vernalis: Trollius, Delphinium, Actaea, Aquilegia, Ranunculus, Eranthis.*

This is a similarity rating only in relation to one species of one genus, and it permits only a linear array of genera to be drawn up, unlike the multidimensional natural distances between taxa. Use of other antisera should help to arrange these genera more accurately. Jensen had nine other antisera to use.

Absorbed antisera provided a further way to check the tentative schemes of serological relationships which were emerging. Figure 11.6 shows a table of results obtained with samples of antiserum to *Hydrastis canadensis,* which were absorbed individually with antigen extracts of 21 other species. When *H. canadensis* antiserum is pre-absorbed with *H. canadensis* antigens, not unnaturally the absorbed preparation gives no reaction to any antigen extract, because all the homologous antigen–antibody systems have been removed. But when *H. canadensis* antiserum is absorbed with *Thalictrum saxatile,* for instance, a strong serological reaction to *H. canadensis* antigens persists in the absorbed preparation. This means that hardly any of the *Hydrastis* antigen–antibody systems can be removed by absorption with *Thalictrum saxatile,* and the two genera may be considered only distant relatives in serological terms. In Fig. 11.6, a strong homologous reaction of an absorbed *Hydrastis* antiserum (i.e. reacting with *Hydrastis* antigens) indicates a distant relationship between *Hydrastis* and the extract used for absorption.

Whatever extract is used to absorb *Hydrastis* antiserum, the residual homologous reaction is still strong. This implies that *Hydrastis* is serologically distant, or isolated from other genera which were tested.

By integrating the results obtained by using all the different antisera, Jensen made a chart to express the serological relationships of the ranunculaceous genera, in two dimensions (Fig. 11.7). It is striking that *Hydrastis* shows a closer serological similarity to Ranunculaceae than to the Berberidaceae (e.g. *Jeffersonia* and *Mahonia*) in which it is often classified. Many taxonomists regard *Hydrastis* as a Berberidacean link with Ranunculaceae. Jensen's work shows it to have more in common with the Ranunculaceae, especially the

Fig. 11.6 Table showing reactivity of absorbed antisera to *Hydrastis canadensis*, to genera of Ranunculaceae, Magnoliaceae and Berberidaceae. Key to symbols: ●, strongly positive reaction; O, moderately strong positive reaction; +, feebly positive reaction; ?, doubtful or inconsistent reaction; −, negative reaction. The zero column (extreme right) refers to unabsorbed *Hydrastis* antiserum. (After Jensen.[254])

Antigen extracts used to absorb *Hydrastis* antiserum

Antigen extracts tested with absorbed *Hydrastis* antisera

Columns (absorbing extracts): Normal serum; Hydrastis canadensis; Aquilegia einseliana, vulgaris; Leptopyrum fumarioides; Thalictrum saxatile; Coptis asplenifolia; Actaea (4 spp.); Cimicifuga racemosa; Trollius chinensis, europaeus; Adonis autumnalis, vernalis; Caltha scaposa; Delphinium ajacis; Ranunculus (3 spp.); Aconitum napellus; Myosurus minimus; Helleborus niger, viridis; Clematis vitalba; Anemone nemorosa; Nigella damascena; Eranthis hyemalis; Magnolia spp.; Mahonia aquifolia; Jeffersonia dubia; O

Rows (antigen extracts tested): Hydrastis canadensis; Aquilegia einseliana, vulgaris; Leptopyrum fumarioides; Thalictrum saxatile; Coptis asplenifolia; Actaea (4 spp.); Cimicifuga racemosa; Trollius chinensis, europaeus; Adonis autumnalis, vernalis; Caltha scaposa; Delphinium ajacis; Ranunculus (3 spp.); Aconitum napellus; Myosurus minimus; Helleborus niger, viridis; Clematis vitalba; Anemone nemorosa; Nigella damascena; Eranthis hyemalis; Magnolia spp.; Mahonia aquifolia; Jeffersonia dubia; Berberis vulgaris; Menispermum canadense

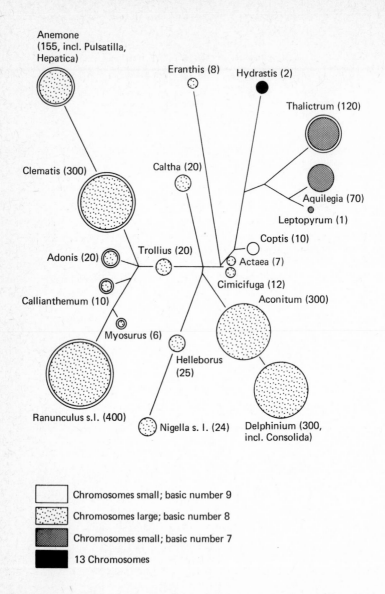

Fig. 11.7 An arrangement of genera in the Ranunculaceae on the basis of serological evidence. Numbers are of species in the various genera. (From Jensen.[254])

genera *Thalictrum, Aquilegia, Leptopyrum, Coptis, Actaea* and *Cimicifuga.*

The general agreement that *Aconitum* and *Delphinium* are closely related is supported by the serological evidence. *Anemone/Clematis* and *Ranunculus/Myosurus* are associated by the protein data, both pairings being a feature of most orthodox classifications.

Eranthis is serologically isolated from the other genera, as is *Nigella. Caltha* and *Trollius* are less similar on serological criteria than might have been predicted from morphology. *Trollius* more closely resembles *Adonis*, which Jensen and others regard as a taxon linking the follicle- and achene-fruited genera in the family.

Striking correlations of serology with karyotype analyses[190] are noted in Fig. 11.7. There is further supporting evidence from ranunculin alkaloid distribution and from pollen anatomy. Jensen has used the serological evidence as a major source of taxonomic characters to construct a revised classification of the Ranunculaceae.

The classic work on potato species by Gell, Hawkes and Wright[177] subsequently continued by Hawkes and Lester,[217,218,300] may herald a new phase of serotaxonomy.[268] Potato species were compared using antisera raised in rabbits to clarified tuber saps. On the basis of double diffusion tests, with absorbed and unabsorbed antisera to *Solanum tuberosum*, Mexican species fell into three groups: a group with three precipitin lines (4 with electrophoresis), a group with two lines, and a group with one line. All extracts of South American species resembled the reaction of *S. tuberosum* antigens, i.e. produced a three line precipitin spectrum. *Solanum morelliforme* alone of all the species produced the one line reaction. This serological evidence confirms the idea that *S. morelliforme* is only distantly related to other tuber-bearing *Solanum* species.

The work of Gell *et al.* showed striking agreement with morphological classification and with the unusually detailed knowledge of the breeding relationships of these important species. Some of the discrepancies between the lines of evidence were followed up with greater use of immuno-electrophoretic analysis.[217,218,300] Intraspecific variation was noted in some species (e.g. *S. bulbocastanum*) but it did not frustrate the use of the serological data.

Considerable research has been undertaken into the application of serological methods to the taxonomy of legumes. Not only are they an important and interesting group, but the storage globulins in their cotyledons are a rich source of readily extracted protein, and they produce excellent antisera. In Prague, the laboratory of Kloz has obtained valuable data relating to the general principles of serology from studies of legume antigen–antibody systems. A

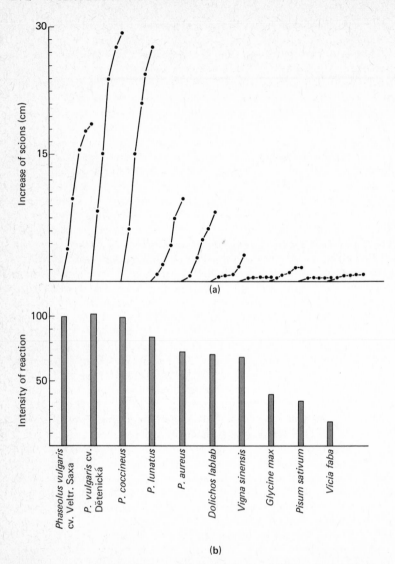

Fig. 11.8 (a) The growth of scions and species on stocks of *Phaseolus vulgaris* ssp. *vulgaris* cv. Veltruská Saxa. Increases were measured weekly for five weeks. (*n* = 30 in each combination). (b) Quantitative evaluation of intensity of precipitin reactions between soluble proteins (hypocotyl and root) of various species, and antisera against soluble proteins of *Phaseolus vulgaris* cv. Veltruská Saxa. Homologous reaction expressed as 100%. (From Kloz.[268])

comprehensive review documents the application of serology to the systematics of Leguminosae, including results of gel diffusion, immuno-electrophoresis and Boyden methods, on globulins and other protein types.[268]

Figure 11.8 presents data from the work of Kloz which shows the strong correlation between quantitatively evaluated precipitin reactions to an antiserum of *Phaseolus vulgaris* cv. Veltruská Saxa, and the growth of scions of different species when grafted on to stocks of *P. vulgaris*.[269] These results recall the much earlier experiments of Rives.[405] It is clearly shown that the graft affinities of the tested species to *P. vulgaris* are in the same order as that indicated by standard precipitin reactions. Perhaps a similar kind of recognition phenomenon is involved in both processes.

The strong American tradition of serotaxonomic research continues at Rutgers University, New Jersey. Fairbrothers provides an American view of the modern uses of serology for systematic purposes.[155] Recent work of this school has been particularly wide-ranging, covering groups as diverse as *Magnolia*[380] and *Typha*.[294]

Serotaxonomic investigations of the grass family were among the earliest researches, as already noted. Smith has applied modern serological techniques to the taxonomy of critical groups,[439,440] and also in a broader survey of the family.[442] In what may be the first example of provisional recognition of a new species on the basis of anomalous serological reactions,[440] it was discovered that *Bromus pseudosecalinus* was probably specifically distinct from the closely similar species *B. secalinus* (see Chapter 14).

Application of serological methods in critical taxonomic groups, such as *Bromus*, provides a valuable means of testing new orthodox classifications against data from a very different source of phenetic observations. Smith produced a new classification of annual *Bromus* species, on the basis of morphology, kayology and cytogenetics and then checked it against a serological survey.[444] In many ways the serological evidence agreed with the classification, but in several ways it did not. After the serological data had been incorporated, a revised version of the classification was adopted.

One feature of the serological approach was the use of immuno-electrophoretic spectra as taxonomic characters. Some of these are illustrated in Fig. 11.9. The homologous reaction (to the tetraploid species *B. hordeaceus*) varied little between different accessions of the homologous species. It is easy to see that some seed protein spectra resemble the homologous reaction quite closely (e.g. *B. interruptus*, and *B. lepidus*). *B.* × *pseudothominii*, an amphidiploid of *B. lepidus* and *B. hordeaceus*,[439] likewise has a homologous-type reaction.

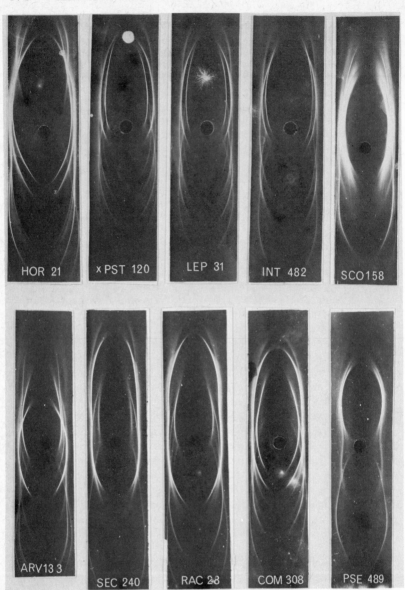

Fig. 11.9 Immuno-electrophoretic spectra of seed protein extracts of *Bromus hordeaceus* (HOR), *B. pseudothominii* (PST), *B. lepidus* (LEP), *B. interruptus* (INT), *B. scoparius* (SCO), *B. arvensis* (ARV), *B. secalinus* (SEC), *B. racemosus* (RAC), *B. commutatus* (COM), *B. pseudosecalinus* (PSE). Antiserum to HOR. (From Smith.[444])

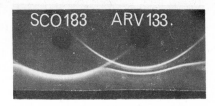

Fig. 11.10 Double diffusion reaction of seed protein extracts of two diploid grasses (*Bromus scoparius*: SCO; *B. arvensis*: ARV), to antiserum raised to their putative tetraploid descendant *B. hordeaceus*. Each reaction includes single antigen–antibody systems lacked by the other, but possessed also by *B. hordeaceus*. (After Smith.[444])

Slightly more different reactions are shown by the tetraploids *B. secalinus*, *B. racemosus* and *B. commutatus*, all of which are morphologically similar. Of the diploid species, *B. arvensis* and *B. scoparius* show greatest resemblance to the homologous reaction,

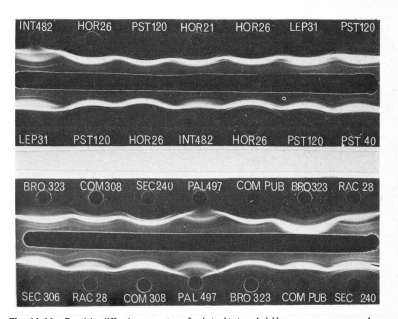

Fig. 11.11 Double diffusion spectra of related tetraploid brome-grasses, and one more distantly related diploid (PAL). Key to symbols; *Bromus interruptus* (INT), *hordeaceus* (HOR), *pseudothominii* (PST), *lepidus* (LEP), *bromoideus* (BRO), *commutatus* (COM), *secalinus* (SEC), *palaestinus* (PAL), *commutatus* var. *pubens* (COM PUB), *racemosus* (RAC). (From Smith.[444])

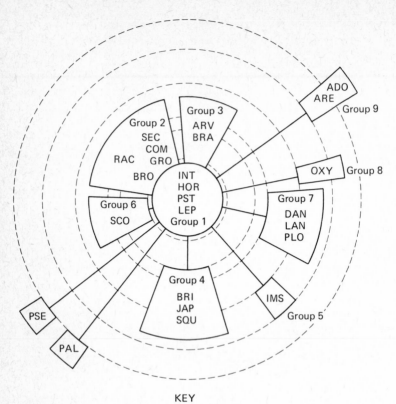

KEY

Abbreviation	Species	Abbreviation	Species
ADO	*B. adoensis*	JAP	*B. japonicus*
ARE	*B. arenarius*	LAN	*B. lanceolatus*
ARV	*B. arvensis*	LEP	*B. lepidus*
BRA	*B. brachystachys*	OXY	*B. oxyodon*
BRI	*B. briziformis*	PAL	*B. palaestinus*
BRO	*B. bromoideus*	PSE	*B. pseudosecalinus*
COM	*B. commutatus*	PST	*B. × pseudothominii*
DAN	*B. danthoniae*	PLO	*B. pumilio*
GRO	*B. grossus*	RAC	*B. racemosus*
HOR	*B. hordeaceus*	SCO	*B. scoparius*
IMS	*B. intermedius*	SEC	*B. secalinus*
INT	*B. interruptus*	SQU	*B. squarrosus*

Fig. 11.12 Chart showing serological relationships in annual bromes (*Bromus* spp.). (After Smith.[444])

while *B. pseudosecalinus*, though morphologically resembling *B. secalinus*, has a very different kind of IEP spectrum. Figure 11.10 shows that *B. scoparius* and *B. arvensis* possess different antigens in common with *B. hordeaceus*. A mixture of the two extracts produces an homologous-type reaction. It therefore seems possible from the serological evidence that *B. scoparius* and *B. arvensis* may be the diploid progenitors of *B. hordeaceus,* or perhaps close relatives of its progenitors. There is some cytological and morphological evidence for this.

Figure 11.11 shows how species extracts behave in double diffusion reactions with *B. hordeaceus* antiserum. On the whole the tetraploid species, which are so subtly different in morphology that they comprise a critical group, are very similar, most of the precipitin bands being shared by the reactions of all extracts. There is a comparatively minor difference between *B. commutatus* var. *pubens* and the other tetraploid species, and a slight difference between the very similar species *B. hordeaceus* and *B. interruptus.* The strong central precipitin band is a complex reaction of several strong lines, separated properly only by immuno-electrophoresis. This complex of antigens, evidently characteristic of most of the brome species tested, is completely absent from *B. palaestinus.* This diploid species therefore is reckoned to have a low serological affinity with most of the other species tested, which belies its morphological resemblance to them.

Figure 11.12 is a chart summarizing apparent serological relationships in this group of grasses. *Bromus hordeaceus* antiserum was mainly used to obtain the data, but results using antisera to other species substantially confirm the general arrangement.

The return of taxonomic information and the evidence of relationships gained from a comparatively modest programme of serological research is clearly quite high. Now that the underlying theory of the production and *in vitro* use of antisera is so much better established, these inexpensive methods will probably be more systematically applied in future. Their popularity will be restricted only by fancied difficulties of interpretation and the requirement for the use and management of animals.

12

Nucleotide Variation and Plant Taxonomy

Nucleotides are fundamentally important in the physiology and biochemistry of plants. Many are so important and ubiquitous that they are instantly recognized by their widely used abbreviations. Thus ATP is adenosine 5-triphosphate, and NAD is nicotinamide-adenine-dinucleotide. Both are coenzymes. Nucleotides of this type show few discontinuities between different plant groups and so are not very useful taxonomic characters. The situation is very different when natural polynucleotides are considered. Deoxyribose nucleic acid (DNA) is a nucleotide polymer which is the physical manifestation of the genetic code. The sequence of nucleotides in DNA is a language in which the specification for the form and physiology of an organism is written. The code also incorporates a workshop manual for constructing and maintaining an organism of that specification. Almost all individuals have a genetic code unique to themselves.

Though much remains to be discovered about the genetic language, it is clear that the nucleic acids of different organisms are treasuries of taxonomic evidence. Taxonomists operate by compiling, and then classifying, specifications of organisms. In the nucleic acids the natural specifications are available for their inspection and use.

Though discovered in the nineteenth century, nucleic acids have begun to unfold their biological complexity only over the last twenty years. The pace of advance in analytical techniques has been especially rapid since the Watson–Crick double-helix hypothesis of the structure of DNA was published in 1953. Establishment of the structures of DNA and ribose nucleic acid (RNA) had to precede the comparison of polynucleotides from different taxa. The stage is now set for an expansion of such comparative studies, particularly in higher plants.

It was perhaps inevitable that much early effort should be devoted to phylogenetic interpretations of the sparse comparative data which became available at first. When it was recognized that mutations were changes in the nucleotide sequence of DNA, the acid was regarded as an evolutionary record of the mutations by which two related taxa had diverged. Theoretically the number of mutations should be enumerable. Though technique might not at first permit such an enumeration, any method of offering a cruder measure of the similarity of nucleic acids from two or more taxa should also indicate their evolutionary relationship. If a standard rate of mutation is assumed, at least over long periods of time, it might even be practicable to arrive at a figure for the period which has elapsed since two taxa diverged. Nucleic acid differences might be useful taxonomic characters, but because of the functional significance of the molecules, the differences might also indicate pathways of descent. The latter are of greater general interest, in higher plants particularly, since fossil studies are frustrated by lack of material. Chemotaxonomists have therefore tended to use comparative nucleotide data as a phylogenetic yardstick against which to measure the evolutionary accuracy of traditional classifications. Even allowing for all the unstated assumptions which such tests require, the outcome is often vaguely described as a 'phylogenetic classification', so confounding cause and effect.

Where classical systems of taxonomy are less well-founded than in the higher plants, nucleic acid comparisons are seen less in terms of phylogenetic considerations than as a source of taxonomic evidence. Work on the nucleic acids of bacteria strikingly emphasizes this (see Chapter 13).

CHEMISTRY AND BIOLOGY OF NUCLEOTIDES AND NUCLEIC ACIDS

Certain basic chemical facts must be outlined in order to set the taxonomic application in perspective. Nucleic acids from the

biochemical viewpoint are well reviewed in the latest edition of
Davidson's classic monograph.[117]

Mononucleotides consist of a purine (I) or pyrimidine (II) base
linked to a sugar, which in turn carries one or more phosphate
groups. ATP (III) is an example of a triphosphate. Purine and
pyrimidine bases occur free in plants, and by no means all of them
occur in nucleotides. Theobromine (from cocoa) and caffeine (from
coffee) are purine bases normally treated as alkaloids (see Chapter
8).

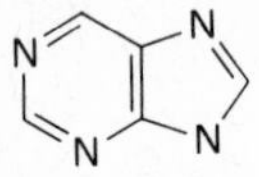

I Purine 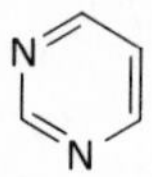   II Pyrimidine

Dinucleotides consist of two nucleotides joined by an esterifica-
tion of the sugar components (e.g. NAD(IV)). NAD is a hydrogen-
carrying coenzyme in oxidation–reduction reactions.

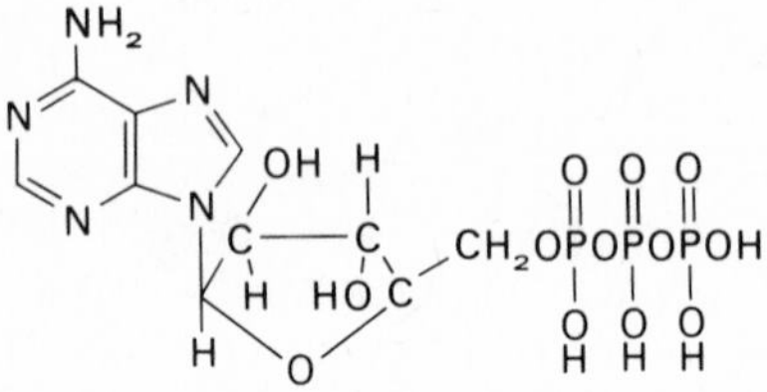

III ATP

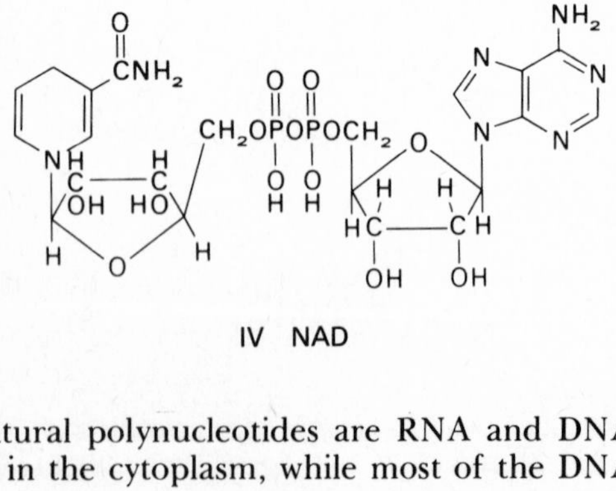

IV NAD

The two natural polynucleotides are RNA and DNA. RNA is
found mainly in the cytoplasm, while most of the DNA is in the

nucleus. RNA and DNA were once thought to characterize the tissues of plants and animals respectively, but this striking tax-onomic discontinuity was soon shown to be fallacious. It arose from the extreme nucleus : cytoplasm ratios in the tissues chosen by chance as the first experimental materials. DNA is a large, complex polymer of nucleotides of the purine bases adenine (A) and guanine (G) and the pyrimidines cytosine (C) and thymine (T), in combina-tion with the sugar deoxyribose. In RNA the sugar is ribose, and uracil (U) replaces thymine. In DNA, cytosine is sometimes replaced by methyl-cytosine.

Figure 12.1 shows a small portion of the double helix of DNA. Phosphate forms a diester link between the sugar molecules of adjacent bases in one helix. The bases of the two helices are linked together by hydrogen bonds, so that A always pairs with T, and C always pairs with G.

Both RNA and DNA can be fairly readily extracted and isolated from plant tissue. Techniques are given by Davidson, together with methods of hydrolysis and details of the chemical properties of the compounds.[117]

DNA is the master copy of the genetic language which is written in codons—units of three bases in sequence which code for a particular amino acid. Table 10.1 (p. 132) gives the amino acid translation of the codons. The code is degenerate in that several codons code for the same amino acid. This means that a difference in base sequence, or base composition, does not necessarily imply a difference in the protein eventually produced. Similarly, production of an identical protein in two species would not *necessarily* imply the existence of identical DNA base sequences coding for the protein in both species. Proteins and nucleic acids are both such large molecules that substantial differences in either almost certainly reflect equally real differences in the other.

Many copies of some parts of the DNA code exist in higher plants, whereas other parts of the genome are represented only by single copies. Some sequences may be repeated as much as a million times, each copy apparently belonging to a 'family' of copies which shows small divergences in sequence from other 'families'. The repeated DNA is described variously as repetitious or redundant DNA. It does not occur in bacteria. Bacterial genes therefore seem to be represented only once in the DNA of a cell.

DNA functions as a template upon which various kinds of RNA are assembled. RNA is thus produced in the nucleus, but it operates chiefly in the cytoplasm. **Transfer RNAs** are short sequences which can attach to particular amino acids. They function by bringing the

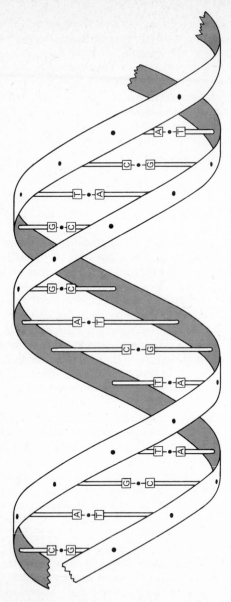

Fig. 12.1   Double helix of DNA. The ribbons are two sugar phosphate chains held together by base-pairs (A = adenine; C = cytosine; G = guanine; T = thymine). The bases are held together by hydrogen bonds (-•-).

appropriate amino acid to the ribosomes in the cytoplasm, which are the main sites of protein synthesis. Ribosomes are organelles consisting of **ribosomal RNA** and protein. A smaller and a larger sub-unit are distinguishable in a ribosome. Ribosomal RNA is the transcription product of a particular gene (DNA sequence), and it is produced in large quantities, especially in cells which actively synthesize protein. Comparisons of ribosomal RNAs from different organisms are comparisons of the sequence of a single homologous gene. Many slightly different copies of the ribosomal RNA gene exist, so it is perhaps not quite accurate to state that only one gene sequence is being compared. The apparent homology, stability and concentration of ribosomal RNA recommend it as a most useful potential source of chemotaxonomic evidence. **Messenger RNA** is the RNA translation of particular DNA sequences (particular genes). It acts as a guide to the sequence in which the transfer RNAs assemble amino acids into proteins at the ribosome.

It is assumed that the DNA from different parts of the same individual is uniform in molecular size, base sequence and level of redundancy. Nuclear DNA is not identical with chloroplast DNA, and the variations are confounded if total DNA is taken for comparison. Ribosomal RNA seems to be homogeneous within an organism,[186] but the absolute size of the ribosome, and the relative sizes of its two sub-units differ in diverse plants. Higher organisms have larger ribosomes.

Certain basic questions about variation of nucleic acids are relevant to their usefulness in taxonomy. Are the ribosomal and transfer RNAs of different species the same, or to what extent do they differ? Are the messenger RNAs produced by homologous genes identical in base sequence in different taxa? Unfortunately, transfer and messenger RNAs are either produced fleetingly or in low concentration, and so are difficult to compare between taxa. Ribosomal RNA is relatively stable. How does it differ between species and between higher taxa?

Nuclear DNA exists in repetitious and 'unique' forms, and in every intermediate condition. Does a standard proportion of unique DNA characterize members of a taxon? Is the unique DNA unique also in a taxonomic sense? To avoid confusion in comparative studies, unique DNA is better referred to as **non-repeated DNA.**

Molecular biologists are still working on these problems, but what has so far been discovered should be of great interest to taxonomists. In taxonomic applications of nucleic acid chemistry which are cited later in this chapter, provisional answers to some of the questions are indicated.

ANALYSIS AND VARIATION

The digestion of DNA or RNA by acid hydrolysis releases the component nucleotides which can be separated and identified chromatographically. The information gained relates only to the ratios of the four bases in the sample hydrolysed, and seems to have low taxonomic potential.

Resting or dividing nuclei can be stained with the DNA-specific Feulgen method and the DNA content calculated by scanning the nuclei with an integrating micro-densitometer. Studies of the nuclear DNA content of 45 species of *Vicia* showed a six-fold variation in nuclear DNA content in the sample.[91] In the primitive sections of *Vicia* (Ervum and Cracca) there was continuous variation in nuclear DNA. Greater variation characterized advanced species, where higher values occurred. There is evidence in this work that evolution from the perennial to the annual species in section Cracca has been accompanied by a loss of DNA.

If nucleic acid is centrifuged at high speed in a caesium chloride solution a density gradient is set up. The banding of the nucleic acid sample in the gradient can be visualized by photographing the separation in ultraviolet light. Buoyant densities of nucleic acids can be calculated by reference to a known marker sample, usually of bacterial DNA.[459] An analytical ultracentrifuge is necessary for this method. Many plant DNAs produce a single band, i.e. are homogenous in density, but many others have both main band and satellite-band DNA. The buoyant densities of main band and satellite DNAs have now been established for many species of plant. Satellite DNA seems to contain many copies of the sequences complementary to high-molecular-weight RNA.[325] The taxonomic significance of the incidence of satellite DNA is not yet clear. Satellite DNA is commonest in the Rutaceae and the Cucurbitaceae, and is apparently absent from monocotyledons.[248] In the Leguminosae, *Phaseolus* contains satellite DNA but *Pisum* and *Vicia* do not. In general there is no correlation between the species distribution of satellite DNA and taxonomy. Of two species of *Linum* examined, one had satellite DNA and one did not.[248]

There seems little difference in the buoyant densities of main-band DNA between monocots and dicots, though some monocots seem to have a rather higher density than the average of dicots (see Table 12.1). Too few taxa have in any case been studied for meaningful conclusions to be drawn.

The underlying factor determining buoyant density is base composition, i.e. the properties of the different purine and pyrimidine

Table 12.1 Buoyant densities and base compositions of some angiosperm DNAs.

	Buoyant density[248]	Moles % GC[54]
Dicotyledons		
Beta vulgaris	1.693	38.0
Cucumis melo	1.692	41.4
Citrullus vulgaris	1.693	41.0
Luffa cylindrica	1.696	41.9
Vicia faba	1.694	40.0
Pisum sativum	1.695	38.5
Phaseolus aureus	1.692	39.7
Lycopersicon esculentum	1.694	37.3
Monocotyledons		
Allium cepa	1.691	36.8
Zea mays	1.701	47.8
Triticum aestivum	1.703	47.5

bases present in the nucleic acid. Base composition can be calculated from buoyant density,[426] and expressed as moles per cent guanine plus cytosine (G + C) or as an AT/GC ratio. Chemical methods have revealed few discontinuities in base composition among 61 angiosperms studied[54] (see Table 12.1). This fits well with the similar poverty of variation in buoyant density and seems to show that little of taxonomic value will emerge from studies of base composition of higher plant DNA. Sylusorenko *et al.* assert that base composition studies may have some value, and cite variations in the G + C component of DNA of monocots which they relate to the level of specialization of the different groups. G + C was found to be highest in 'phylogenetically young' groups. The incidence of methylcytosine was highest in the Liliales.[463]

Base composition variations have obvious connections with sequence differences, and it is possible to calculate the minimal difference of sequence homology which can accommodate a given change in base composition.[126] Such calculations may be wholly academic, giving an insufficiently precise measure of actual nucleic acid differences.

The rather disappointing yield of taxonomic evidence from base composition studies of angiosperms strikingly contrasts with the situation in lower plants. Wider variations have been reported in the base compositions of fungal DNA,[457] and the taxonomic promise of these findings has been confirmed by useful agreements and discrepancies found between orthodox classification and base composition in the Oomycetes—a refractory group where the taxonomy has been sometimes conjectural and always controversial.[188] Base compositional studies have proved their worth in taxonomy in the blue-green algae,[142] the actinomycetes[470] and the bacteria[321] (see Chapter 13).

The molecular weight of RNA has been determined in a wide range of organisms, with a view to detecting any evolutionary trends which are present[307] but the differences are not manifested at low hierarchical levels, and so the character has only a limited taxonomic value. Gould lists 'significant variations' in the base composition of ribosomal RNA,[186] but again the differences quoted are between organisms as distantly related as rabbits, yeast and *Drosophila*. Lava-Sanchez *et al.* assert that meaningful differences occur among the ribosomal RNAs of plants in terms of buoyant density (i.e. base composition) but their data compilation seems to indicate that, compared with animal RNAs, plant ribosomal RNA is a very conservative molecule indeed.[293]

Though it therefore seems doubtful at present that overall base composition studies of nucleic acids can offer much to the taxonomist of higher plants, the distribution of individual bases may occasionally be of interest (e.g. of 5-methyl cytosine in *Gossypium*[152]). 5-methyl cytosine replaces cytosine in wheat germ DNA and accordingly decreases the buoyant density.[265] The moles percent $G + C$ is therefore underestimated. If such replacements are commoner than is supposed[463] the reliability of buoyant density estimations of base composition may be undermined.

The *sequence* of bases in nucleic acids seems the most potent source of taxonomic evidence. Base composition offers only a hazy guide to sequence. Though the base compositions of DNA from *Pisum sativum* and *Phaseolus vulgaris* (both Leguminosae) are closely similar, large sequence differences exist.[45] Unfortunately, the technology for sequencing nucleic acids is much less advanced than that earlier described for proteins,[79,511] Selective enzymes which cleave polynucleotides at particular points can be used to produce fragments of the chain. The end bases of these fragments are known because the specialized properties of the digesting enzyme are known. Ribonuclease, of which there are numerous variants, splits the linkage between the phosphate group on a pyrimidine nucleotide and the next nucleotide in sequence. It is a specific phosphodiesterase, attacking only RNA. Nucleases from different sources cleave nucleotides preferentially in different positions. By integrating the data from many such digestions, it may be possible to determine the sequence, after much effort.

Biochemical short-cuts to the sequences are the only possible ways of releasing the information on a scale and at a speed which creates usable taxonomic evidence. A few short-cut methods have been developed, and, as in most other cases, their yield of systematic data far outweighs the meagre output from more fundamental approaches.

A short-cut method resembling the fingerprint technique for proteins has been described. RNA is digested with a specific nuclease, e.g. ribonuclease T_1, attacking only guanine linkages.[186] Digests are subjected to electrophoresis in acrylamide gels of different pore sizes. The molecular weight of the fragments is easily determined from their mobilities. Electrophoretic differences between fragments do not exist, since every nucleotide has a single negatively charged phosphate group. Molecular size, or fragment size determines the rate of movement in the gel. Patterns from *Escherichia coli* and *Saccharomyces* resembled each other more closely than they did the animal fingerprints. Both samples were very susceptible to the enzyme, and the digests consisted of very small, rapidly migrating fragments. The RNAs of higher plants should be studied by this interesting method.

Like the protein fingerprinting method, this technique examines the overall conformation of the molecules digested in that only a few places in the polymer chain can be shown to be the same or different. Sequence variations are still masked to a degree, and fingerprints may therefore not always represent the true similarity between samples. The RNAs of the closely related bacteria *Bacillus subtilis* and *B. niger* are indistinguishable by the fingerprint pattern.[186] The sequence homology of these two species is no more than 50%[136] though Gould[186] suggests that this is an overestimate of the difference.

A promising short-cut approach to the comparison of polynucleotide sequences from different taxa is offered by hybridi-ation methods. DNA exists as a double helix, but the two complementary strands can be separated (dissociated) from each other by heating to 100°C and cooling quickly. In suitable conditions they can later be made to re-associate. Figure 12.2 illustrates how this property can be used to indicate sequence homologies between DNA of different sources. If single-stranded DNA from species A and B is mixed together, and conditions promoting re-association (annealing) are provided, hybrid DNA helices should form if there is some degree of sequence similarity between the two DNA samples. The amount of hybrid DNA can easily be ascertained if one of the original

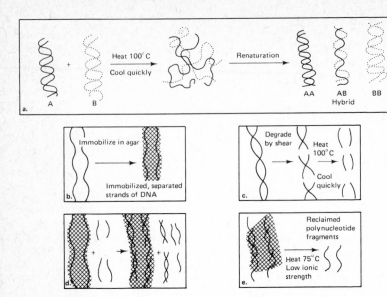

Fig. 12.2 (a) Principle of DNA hybridization technique. Native DNAs from species A and B are denatured. On renaturation of the mixture, some hybrid DNA forms if there is similarity between the two DNAs. (b)–(e) Schematic representation of DNA–agar procedure. (From Kohne.[275] Courtesy of the Systematics Association.)

samples is labelled with a radioactive isotope. Separation of the hybrid and non-hybrid helices, and single-stranded remnants can be achieved by the DNA–agar technique[241] (Figure 12.2). Long single strands of DNA from species A are immobilized in agar. DNA from species B is radio-labelled and then broken into short lengths (sheared) by pressure or repeated passage through a small-bore needle. The short lengths of double helix are dissociated and reacted with the immobilized single strands of species A. After a time the unreacted short lengths of species B DNA are washed away. The amount of labelled B DNA which has hybridized with species A DNA is measured by reclaiming the labelled polynucleotides and measuring the amount of label.

Hybridization reactions depend on chance collisions between DNA molecules, and are therefore faster at high DNA concentrations. Evidently, repetitious DNA sequences will hybridize much more quickly than the unrepeated DNA. Studies of hybridization by the DNA–agar method involve only the repetitious DNA in higher plant comparisons. Bacterial DNA comparisons involve the entire genome.

A variant of the DNA hybrid method using hydroxyapatite to separate single- and double-stranded DNA has been described,[77] and its applications to plant taxonomy discussed.[295] In appropriate conditions, hydroxyapatite columns will absorb only double-stranded DNA, e.g. hybrid DNA. Unre-associated DNA passes through the column. Hybrid DNA can then be easily eluted from the column by adjusting the temperature. The label in the eluted double-stranded DNA is a direct measure of the degree to which DNA hybridization has occurred (see Table 12.2). Maximum hybridization takes place when the DNA of a species hybridizes with itself. In bacteria this maximum degree of hybridization is commonly 100%, as explained above, while in higher plants much less of the DNA hybridizes in homologous hybridization experiments. Hydroxyapatite fractionation of hybridized DNA is hence a rapid method of testing how much of the DNA of an organism is repetitious. The slowly re-associating, non-repeating DNA can be separated and is available for taxonomic studies.

Table 12.2   DNA hybridization estimates of relatedness of bacterial species to *Escherichia coli*. (After Kohne.[275])

Bacteria	Relatedness to *E. coli*
Escherichia coli	100%
Shigella flexneri	85%
Salmonella typhimurium	35%
Aerobacter aerogenes	35%
Proteus mirabilis	2–5%

The conditions of DNA hybridization experiments (e.g. of salt concentration and temperature) greatly affect the result and so need to be carefully controlled and recorded. Stringent and non-stringent conditions can be defined[93] in which a greater or lesser proportion of the DNA will hybridize. The accuracy of base-pair matching in hybrid DNA varies with reaction conditions and can be measured fairly easily. Native DNA is assumed to have perfect base-pair matching in the double helix, both strands being fully complementary. The helices have a certain thermal stability, and a defined temperature at which they dissociate. Hybrid DNA, in which some mis-matching occurs, has a lower thermal stability than that of re-associated native DNA. The temperature at which 50% of a hybrid DNA is dissociated is the mean thermal dissociation temperature (T_m). This is a measure of the accuracy of base-pair matching. A T_m difference of 1°C corresponds to about 1.5% of base substitutions between two DNAs.[288] T_m is not an absolute value, but varies with the stringency of the hybridization conditions.

Figure 12.3 shows the thermal stability profiles of four DNA/DNA duplexes. Tritium-labelled DNA from barley was hybridized with DNA from oats, rye, wheat and barley. The T_m of the barley–barley (homologous) duplex is about 73°C, whereas the hybrid DNAs (barley–oat, barley–wheat and barley–rye) all have a T_m of less than 70°C.

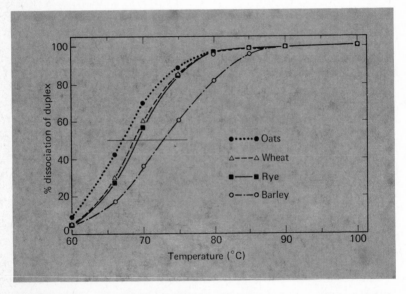

Fig. 12.3 Thermal stability profiles of DNA/DNA duplexes of barley–oats; barley–wheat; barley–rye; barley–barley. Barley DNA was immobilized on filters in each case. (From Bendich and McCarthy.[46])

DNA can be hybridized with RNA. This opens up the fascinating possibility of hybridizing the DNA which codes for ribosomal RNA (rDNA) with its own transcription product—ribosomal RNA (rRNA). rDNA/rRNA hybridization should reveal what proportion of the genome codes for rRNA. There might be taxonomic differences in this proportion.

TAXONOMIC APPLICATIONS OF DNA HYBRIDIZATION

DNA hybridization is so far the only short-cut technique to have been systematically applied to the study of polynucleotide variation in higher plants. Its usefulness in bacterial taxonomy is well-established, and is discussed in Chapter 13. Higher plant studies are as yet few and the true value of the method cannot be assessed until much more work has been completed.

Early studies applied the DNA–agar technique to legumes and cereal grains.[45] Initial results were somewhat disappointing to taxonomists[230] who were disconcerted by the size of the differences in DNA between relatively similar organisms. Bendich and Bolton[45] showed that only about 20% of the nucleotide sequences of *Pisum* and *Phaseolus* were similar, and only 50% of the sequence of *Pisum* and *Vicia* was held in common. Though in general agreement with most classifications of the genera, the data seemed a rather crude indication of relationships, and held out little hope of sequence homologies being detectable between less closely related taxa.

DNAs from grass species have been compared by means of base composition measurements (buoyant density method) and T_m.[46] Results appear in Table 12.3 and show the DNA of the species to be rather uniform in these features.

Table 12.3 Relationship between buoyant density in CsCl, base composition and thermal denaturation temperature in some cereal grain DNAs. (From Bendich and McCarthy.[46])

Source of DNA	Density	T_m(°C)	Mole % G + C calculated from:	
			Density	T_m
Barley	1.701	85.2	42	39
Oats	1.700	—	41	—
Rye	1.702	86.4	43	42
Wheat	1.702	85.2	43	39

Hybrids were made between repetitious DNAs of the four species, all sixteen possible hybrids being produced. The extent of hybridization and thermal stabilities of hybrids were determined in each case. Table 12.4 shows the relative homology between the four DNAs and their thermal stabilities. Figure 12.4 illustrates the proposed phylogenetic relationships of the four species. There is good agreement with the generally accepted classification of the four genera. Barley, rye and wheat DNAs (tribe Triticeae) show

Table 12.4 Relative percent binding (%) and decreases (ΔT_m) in thermal stabilities of cereal grain ^{3}H DNA/filter-bound DNA duplexes. (After Bendich and McCarthy.[46])

Filter-bound DNA	^{3}H-labelled DNA							
	Barley		Oats		Rye		Wheat	
	ΔT_m	%	ΔT_m	%	ΔT_m	%	ΔT_m	%
Barley	—	100*	6.4	19	5.4	58	3.4	72
Oats	5.5	12	—	100	7.2	15	5.0	17
Rye	3.6	59	6.1	22	—	100	0.7	100
Wheat	4.0	48	6.1	16	4.1	60	—	100

* Range was 90–105%.

much more base sequence complementarity to each other than any of them do to oats (Aveneae). *Avena* thus seems isolated from the other three genera. Wheat and rye are more related in nucleotide sequence than either is to barley, which fits well with the fact that they are able to produce the inter-generic hybrid, *Triticale*.

It is noteworthy that reciprocal DNA hybridizations do not always produce the same kind of hybrid DNA in terms of thermal stability. This is probably because the repetitious DNA in some species is more heterogeneous than in others. In experiments by Bendich and McCarthy,[46] labelled (^{3}H) wheat DNA/rye DNA hybrids approach the thermal stability of wheat/wheat duplexes because the wheat

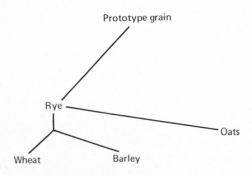

Fig. 12.4 Proposed phylogenetic relationships among the principal grains. The length of the lines between species is proportional to the divergence between the species. (From Bendich and McCarthy.[46])

repetitious DNA is not very uniform. ^{3}H-labelled rye DNA/wheat DNA hybrids are much less thermostable than rye/rye duplexes because the wheat component in the hybrid DNA is non-uniform and base-pair matching must inevitably be poorer. The rye/rye duplex is more stable than the wheat/wheat duplex for the same reason. Taxonomists will have to allow for this kind of reciprocal variation when they interpret hybridization data.

At the same level of stringency, more of the rye genome is shown to be repetitious than is the case in wheat. Bendich and McCarthy propose that evolutionary specialization is characterized by sequence divergence of repetitious DNA, and therefore by a greater proportion of non-repeated DNA. On this basis, rye is shown to be most primitive of these four grass genera. It was shown that the non-repeated DNAs of wheat and rye, isolated by the hydroxyapatite technique, were less similar than the repetitious DNA of these two species. Comparisons of repetitious DNA may therefore underestimate the actual sequence divergence between two plants. Since the repetitious DNA is a fraction of total DNA defined only by the conditions of the experiment, there can be no single number which characterizes the nucleotide sequence relatedness of two plants. Taxonomists will find this fact interesting but perhaps disappointing.

In an associated paper Bendich and McCarthy report on the same hybridization techniques applied to DNA from three species of *Triticum* and one species of the closely related genus *Aegilops*, which have different genomes.[47] Although the sequence differences appear small the results indicate greater divergence between the A (diploid wheat) genome and the D (*Aegilops*) genome than between A and AB (tetraploid wheat) or ABD (hexaploid wheat genomes). Thus DNA base sequence differences within a single genus, compatible with known breeding behaviour, are detectable using the DNA hybridization method.

Rather little DNA hybridization work on higher plants has been undertaken at the intrageneric level despite the facts that it is here that the results can most easily be compared with other taxonomic evidence and that comparisons between similar genera have often revealed surprisingly large differences. Chooi[92] studied the DNA hybridizations of six species of *Vicia*, already shown to have a six-fold variation in nuclear DNA content.[91] He found that the degree of repetition in the DNA was different in each species, the percentage of rapidly re-associating ('fast') DNA varying from 15–38%. Four of the *Vicia* species showed a high level of homology with each other, and with *V. faba*, in competition experiments (see

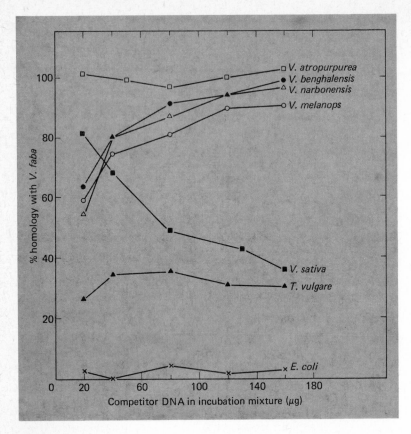

Fig. 12.5 The percentage homologies of the DNAs of five *Vicia* species, *Triticum vulgare* and *Escherichia coli* with the DNA of *Vicia faba* are plotted against the amount of competitor DNA in the incubation mixture. (From Chooi.[92])

Fig. 12.5). *Vicia sativa* was an exception, competing very poorly with *V. faba* DNA.

Little work on DNA/RNA hybridization has so far produced clear taxonomic conclusions. Base sequence similarities in the rRNAs of different plants have been studied.[48,325,475] Vodkin and Katterman confirmed earlier indications that most dicotyledon rRNAs hybridize equally well to any given dicot DNA, indicating that rRNAs are all rather similar.[492] Their data on the percentage of DNA maximally hybridizing with rRNA are given in Table 12.5. In

Table 12.5 Percent of DNA hybridized with rRNA at saturation in some monocot/dicot hybridization experiments. (After Vodkin and Katterman.[492])

| | Source of DNA | | | |
| | Monocot | | Dicot | |
Source of rRNA	Barley	Wheat	Cotton	Pumpkin
Monocot				
Barley	0.73 (100)*	0.15 (68)	0.55 (77)	1.76 (94)
Wheat	0.42 (58)	0.22 (100)	0.46 (65)	1.50 (80)
Dicot				
Cotton	0.34 (47)	0.13 (59)	0.71 (100)	2.07 (110)
Pumpkin	0.29 (40)	0.11 (50)	0.45 (63)	1.88 (100)

* The numbers in parentheses refer to relative percent of DNA hybridized with rRNA at saturation, with the homologous reaction normalized at 100%.

general the nucleotide sequences of dicot rRNAs seem to be highly conservative, so confirming the general view gained from studies of base composition. The general nucleotide sequence homology of dicot DNAs varies from 5–55%.[45] Homologies of rRNA vary from 63–110%.[492] rDNA must therefore have been conserved much more than most other DNA sequences. By contrast, monocotyledon rRNAs hybridize unequally to any given DNA. The homology of wheat rDNA and barley rDNA seems to be about 60%, taking into account reciprocal differences. Though the rDNA is conserved more than other DNA sequences in monocots, it seems possible that it is conserved much less than in the majority of dicots, i.e. has diverged more between taxa.[492] Further work will be necessary to confirm this indication.

Reciprocal rRNA/DNA hybrids of monocots with dicots differ, presumably due to different levels of heterogeneity in the repetitious DNA of the various taxa. Nevertheless it is clear from Table 12.5 that the minimal estimate of homology between monocot and dicot rDNAs is 40% (pumpkin/barley). Monocot/dicot DNA hybrids had considerable base-pair mis-matching. Bendich and Bolton found a maximum sequence homology of only 10% between monocot and dicot DNAs.[45] Evidently, in the angiosperms as a whole, rDNA has diverged much more slowly than the rest of the genome. It will be interesting to learn what this conservative gene has to reveal to taxonomists when sequencing methods are applied to it systematically.

Goldberg *et al.* recently applied DNA hybridization techniques to the taxonomy of *Cucurbita,*[181] which has been thoroughly studied from more orthodox standpoints.[44,498] All thirteen species of *Cucurbita* which were tested proved to have mainband and satellite DNA. The densities of these were constant throughout the genus. *Cucurbita* rRNAs were hybridized with DNAs in reciprocal saturation experiments in order to determine what proportion of the cucurbit genomes codes for rRNA. Results showed that considerable variation occurred among the thirteen species (see Table 12.6) which did not correlate at all well with the infrageneric classification of *Cucurbita*. Different proportions of rDNA occurred in similar species (e.g. *C. andreana* and *C. maxima*) while sometimes rather different species (e.g. *C. andreana* and *C. sororia*) had the same proportion.

Table 12.6 Percent homology of *Cucurbita* DNAs to rRNA. (After Goldberg *et al.*[181])

Species group	Species	Exp. 1*	Exp. 2	Exp. 3	Average
Sororia	*C. sororia*	1.7	—	1.7	1.7
	C. mixta	2.5	2.3	2.7	2.5
Pepo	*C. pepo*	2.6	2.0	2.5	2.4
	C. texana	1.7	—	1.7	1.7
Maxima	*C. maxima*	3.3	—	2.8	3.1
	C. andreana	1.7	1.5	2.0	1.7
Digitata	*C. palmata*	—	—	1.5	1.5
	C. digitata	1.6	1.6	—	1.6
Lundelliana	*C. okeechobeensis*	1.4	1.4	—	1.4
	C. martinezii	1.7	—	1.7	1.7
Ecuadorensis	*C. ecuadorensis*	1.7	—	1.8	1.8
Moschata	*C. moschata*	1.4	—	1.3	1.4
Pedatifolia	*C. pedatifolia*	1.7	1.5	—	1.6

*1μg of membrane-fixed DNA was hybridized to 1μg of ^{3}H-tobacco rRNA (specific activity of 54 300 cpm/μg) at 69°C for 18h in 1 ml of 2 × SSC (0.15 M NaCl and 0.015 M Na citrate). Each value represents an average of three replicates within each experiment.

DNA/DNA hybridizations, in stringent annealing conditions, produced the percentage homologies listed in Table 12.7, and were used to construct the relationship chart in Fig. 12.6. In the conditions provided, only 8.5–18.6% of tritium-labelled homologous DNA would hybridize with homologous DNA immobilized on a filter. Only the most repetitious DNA was therefore being studied. Heterologous values were expressed as percentages of the homologous reaction, which was thus taken to be 100%. Homologous and heterologous hybrids had very similar thermal stabilities, so that

Table 12.7 DNA/DNA hybridization of DNAs from species in the genus *Cucurbita*. (From Goldberg *et al.*[181])

Species group	Filter-bound DNA*	^{3}H-DNA				
		C. palmata				*C. lundelliana*
		Exp. 1	Exp. 2	*C. maxima*	*C. pepo*	
Digitata	*C. palmata*	100†	100	74	68	72
	C. digitata	86	—	51	—	—
Maxima	*C. maxima*	75	—	100	87	105
	C. andreana	—	73	—	—	—
Pepo	*C. pepo*	—	—	82	100	99
Sororia	*C. sororia*	70	—	—	—	—
	C. mixta	—	66	—	—	—
Lundelliana	*C. lundelliana*	—	—	—	87	100
	C. okeechobeensis	—	75	—	—	—

* 6 μg of unlabelled DNA were bound to nitrocellulose membranes and annealed to 0.3 μg of labelled DNA for 18 h at 70°C. The numbers are the average of three independent experiments.

† Homologous hybridization values were 18.6% for *C. maxima*, 10.9% for *C. palmata* (Exp. 1), 8.5% for *C. palmata* (Exp. 2), 11.2% for *C. pepo*, 9.2% for *C. lundelliana*.

base-pair mis-matching seems to have been minimized by the annealing conditions.

The results show that *C. palmata* is most distantly related to the other four species used as homologous taxa. It is a xerophyte. Such a finding fits well with the conclusion[498] that xerophytic cucurbits are genetically isolated from the rest of the genus, and with data from cucurbitacin and fatty acid distribution.[224] It is interesting that DNAs of *C. lundelliana*, *C. pepo* and *C. maxima* are so similar, because Whitaker and Bemis[498] believed that *C. lundelliana* was a progenitor of the other two. Each is more similar to *C. lundelliana* in nucleotide sequence then either is to the other.

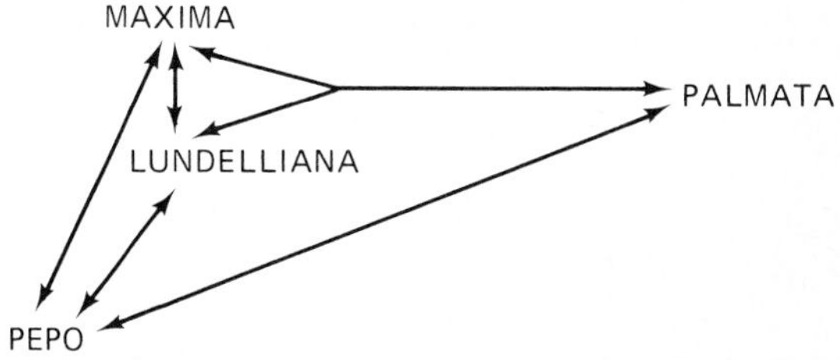

Fig. 12.6 Relationships between species of the genus *Cucurbita* inferred from DNA/DNA hybridization experiments. Length of lines is proportional to DNA differences. (From Goldberg *et al.*[181])

EVALUATION OF NUCLEOTIDE EVIDENCE

The kind of information so far revealed by DNA hybridization studies augurs well for future extended applications in taxonomy. Greater understanding of the method and its limitations should make taxonomic interpretations easier. It is somewhat difficult to reconcile statements that a 10% DNA sequence homology can be demonstrated between dicots and monocots, with others which indicate that the homology between *Pisum* and *Phaseolus* is only 20%. When the matter is investigated, most of the apparent contradictions can be explained, but it remains disappointing that no absolute indication of nucleotide sequence similarities can be obtained without laborious and impractical sequencing. Different indications of homology can be gained merely by changing experimental conditions. The DNA of higher plants is heterogeneous, and it is not possible to say which part of it should be used as a taxonomic guide. Overall sequence homologies would give only a cloudy indication of relatedness, yet it was hoped to find in nucleic acid variations the final, objective solutions of taxonomic problems. There is evidently much more room for refinement of technique.

Boyden[70] and Alston[7] have both sounded cautionary notes. Similarities of portions of DNA may well not reflect the similarity of the whole complement. DNA changes are not linked proportionately with phenotypic expression. Gross phenotypic changes, with considerable evolutionary significance, may in principle arise from minor base changes so trivial that the hybridization process is not detectably affected. Only wider application of the available methods and their continual improvement can show how important such objections may be.

More fundamental knowledge of the genome of higher plants is an urgent desideratum if nucleic acids are to be sources of useful taxonomic evidence. For instance, it would be interesting to know if the non-repeated DNA, supposing it to be definable, is taxonomically unique, coding for recently evolved characters.

Much may be hoped for from future nucleotide comparisons. Only technological limitations have so far restricted what has been achieved in the taxonomic context. The science of nucleic acid chemistry is still very young. We must neither condemn its taxonomic contributions for their lack of detail, nor expect that the genetic code, once written *en clair*, will solve all systematic and evolutionary problems. Missing links will frustrate students of nucleic acid as they do comparative morphologists. Several thousand years have passed while the present orthodox system of classification was developing. How much longer the nucleotide data will take to compile and integrate is anyone's guess. So far we know something of the nouns and punctuation of the genetic language, but little or nothing of its verbs and prepositions. Comparing nucleotide sequences in a wide range of plants, when technically feasible, perhaps gene by gene, may be uncomfortably like comparing grammar and style in a range of essayists.

PART 3

Applications

13

The Case of the Bacteria

A taxonomist concerned with higher plants experiences some of the difficulties which confronted his eighteenth century forebears, when he reviews the field of modern bacterial taxonomy. New organisms abound, reference collections are scattered and incomplete, and descriptions are ambiguous or overlapping, because variation is insufficiently explored and charted. The student of angiosperms is at first refreshed and rejuvenated by his step back in time, then becomes disconcerted as the magnitude of the problems is made plain.

Basic reasons for the difficulties include the small size of bacteria which precluded their study by natural historians until microscopical science was well-established. Bacteria were noted for the first time by Leeuwenhoek in 1676. Bacterial taxonomy therefore has a much shorter history than that of higher plants. Bacteria are rather simple in structure, both internally and externally, and, though electron microscopy is producing more morphological evidence than has ever been available, the possibility of a totally morphological classification of bacteria still does not exist. The great value of morphology as a source of taxonomic evidence is that its facts are quickly gathered, easily described and thus readily communicated. Bacterial taxonomy did not enjoy this assistance, nor did it permit the participation of the enthusiastic amateurs who have contributed many observations on the natural history of higher organisms.

Bacteria are found almost everywhere in large numbers, and there was and is great difficulty in ensuring that every new isolation is correctly identified. With the paucity of structural characters and consequent vague descriptions, bacteriologists in different areas often gave the same taxon different names. There was almost no way to determine whether or not a new isolate had been named previously. Nevertheless the organisms were found to be so important in nature and in human life as agents of decay and disease that the fundamental difficulties with their classification and identification had to be swept aside for the moment. Naming and classification proceeded rapidly in many centres, on an *ad hoc* basis, with little integration. Synonyms for well-characterized bacterial species often seem almost numberless.

A partial solution to the shortage of taxonomic evidence was found in the metabolic diversity of bacteria. The group as a whole is characterized by unrivalled synthetic powers, and a considerable range of energy sources. Thus physiological and chemical characters were soon seen to be vital to the furtherance of microbial systematics. Bergey's *Manual* is largely a treatise on physiological taxonomy.[71] This degree of emphasis on chemical data is unique among plant groups and is the reason for giving the bacteria special attention in this book.

Table 13.1 Some orthodox morphological, physiological and chemical characters in bacterial classification.

Morphological characters	Physiological/chemical characters
Cell shape (rods, cocci, spirilli, etc.)	Growth rate (on range of media)
Cell size	Growth rate (at various pHs/temps.)
Cells single or massed in colonies	Aerobic/anaerobic
Colony shape and variation	Photosynthetic/non-photosynthetic
Cells in chains or filaments	Range of possible respiratory substrates (carbohydrates, gelatin, etc.)
Cells motile or non-motile	Metabolic products (acids/gases/complex products)
Presence/absence/position of flagella	Pigment production
Spores formed/spores not formed	Nitrate reduction
	Energy source organic/inorganic; Gram-positive/Gram-negative; cells with free sulphur, etc.
	Pathogenicity

Table 13.1 lists some of the principal morphological and chemical characters traditionally used for classifying bacteria. It is obvious that considerable culture work is necessary to produce the facts about how a particular bacterial strain grows in different conditions, and what it accumulates or excretes. Identification of bacteria remains difficult because of the time taken for completion of the necessary tests, and also because of variation in the bacterial species, which may be overlooked or simply undiscovered. Production of particular compounds by two cultures may not imply a relationship since the pathways by which the compounds are formed may not be the same in both (see Chapter 1). Much of the older work was done with impure cultures, resulting in the confusion of chemical properties from several taxa in a single description.

When a relatively clear-cut group of bacterial isolates has been defined on correlated morphological and chemical grounds, the next problem is to decide what rank to give it. Are minor chemical differences more or less significant than minor morphological ones? Supposing each isolate differing slightly from others to be a species, which criteria define a bacterial genus? If a few genera have been defined, on whatever criteria, what level of similarity between such genera would indicate the boundary of a family, or an order? Such questions were virtually insoluble on rational grounds. Bacterial taxonomists therefore produced diverse schemes of classification—some weighting chemical evidence more than morphological data, and *vice versa*. Despite the wealth of metabolic differences there was still no third source of evidence to which they might turn for guidance. Uncertainty of identification frustrated the use of pathogenicity and host specificity among parasites. For a time it seemed that any bacterium isolated from a new host must *ipso facto* be named a new species. Bacteria with particularly striking attributes tended to be the foundation of monotypic genera, families and orders. At least the angiosperm taxonomists of the eighteenth century had more evidence available than the bacteriologists of the early twentieth century.

Bergey's *Manual* (1923–1957) traces the evolution of bacterial classifications before and after the incorporation of chemical and physiological data.[71] It is interesting that *generic terms* are spoken of, rather than genera, implying more strongly than any work on angiosperm taxonomy that taxa are concepts, not actualities. Old generic terms have been constantly re-defined, as cycles of splitting have succeeded cycles of lumping. Despite the incorporation of chemical facts, microbial classifications still seemed as insubstantial and ephemeral as the organisms themselves. Given the miscellaneous nature of bacteria on the crude evidence available, it is hard to see how the situation could have been different. Though chemical evidence greatly aided bacterial identification and recognition, it did little to indicate relationships, and made attribution of rank even more controversial. The obscurities and confusions of the early days have an eternal relevance because bacteriologists have selected 1753 as the starting date for nomenclatural priority—a time when scientific microbiology scarcely existed.

Chemotaxonomic developments in the twentieth century have had important consequences for the classification of bacteria. Surface structures of bacterial cells were found to act as powerful antigenic determinants. Serological data on bacterial diversity have been increasingly available from the nineteen-twenties, and serology is now a vitally important and very convenient method for typifying bacterial isolates, and determining possible phylogenetic relationships.

Biochemical methods for studying pathways of synthesis are now available, using radioactive isotopes. It is technically feasible, given time, to determine whether or not a given metabolic product is produced by the same pathway in two or more bacterial taxa. Stanier's work on this topic has already been cited (Chapter 1), and the subject is reviewed by Mandel.[317] Enzymes responsible for metabolic interconversions can be extracted, purified and compared using all the powerful techniques of the protein chemist (Chapter 10). The complexity of the bacterial cell wall is recognized as a new source of taxonomic facts. Nucleotide variation in bacteria is a field of active research aimed at providing taxonomic and phylogenetic evidence (see Chapter 12). Connected with the new work on bacterial genomes from the chemical standpoint, but beyond the scope of this chapter, are the various ways of determining limits of genetic exchange between bacterial taxa by the transference of bacteriophages and bacteriocins.[259]

With such a dearth of taxonomic data on bacteria, it is not surprising that all these newer developments have been vigorously applied. In the same way, the concepts of numerical taxonomy have found widest acceptance in bacterial systematics because existing schemes of classification have been uniquely unstable, and the species concepts uniquely diverse.

TAXONOMIC DATA FROM CELL WALLS

Cummins and Harris pointed out the potential value of cell-wall composition studies as an aid to bacterial taxonomy,[111] though the fundamental idea of wall chemistry as a source of taxonomic facts about miro-organisms is much older. Different properties of the bacterial cell wall underly the Gram-positive and Gram-negative reactions, which is based on whether an iodine-dye complex is retained by the wall, or is removed by alcohol. Many serological properties of bacteria arise from wall-surface antigens, so it would not be surprising if cell-wall composition proved taxonomically useful. Work and Dewey had earlier commented on the taxonomic distribution of the common wall component α-ε-diaminopimelic acid (DAP) in a range of micro-organisms.[508] The principal compounds of interest are amino acids and amino sugars. Salton reviews the general structure of bacterial cell walls.[421].

Ikawa has reported on the taxonomic significance of wall chemistry in lactic acid bacteria.[245] Of these the lactobacilli and streptococcoid members all had walls containing glutamic acid, alanine, lysine or DAP, glucosamine and muramic acid. Aspartic acid was normally absent from *Streptococcus* cell walls, but occurred wherever lysine was present in the walls of *Lactobacilli*. Distribution of sugar alcohols and reducing sugars paralleled the amino acid differences. Ikawa commented on the fact that, unlike the amino acids of higher plants, those generally found in bacterial cell walls are of the uncommon D-configuration. He speculated on the possible phylogenetic significance of this association of D-acids with the prokaryotic condition. There are similarities between the cell walls of bacteria and those of blue-green algae.[86,135]

Cell wall chemistry has become a recognized source of evidence for microbial classification. The saprophytic coryneform bacteria *Mycobacterium*, *Corynebacterium* and *Nocardia* have identical wall compositions.[112] Subsequently they were found to be serologically very similar.[110] Cell wall composition in *Cellulomonas* is highly uniform[262] while in another coryneform genus, *Microbacterium*, every species tested proved to have different cell wall components.[409] Conclusions on the respectability of bacterial taxa from cell wall composition alone are plainly unwise, but it is encouraging that at least in some cases there may be serological correlation.

In a substantial review, Schleifer and Kandler recommend the application of peptidoglycan variation in taxonomic studies.[427] Peptidoglycans—macromolecules of strands of polymerized amino sugars cross-linked through short peptides—are the only cell wall polymers common to both Gram-positive and Gram-negative bacteria, and so should be comparable over a wide range of genera. They are complex in structure, and at least twenty enzymes seem to be involved in the synthesis of even the simpler types. As polygenic characters they are unlikely to be subject to convergent evolution. Most peptidoglycan diversity occurs within Gram-positive bacteria, where it is hoped that the numerous discontinuities may have a taxonomic meaning.

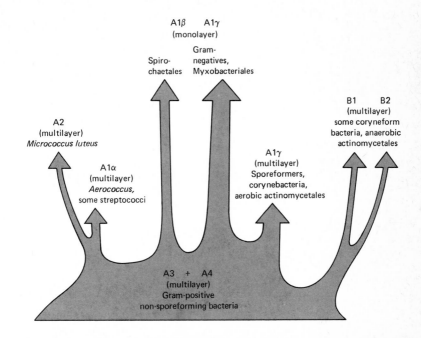

Fig. 13.1 Possible phylogenetic relationships between bacterial groups based on 8 types (A1α, A1β, A1γ, A2, A3, A4, B1 and B2) of peptidoglycan cell-wall structures. (From Schleifer and Kandler.[427])

Figure 13.1 represents a possible phylogeny of bacterial groups based on the incidence of eight types of peptidoglycan. Schleifer and Kandler assume that the evolutionary trend has been towards simpler peptidoglycan structure and metabolism. The most primitive groups thus have complex peptidoglycans in multilayered walls. On this basis, the Gram-negative bacteria and myxobacteria seem to be generally the most advanced groups, and it is of interest that the same kind of peptidoglycan occurs in walls of blue-green algae.

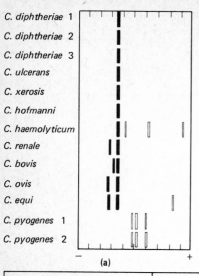

C. diphtheriae 1
C. diphtheriae 2
C. diphtheriae 3
C. ulcerans
C. xerosis
C. hofmanni
C. haemolyticum
C. renale
C. bovis
C. ovis
C. equi
C. pyogenes 1
C. pyogenes 2

(a)

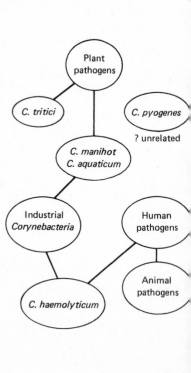

C. fascians 1
C. fascians 2
C. tritici
C. betae
C. poinsettiae
C. flaccumfaciens
C. manihot
C. aquaticum
C. mediolanum
C. acetoacidophilum
C. rubrum

(b)

Corynebacterium		Enzyme distribution		
Species	Ecology	No. of Esterases	No. of Catalases	No. of Peroxidases
diptheriae 1		—	1	—
" 2		—	1	—
" 3	HUMAN PATHOGENS	—	1	—
ulcerans		—	1	—
xerosis		—	1	—
hofmanni		—	1	—
haemolyticum		3	1	—
renale		—	2	—
bovis		—	2	—
ovis	ANIMAL PATHOGENS	—	2	—
equi		—	2	—
pyogenes 1		3	—	—
pyogenes 2		3	—	—
fascians 1		2	2	1
fascians 2		3	2	1
tritici	PLANT PATHOGENS	2	1	1
betae		4	1	1
poinsettiae		1	1	1
flaccumfaciens		1	1	1
manihot		2	1	1
aquaticum	SAPROPHYTES	4	1	1
mediolanum		2	1	—
acetoacidophilum		1	1	—
rubrum		4	2	—

(c)

Plant pathogens

C. tritici

C. pyogenes
? unrelated

C. manihot
C. aquaticum

Industrial *Corynebacteria*

Human pathogens

C. haemolyticum

Animal pathogens

(d)

ENZYME AND PROTEIN STUDIES

Electrophoresis of enzyme extracts, followed by staining the separated enzymes with appropriate substrates and dyes to produce a 'zymogram', has been widely applied in bacterial taxonomy. Figure 13.2 shows some results of Robinson[409] on the esterases, catalases and peroxidases of 24 strains of *Corynebacterium*. Robinson considered that esterase analyses revealed useful variation at the strain level, while presence of peroxidases seemed to indicate that the bacterium was associated with a host plant. Catalases seemed most useful as evidence of similarity above the species level. Some of his findings are supported by conclusions from serological and wall-chemistry data.

Lund produced electrophoretic evidence of esterase variation, and variation in other proteins, in strains of *Streptococcus*.[310] In esterases, and in other proteins, the strains fell into a *S. faecalis* group and a *S. faecium/durans* group. This result fits well with patterns of variation established in the metabolic properties of these bacteria.[502]

Other examples of the use of zymograms in taxonomy are mentioned in Mandel's review [317] who points out that the commonly studied esterase reaction can be achieved by a wide variety of enzymes. Bands of similar electrophoretic mobility, even with the same reaction to a substrate, may not indicate presence of the same catalytic protein. Mandel considers catalase zymograms a surer basis for comparison. Aspartate aminotransferases of *Rhizobium* strains differ in ways potentially useful for classification.[416]

Amino acid sequencing of bacterial proteins has been possible for some time,[13] along with amino acid analysis and peptide mapping. Bacterial enzymes appear not to be homologous with their counterparts in higher organisms. Though few bacterial protein sequences have been compared over a range of taxa, owing to the labour involved, there can be little doubt that sequence studies will be an important source of taxonomic evidence, expecially when techniques improve. Ancillary short-cut techniques, such as fingerprinting (see Chapter 10), applied to the same proteins would speed up the work considerably.[14] Ambler reports on the sequence of the blue,

Fig. 13.2 Results of zymogram analyses of *Corynebacterium* spp. (**a**), (**b**) Zymograms of esterases (open blocks), catalases (filled blocks) and peroxidases (lined blocks). (**c**) Table of results compared with ecology of species. (**d**) Possible relationships between species indicated from the data. (Figures (**a**) and (**b**) from Robinson.[409])

copper-containing azurin proteins of five bacterial species.[13] Only about half the sequence is common to all, and most of the remaining half proves to be characteristic of each species. Bacterial cytochromes are obvious candidates for extensive comparisons in future.

SEROLOGY AND BACTERIAL TAXONOMY

Serological tests have been applied to bacteria for many years, and in some groups they are of great importance in classification. Bacterial antigens are chemically diverse, consisting of proteins, lipopolysaccharides or polysaccharides. Flagellar (H-antigens), wall surface (O-antigens) and intracellular antigens released by grinding or sonication, can all be compared relatively easily with antisera prepared in the ways described earlier (Chapter 11). According to the type of test or antibody employed, bacteria are lysed, agglutinated or immobilized. Precipitin reactions are widely used to detect intracellular antigens, *in vitro*.[298] Location of bacterial antigens can be determined by placing the cells in solutions of antibodies which have been coupled with fluorescent dyes.

Sharing of identical antigens is widespread in many bacterial groups, and absorption techniques are necessary to distinguish between such cases, and those where genuine cross-reactions are exhibited by related heterologous antigens.

Cowan uses the Enterobacteriaceae to exemplify the taxonomic difficulties arising from sharing of antigens.[99] *Salmonella, Arizona* and *Escherichia* differ by numerous, if trivial, metabolic properties. Hundreds of naturally occurring combinations (serotypes) of *Salmonella* O-antigens have been detected, which are shared with

Table 13.2   Use of different kinds of chemical evidence in the attribution of rank in different bacteria. (From Cowan.[99])

Rank	Strepto-coccus	Salmonella Kauf.	Salmonella Others	Arizona	Escherichia
Genus	B	B	B	B	B
Species	B and/or S	SBP	B	B	B
Subspecies	S/B	·	S	S	S
Sub-subspecies	S		P	·	·

Key: Kauf. = according to Kauffman   P   = bacteriophage typing
       B   = biochemical characters   S   = serology

Arizona and *Escherichia.* Over a hundred *Escherichia* serotypes, and about sixty *Arizona* serotypes have additionally been described. If serotypes are to be regarded as species,[261] these three genera evidently cannot be maintained as discrete entities. If metabolic criteria were given greater weight, the genera could be preserved, and the serotypes might then be used to indicate subspecies. A quite different situation exists in *Streptococcus,* where the different serotypes can also be distinguished by major biochemical characters. Serological evidence contributes to the definition of taxa at different levels of the hierarchy in different genera (see Table 13.2). Clearly 'species' of *Streptococcus* and 'species' of *Salmonella* may not be of comparable rank.

Cowan considers that serological variation should be applicable only at the subspecific level, and be regarded as a bonus when it occasionally correlates with biochemical (i.e. specific or generic) discontinuities. Most bacteriologists now accept that serotypes are relatively minor variants and should not be used as a species concept. Nevertheless, bacteria are so variable in the degrees to which serotypes and other lines of evidence correlate that generic and specific concepts for the bacteria as a whole may be impossible to define. Cowan understandably recommends abandonment of the hierarchical principle for microbial classification in favour of a linear spectrum into which any bacterial strain might be fitted. Rank attribution would no longer be necessary.

Whatever changes may eventually be made to the form of bacterial classification, it is clear that serological facts will continue to be important, particularly in the recognition and identification of minor variants. Kwapinski's *Analytical Serology of Micro-organisms* is a detailed systematic treatment of serological evidence and taxonomic conclusions in the major groups of bacteria.[287] Mainly concerned with serotyping as a diagnostic aid, it also incorporates material about bacterial taxonomy and relationships. Angiosperm taxonomists have no comparable presentation of organized serological data. Problems of weighting evidence and rank attribution recur throughout this work, mainly because of variation in the degree to which antigens are shared (group and type specific antigens) and how they correlate with other characters. Slopek's account of the serology of *Shigella* (dysentery bacteria) exemplifies the difficulties.[438] Most antigens of *Shigella* serotypes are shared with *Escherichia,* but four serotypes are completely unrelated, having no shared antigens. Serotypes indistinguishable from *Escherichia* occur in *Shigella dysenteriae, S. sonnei* and *S. boydii.* Therefore part of *Shigella* is very distinct, part is related to *Escherichia* and part can be assigned either to *Shigella* or *Escherichia*. Though serotypes are often indispensable for identification, as guides to specific or generic delimitation they are not always helpful.

Reliably typed bacteria may sometimes be useful in higher plant taxonomy. Baldwin *et al.* described groups of legume species which could be inoculated with particular strains of *Rhizobium*.[23] The groups distinguished by the bacterial strains proved to differ from each other in seed proteins.

NUCLEIC ACID STUDIES

Possibilities of elucidating the structure of the genome by nucleic acid comparisons have been eagerly explored by microbial taxonomists. DNA base ratios and DNA hybridization have both given considerable taxonomic information. Bacterial genomes are inevitably less complex than those of higher plants, and do not include numerous copies of genes. Even the rDNA is a very small fraction of total DNA. Almost all the DNA will hybridize fairly rapidly. The theory underlying the use of moles percent GC as a taxonomic guide (see Chapter 12) was proposed by Lee *et al.*[295] and developed by De Ley.[126] A 20–30% difference in GC ratio between two bacterial DNAs means that there can be virtually no common nucleotide sequences. Very similar organisms have very similar GC ratios. In well-established bacterial species, strains rarely differ by more than 2.5% GC and often much less. Wide variations occur in genera such as *Vibrio*[489] which are noted for their unsettled taxonomy. Numerous applications of GC ratios to taxonomy are published every year; clearly much is expected from the method. General reviews of nucleic acid evidence in bacterial classification are given by De Ley[125] and Mandel.[317]

Nucleotide composition and DNA hybridization have both been used in an attempt at more rational classification of the common brewers' yeast contaminant *Obesumbacterium proteus* (Achromobacteriaceae).[388] *Obesumbacterium* is monotypic, the single species being recognized by its property of growing alongside yeast in brewery fermentations. Clearly this esoteric character is circumscribed in use because of the closely defined, artificial habitat in which it is manifested. Nineteen isolates of *O. proteus* and eighteen strains of enterobacteria were compared. Conventional biochemical tests revealed that *O. proteus* satisfied the requirements for membership of the Enterobacteriaceae. The GC ratio of *O. proteus* was 48%, closely similar to *Hafnia alvei* (48.5%). Table 13.3 shows the results

Table 13.3   DNA relationships of *Obesumbacterium proteus* shown by competition hybridization experiments. (After Priest *et al.*[388]).

Competitor DNA	Percent competition with *O. proteus* DNA	
	O. proteus strain 502	*O. proteus* strain 511
O. proteus 511	100	100
O. proteus 502	100	100
O. proteus 510	100	95
O. proteus 501	77	85
O. proteus 530	65	20
Hafnia alvei	70	82
Salmonella gallinarum	17	0
Escherichia coli	53	21
Proteus mirabilis	0	0

of DNA hybridization tests. *O. proteus* single-stranded, labelled DNA was made to compete for filter bound single-stranded *O. proteus* DNA with DNAs from other bacteria. High percentage competition implies similarity of the heterologous DNA with *O. proteus* DNA. From Table 13.3, two groups of *O. proteus* can be distinguished. DNAs from *Escherichia coli* and *Hafnia alvei* both show high ability to compete with *O. proteus* DNA, indicating a high level of sequence homology. Priest *et al.*[388] finally demonstrated that at least two strains of *Hafnia alvei* could grow with yeast in simulated brewery conditions, so satisfying the criterion for *Obesumbacterium*. From this and the obvious nucleotide similarity they very reasonably recommended that *O. proteus* be renamed *Hafnia protea*, and that the genus *Obesumbacterium* be abolished.

THE HISTORY OF *ERWINIA*

The dominant position of chemical and physiological characters in modern bacterial taxonomy cannot be better shown than by considering the evidence offered by protagonists for a major taxonomic change, and how they marshal it.

The genus *Erwinia* has for generations been the resting place for numerous 'species' of bacteria causing soft rot diseases of plants. *Erwinia amylovora*, the first named species, was the first bacterial phytopathogen to be demonstrated. It is not a soft rot, but causes fire-blight of pears. The soft rot organisms fitted the inadequate description of *Erwinia amylovora*, all having peritrichously flagellated, Gram-negative, rod-shaped cells. They were named as new species of *Erwinia*, the first being *E. carotovora*. Certain yellow bacteria growing as epiphytes on plants were also assigned to *Erwinia*, which was made the basis of a monotypic tribe, Erwinieae, in the Enterobacteriaceae.

Starr and Chatterjee develop the idea that this concept of *Erwinia* is inaccurate and misleading and review chemical characters which might help to clarify the situation.[450] Many of the characters seem to have been little studied. Pigments and wall-chemistry have been studied but not related to other genera. A little serological work on *Erwinia* showed *E. nigrifluens* to be highly uniform, and that *E. carotovora*, *E. atroseptica*, *E. aroideae*, *E. amylovora* shared common antigens.[513] Some of these were shared also by *Escherichia coli*, an enteric bacterium common in animals.

Comparatively little work has been completed on the biosynthetic pathways, regulatory mechanisms and general metabolism of *Erwinia*, except for the establishment of the test media necessary for identification of strains. Most *Erwinias* grow in a glucose–salts medium, but in a few cases supplements are required. *E. amylovora* requires added nicotinic acid. Many strains of *Erwinia* have been thought unable to reduce nitrate to nitrite, and this has become a method by which they can be distinguished from the enterobacteria, such as *Escherichia* and *Shigella*. However, if the growth medium is supplemented with KNO_3 and nicotinic acid, even the 'nitrite-negative' *Erwinias* will readily produce nitrite.[462]

White and Starr extended observations of carbohydrate metabolism in *Erwinia* by comparing their end-products of fermentation with those of enterobacteria.[500] *Erwinia* end-products were of the 'mixed acids' type—typical of enterobacteria.

One of the most striking properties of the soft rot *Erwinias*, such as *E. carotovora*, is their output of enzymes which can degrade pectic substances. Pectolysis has been so striking a feature that it has tended to reinforce the concept of the genus. Other bacteria have pectolytic properties, however, and avirulent mutants of *Erwinia* are known, which are deficient in several pectinases.[49]

Not much is known about the bacteriophage relationships of *Erwinia* and other plant pathogenic bacteria, though polyvirulent and more specific phages have been isolated from fire-blight organisms. Genetic relationships between *Erwinia* and other bacteria have been inadequately investigated, through some exchange of genes between *Erwinia*, *Escherichia*, *Salmonella* and *Shigella* has been reported.[89]

The reason for the apparent neglect of *Erwinia* may be that its position as a phytopathogen with striking pectolytic properties, and its early recognition, gave it unquestioned taxonomic respectability. Ecological study of the group shows that *Erwinia* may not simply be a phytopathogenic genus, by implicating it in infections of fish.[76] Once the concept of specifically phytopathogenic properties of *Erwinia* was seriously challenged, numerous isolations of the *Erwinia* species were made from a wide range of animal and human tissues. Bottone and Schneierson reported that sera of human patients would agglutinate *Erwinia* but not *Escherichia coli*, *Enterobacter*, etc.[61] Isolations from animal sources are entirely compatible with early reports of tissue damage (haemorrhage, septicaemia) caused to animals by inoculations of *Erwinia* from plant sources. Many of the plant *Erwinias* have yellow pigments, and there have been suggestive reports of the isolation of yellow 'coliform' bacteria in cases of septicaemia, multiple abscesses and meningitis.[485]

The classical view of *Erwinia* as a rather heterogeneous group of mainly pectolytic phytopathogens, with a few epiphytic (? avirulent) members, must be re-examined as a result of these incontrovertible ecological observations. The definition of the tribe Erwinieae is too narrowly based. Classical evidence is inadequate to re-distribute the species of *Erwinia*, since comparative data are so few. Starr and Chatterjee believe that the artificial gulf between the fields of plant pathology and medical bacteriology is chiefly responsible for the sparseness of facts.[450] Nonetheless there were some earlier indications, from nitrogen and carbon metabolism, gene exchange and serology, of an affinity between some strains of *Erwinia* and genera in other tribes of Enterobacteriaceae.

It is almost entirely chemical evidence which has been urgently gathered in support of the abandonment of the tribe Erwinieae, and in favour of various replacement schemes of more natural (polythetic) classification. The problem is fundamentally two-fold: firstly are *Erwinia* strains as typical enterobacteria as is, say, *Shigella*, and secondly can *Erwinia* be divided into non-pectolytic (e.g. fire-blight), pectolytic (soft rot) and epiphytic taxa?

The chemical evidence comes mainly from studies of DNA base composition and DNA hybridization. Base composition shows that plant *Erwinia* strains are completely typical of Enterobacteriaceae, with GC contents ranging mostly from 50–58%. Extreme values occur not in the phytopathogens, but in a human *Erwinia* (60.2% GC) and in *Hafnia alvei* (48% GC). *Erwinia amylovora* is indistinguishable on GC ratio from several other fire-blight-type isolates (necroses, galls and wilts), and all might perhaps be lumped together with advantage. *Erwinia salicis* and *E. tracheiphila* might be united on the same grounds. GC ratios of the yellow *Erwinias* (from plant and animal sources) show them to be closely related to *E. amylovora*, *Klebsiella* and *Enterobacter*.

The soft rot *Erwinias* are not separable from the necrotic strains on GC ratio evidence. *E. carotovora* has much the same ratio as five other 'species', all of which could well be lumped together. Two or three other groups of strains (? species) are clustered together on the GC ratio data.

Table 13.4   DNA relationships from hybridization experiments of species of *Erwinia* and other genera. (Data from Brenner *et al.*[74])

Test DNA samples	Relative percent binding at 60°C to DNA of		
	Erwinia carotovora	*Erwinia dissolvens*	*Escherichia coli*
Erwinia carotovora	100	—	17
Erwinia aroideae	67	—	16
Erwinia carnegiana	18	34	32
Erwinia amylovora	23	24	27
Erwinia dissolvens	23	100	34
Escherichia coli	—	32	100
Salmonella typhimurium	13	30	45
Salmonella marcescens	18	21	—
Shigella flexneri	16	31	—
Enterobacter aerogenes	25	36	—
Proteus mirabilis	4	2	9

Equally convincing is a demonstration of substantial homologies between *Erwinia* and the other enterobacteria by DNA hybridization.[74] Table 13.4 summarizes some of these findings. All *Erwinias* showed low to moderate reactions with DNAs of representative enteric bacteria. An 'atypical' *Erwinia*,[140] *E. dissolvens*, shows a higher affinity with *Escherichia coli* than it does to *E. carotovora*. *Erwinia carotovora* seems to have more sequences in common with *Enterobacter aerogenes* than with *Erwinia amylovora* or *E. carnegiana*. There is no support from these results for the idea that the pectolytic *Erwinias* (*Pectobacterium* Waldee) are taxonomically separable from enterobacteria, except in terms of that one, over-valued character. In any case it has been reported that *Enterobacter aerogenes* is pectolytic.[128] It seems that the tribe Erwinieae must be abolished.

CONCLUSION

The *ad hoc* classifications of the early bacterial taxonomists, like those of the earlier angiosperm taxonomists, are understandable since they had so much to name, describe and classify, on a comparatively narrow range of characters. The approach to more natural classification of bacteria is being fuelled largely by advances in chemotaxonomy, which can provide fundamental evidence cheaply and rapidly. Bacterial taxonomists have been quick to recognize their well-deserved good fortune. It seems that they will continue to be biochemical experimenters in the future, as they have been in the past, hence being less naturalists and mystics than their higher-plant colleagues.[317] It is worth noting, however, that even with the fullest applications of new methods and ideas, the classification of some perennially critical taxa is no more settled than before (see for example Dixon[131] on the taxonomy of *Rhizobium* and *Agrobacterium*). Mandel[317] asserted that bacteriologists are fortunate not to have been encumbered with the burden of systematic polemics. Perhaps these halcyon days will pass now that so much quantitative chemotaxonomic information has accumulated. Taxonomic arguments do not stop when facts become available; they just become worthwhile.

14

Chemical Evidence and Taxonomic Problems

Problems for taxonomists arise fundamentally from the nature of the variation patterns exhibited by the taxa which they study. Numerous patterns of variation have been described in different plant groups, and it is likely that many more remain to be discovered. The variation pattern of a group is eventually described in terms of a hierarchical classification, unless the variation is of a kind requiring a special-purpose system, such as biosystematic categorization. To be of most general usefulness the pattern should be interpreted in terms of the orthodox hierarchy of order, family, genus, species and so forth.

Most taxonomic problems arise firstly in the phase of interpretation of complex patterns of variation, perhaps originating from the operation of curious breeding systems, or secondly in the phase in which the variation is represented in hierarchical terms. Difficulties of the first kind are sometimes presented by apomictic or self-pollinating groups, by polyploid complexes and by populations of species which are hybridizing. Taxonomists sometimes have great difficulty in evaluating the significance of incompatibility mechanisms, of continuous variation, and of disjunct distributions of what appears to be the same taxon. Difficulties of the second kind include the circumscription of groups within the variation spectrum which has been demonstrated, that is the requirement for lines to be drawn around 'nodes' of variation to represent species or other taxa. The problem is of course to know where exactly the lines should be drawn. Conflict of different kinds of evidence often occurs during the circumscription stage, in the integration and weighing of data from several or many sources, and eventually in the attribution of appropriate rank to the taxa which are recognized. Finding the right names for the taxa is the last, but seldom the least, of the taxonomist's troubles.

A complete account of the nature of taxonomic problems would comprise a treatise on the principles of taxonomy, for which there is no space. Chemotaxonomists wishing insight into these matters would do well to consult the text by Davis and Heywood[118] for a lucid and comprehensive treatment.

In general, the problems are most acute where the variations demonstrated are small, or where they are found only in cryptic characters. Rather different considerations may apply above and below the species level, according to the group being studied. Genera may be easy to define while their component species are critical; sometimes the species are the obvious units and the genera are not. When species form well-defined groupings within a genus there are possibilities of recognizing sections or subgenera, or of adopting a narrower generic concept by raising the rank of the groupings to the generic level.

Although most taxonomists classify plants in accordance with the maximum correlation of attributes, and do not in principle consider the phylogenetic relationships of the materials they work with, eventually the taxa which have been defined must be placed in some kind of order. The genera within a family can be arranged in many different ways, and likewise the species in a genus may be placed in different sequences which different taxonomists think phylogenetically reasonable. Though fundamental classification *need* not involve phylogenetic concepts, in practice it almost always does. Perhaps this is why natural classifications and 'phylogenetic' classifications are often confused. A natural classification (see Chapter 1) reflects the similarities and differences of plants in every feature which has been studied. If we believe that the major cause of similarity between taxa is community of descent then the natural clasification is *ipso facto* a 'phylogenetic' one. At lower hierarchical levels, where there is plenty of evidence, natural and 'phylogenetic' classifications are probably almost the same thing. At higher levels, above the genus, evidence of similarity and difference is sparser because of the uncertainties of homology and the larger discontinuities. Here the ordering of taxa based on maximum correlation of attributes is less likely to reflect the degree of phylogenetic relationship accurately. Different taxonomists tend to form larger groups less uniformly, because of differences in their intuitive perception of phylogenetic relationships. Most agree on the separation of *Ranunculus* from *Anemone*. Few would agree completely on a scheme of subfamilies in the Gramineae. No two taxonomists would produce the same arrangement of orders and sub-orders of Angiosperms, and those who persist in their attempts to produce better classifications at these higher levels are sometimes unfairly regarded as mere phylogenetic speculators.

The desire to make the arrangement of taxa in a natural system as phylogenetic as possible is another source of taxonomic problems. The commonest example of this is the genus, family or species of uncertain affinity. Isolated taxa which seem to have similarities to more than one established group or to none pose a sometimes insoluble problem. No-one really knows what the affinities of *Adoxa moschatellina* are, though there are several possibilities. Until the problem is solved, taxonomists pigeon-hole *Adoxa* in a family of its own. The best position of the Cactaceae has been hotly disputed for years, some supposing it to be a member of the order Centrospermae, whereas others reserve their judgment pending further research, so making for it a monotypic order Cactales.

This chapter draws together examples of some of these taxonomic problems, considering in each case what contribution to the debate has been made by the availability of chemical evidence, and what contribution might therefore be made by a chemotaxonomic approach in similar cases. Additional examples are, of course, scattered through earlier chapters but there the intention was to illustrate the nature of chemical evidence, not the taxonomic problem which it may have helped to solve.

THE RECOGNITION OF MINOR VARIANTS

In most plant groups, considerable variation exists below the level of the species, which is of course not a standardized concept, comparable between all groups. Traditional forms of taxonomic evidence have been useful in distinguishing subspecies, varieties and forms of species. Previous chapters have shown that infraspecific variation occurs also in chemical characters. In bacteria the serotypes of a species may be recognized as formal infraspecific taxa. Electrophoretic studies on proteins have helped to define and identify wheat varieties for the cereal breeder and baker (see Chapter 10). Mirov's work on turpentines showed that chemical varieties were present in several conifers (see Chapter 9). Penfold and Morrison noted chemical races in species of *Eucalyptus*, based on comparisons of essential oils.[373] Populations of *Trifolium repens* and certain *Lotus* species include cyanogenic and acyanogenic forms.[114] Mention has already been made of chemotypes in lichens, which are especially important since they may frustrate circumscription of species in this group where chemical identification tests are widely used.

Chemical identification of infraspecific variants would clearly be a useful tool in the taxonomy of cultivars. Cultivars are infraspecific variants maintained by cultivation, and may often be clonally propagated. Accurate cultivar identification is essential if materials are to be sold to farmers or horticulturists, and unfortunately it is all too easy for cultivars to be mixed up in nurseries, and during grafting procedures. There can be few people who have not been sold garden plants under the wrong name. Only rarely is there an intention to deceive; there is great difficulty in maintaining pure, correctly labelled stocks. Chemical tests might solve many of the growers' problems, if enough could be worked out. Cultivars of blue spruce (*Picea pungens*) can be correctly identified by comparing the highly conservative monoterpenes of cortical oleoresin.[411] Of forty-five paired cultivars, thirty-seven pairs could be separated with ease on monoterpene content. The chemical data here might well be a surer guide to identity than morphological features, especially in juvenile or recently grafted individuals, and could be provided cheaply and quickly by government agricultural services.

In evolutionary studies, minor chemical variation may often have much to reveal to the taxonomist. Reference has already been made (Chapter 10) to the work of Allard's school in following the fate of genes in barley populations by scoring frequencies of the allozyme proteins for which they code. A fine example of the application of chemistry to population studies, which aim at the demonstration of polymorphisms, their origin, significance and adaptive value, is offered by the researches of Mabry and others on the sesquiterpene lactone variations in species of *Ambrosia* (Compositae).[312]

Ambrosia psilostachya (ragweed), a herbaceous perennial weed common in North America, was studied by Miller *et al.*[338] Sixty-two populations were analysed for their sesquiterpene lactones, and it was found that, although over a dozen characterize the species as a whole, any single population contains only one or two as major components. Almost all the populations sample contained either monolactone-pseudoguianolides or dilactone-pseudoguianolides. Figure 14.1 shows that mainland Texas populations of *A. psilo-*

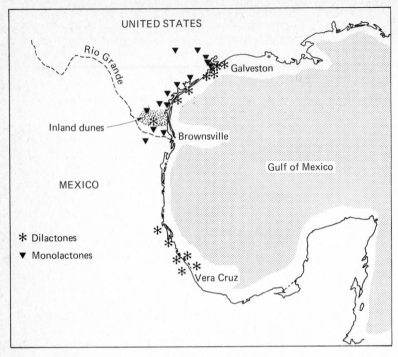

Fig. 14.1 Distribution of monolactone-pseudoguianolide and dilactone-pseudoguianolide populations of *Ambrosia psilostachya* and *A. cumanensis*. (Modified after Miller *et al.*[338] and Potter and Mabry.[385])

stachya contained monolactones, except for one group from inland sand dunes north of Brownsville. In contrast, the populations on the barrier islands five to sixteen kilometres off the mainland (in the Gulf of Mexico) all contained only the dilactone types. Environmental and developmental variation in lactone production was minimal, the characters apparently being under genetic control.

Because of the time of origin, and sequence of fusion, of these offshore islands, Miller *et al.* were led to suggest that the inland dune system, known to be at least 35 000 years old, was the site of a gene pool from which dilactone plants colonized the islands from the south. This colonization may have taken place about 3000 years ago, when the chain of barrier islands was completed to the south. Colonization of the island chain from the north was considered unlikely because the prevailing winds, carrying seeds and pollen, are from the south and south-west, because the islands appear to have had little or no mainland contact, and finally because the plant community on the northern mainland has for a long time been climax prairie, dominated by *Andropogon*. *Ambrosia psilostachya* seems only recently to have penetrated the northern mainland area, as a weed of roadsides.

Chemical evidence therefore favoured a southern origin, possibly from the inland dune system, for the barrier island ragweeds. A later re-appraisal based on wider sampling, and also on volatile terpene distribution, has somewhat altered and extended these conclusions.[385] Population analyses of the related species *Ambrosia cumanensis*, common in Central Mexico, show that plants from the vicinity of Vera Cruz have the same three dilactone pseudo-guianolides as those on the barrier islands lining the Gulf coast of Texas. Most populations of *A. cumanensis* which have been analysed, from Mexico and Colombia, have both dilactone and monolactone sesquiterpenes. Potter and Mabry show also that the *A. psilostachya* populations on the barrier islands resemble the Vera Cruz *A. cumanensis* plants in their volatile terpenes. A dendrogram of the similarities between the *Ambrosia* populations was calculated on the basis of qualitative variations in volatile oils. The Texas islands and Vera Cruz populations were connected at higher similarity levels than were either to the Texas mainland populations. These two sources of chemical data agree with morphological findings, in that the island ragweed populations resemble *A. cumanensis* more closely than mainland populations of *psilostachya*.

It appears from all the evidence that, at some time in the past, *A. cumanensis* (Vera Cruz type) extended further to the north than it now does. During this northward extension, it differentiated into dilactone populations of what is now regarded as *A. psilostachya*. This evolution may well have happened in the inland dune area around the Rio Grande. Subsequently these inland dune populations may have colonized the barrier islands from the south. The evolutionary relationships of *Ambrosia psilostachya* and *A. cumanensis* are not yet clear, but it seems from cytological and genetic data that the latter, a diploid, may have given rise to the former (a diploid–polyploid complex).[338] Morphological and other differences between the two species are inconstant, and they are not always separated by taxonomists. Chemical evidence from these population studies clearly agrees with what is known of their morphology and cytogenetics, forming a valuable supplement to total knowledge of what must be a very complex evolutionary situation.

CHEMISTRY AND THE STUDY OF HYBRIDIZATION

Considerable use of chemical information has been made in studies of hybridization, both at the level of populations and introgressing taxa, and in the detection of amphiploidy. Work on the genome relationships of genera in the Triticinae,[256] and of different polyploid wheats,[255] and that on the rye–wheat hybrid,[199,344] has already been discussed. Johnson *et al.* have reported on genome relationships in *Gossypium*[257] using the techniques of protein electrophoresis. Analyses of turpentines have also extended to the study of pine hybrids.[341] Work on variation in the mustard oils of *Brassica* suggested that the allopolyploid of *B. nigra* and *B. campestris* (*B. juncea*) might have had a polytopic origin, i.e. have developed independently in more than one place.[225] In most cases, hybrid derivatives have been shown to be chemically as well as morphologically intermediate between their parents.

At the level of interspecific relationships and gene exchange between populations, classical work was carried out by Alston and Turner and their school[8,11] on the application of paper chromatography to analysis of variation in *Baptisia* (Leguminosae). Much of the credit for establishing the relevance of chemotaxonomic methods to hybridization studies, and indeed in general, should be given to them. The rigour, soundness and success of their approach subsequently encouraged and enlightened investigations of hybridization in scores of genera. Among these may be cited the work on hybrids in *Viola*, [453] in *Tragopogon*,[73] in *Corchorus*,[174] and in *Dicentra*.[154] Interests in chromatography, phenolic chemistry and hybridization reinforced and fertilized one another, so defining a very characteristic period in the development of chemotaxonomy.

The attractions of phenolic (especially flavonoid) chromatography to the investigator of hybridization include its speed, the possibility of detecting patterns of inheritance of identifiable constituents, and the possible discovery of 'hybrid substances' —compounds absent from the parents which occur in hybrids, commonly in the F_2. Presumably these substances arise via gene interactions which normally do not take place.

All these potential returns were realized in work on inbred lines of *Tragopogon* species and artificial hybrids between them.[43] A total of 1700 plants representing five species and their F_1 and F_2 hybrids was analysed by two-way paper chromatography. On chromatographic pattern *T. balcanicus*, *T. crocifolius* and *T. samaritanii* were very similar to one another, while *T. angustissimus* was somewhat different. *T. pterodes* was very distinct. These findings agreed with placings of the five species on morphological criteria. Hybrid compounds were detected in some F_2 crosses, and sometimes parental compounds were entirely missing from the hybrids. The data were used to detect linkage groups controlling biosynthesis of phenolic compounds in these species.

Taylor investigated claims that *Tsuga heterophylla* (western hemlock) and *T. mertensiana* (mountain hemlock) hybridized in areas where their distribution overlaps in the north-western United States.[467] Morphological intermediacy had been documented over many years, but artificial crossing had failed to produce viable hybrid seed. Paper chromatography of phenolic extracts of these hemlock species revealed 27 major compounds of which 22 were found in both species, three were specific to *T. heterophylla* and two were restricted to *T. mertensiana*. It would be expected that hybrids would contain at least some of the species-specific phenolics from the presumed parents. Of the putative hybrids in Taylor's study, only three contained species-specific compounds from both *T. mertensiana* and *T. heterophylla*, and were thus chemically as well as morphologically intermediate. Taylor concluded that these plants were probably introgressants, since they resembled *T. heterophylla* quite closely, but he considered the frequency of hybridization must be too low, as judged on phenolic intermediacy, to account for all the morphologically 'hybrid' trees. Sparseness of chemical hybrids agreed with the failure of artificial hybridization in suggesting that crossing does not occur to any marked degree in these hemlock populations.

T. mertensiana is a morphologically extreme representative of *Tsuga*, and the fact that its peculiarities are 'spruce-like' has suggested to a number of botanists that it is an intergeneric hybrid of *Tsuga heterophylla* and *Picea sitchensis*. Taylor scrutinized his phenolic data for evidence at this other level of hybridization. In chemical terms, *Tsuga* and *Picea* proved to be fairly similar. Intergeneric comparisons of phenolic patterns showed that those of *Tsuga mertensiana* and *Picea sitchensis* were the most similar, one particular compound being found only in these two species. Though the chemical data are hence compatible with the theory of intergeneric hybridization, Taylor believes it to be unlikely. The presumed parent taxa are markedly dissimilar and were probably not sympatric during the period when the hybridization is postulated to have occurred. Modern sympatric populations of the two species are not characterized by hybrids, certainly not by hybrid swarms. Taylor prefers to consider that the chemical evidence indicates *T. mertensiana* as the most spruce-like hemlock, and that *Picea* and *Tsuga* are closely related. The situation is illustrated in Fig. 14.2.

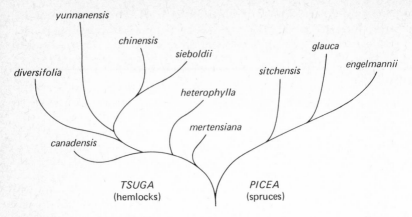

Fig. 14.2 A suggested phylogeny of *Tsuga* and representative species of *Picea*. *Tsuga mertensiana* is indicated as the most spruce-like hemlock, perhaps resulting from an intergeneric hybridization. The scheme is based on similarity values derived from phenolic pigment chromatograms. (After Taylor.[467])

The extent to which the phenolics of hybrid derivatives may indicate their parentage, or indeed their hybrid status, is unlikely to be constant in different plant groups. It has often been demonstrated that phenolic characters are under genetic control, but the extent to which they persist as markers in back-crossing populations is variable. Unless artificial hybrids and back-crosses of the parental taxa can be analysed in parallel with wild populations, it is not possible to estimate with certainty the degree to which different levels of phenolic intermediacy indicate closeness to one or the other parent. Crawford has considered this matter by analysing phenolic patterns of artificial *Coreopsis* hybrids and back-cross progeny.[101] He found that the phenolic characters identified back-cross types more reliably than features of gross morphology. This contrasts with findings in *Baptisia*[329] and in *Liatris*[303] where undoubted back-cross types, identified by morphology, failed to show any phenolic characters from the non-recurrent parent. Obviously if phenolic characters are to be used as reliable guides to hybridization, investigation of the extent to which they correlate with morphological features and of their stability in artificial back-crosses must be undertaken. In groups such as *Coreopsis* they seem to be very sensitive indicators of hybridity, but at least in some individuals of *Baptisia* and *Liatris* they are less useful than morphological characters. In *Baptisia* however it is well established that phenolic chemistry can be used as a test for hybrid status in most cases. It is noteworthy that *Baptisia* phenolics may be more valuable in this regard than are *Baptisia* seed proteins. Very little variation has been demonstrated in seed proteins of *Baptisia* species which in terms of morphology and phenolic constituents were very distinct.[301]

It is not surprising, if chemical and morphological characters of hybrids do not always vary in parallel, that chemical characters of different kinds should differ in stability also. Ideally, taxonomists should investigate the genetics of all chemical characters employed in studies of hybridization, but time, space and material rarely make this a practical proposition. As with morphological evidence of hybridity, work on cultivated plants, for which materials and money are more readily obtainable, has provided basic facts about the segregation, dominance and persistence of chemical characters in hybrids of known parentage (e.g. *Pyrus* hybrids).[88] From such findings the taxonomist of wild plants must often extrapolate.

If hybridization is detectable by morphological and chemical intermediacy, physiological intermediacy can be assumed. Though physiological attributes of plants are susceptible to segregation and recombination following hybridization, it is unusual for them to be closely analysed. Elegant studies of physiological variation in hybrids have been made on a swarm of nothomorphs between *Phlox maculata* subsp. *maculata* and *P. glaberrima* subsp. *interior* at Idaville, Indiana.[196] Morphological intermediacy of hybrids was obvious in many characters, and there was existing chromatographic evidence to support the idea of introgression in this population.[302] Several physiological characters of the plants in the hybrid swarm were compared with the behaviour of 'pure' populations of the supposed parental taxa. Samples were transplanted into pots and then grown in glasshouse or coldframe conditions for $2\frac{1}{2}$ years before the physiological experiments were undertaken.

The most interesting data relate to measurements of net photosynthesis (Ps) and dark respiration (Rs), obtained by determining the CO_2 fixation and evolution of intact flowering shoots in controlled conditions of temperature, light and soil moisture. Figure 14.3 shows a plot of the hybrid index (a measure of morphological intermediacy) against the net Ps/Rs ratio. Pure *P. glaberrima* clearly has a higher net rate of carbon fixation than *P. maculata*, probably connected with the fact that *P. maculata* begins spring growth earlier than *P. glaberrima*. Thus *P. maculata* has a longer growing season, and presumably there is less need to build up carbohydrate stocks rapidly. The hybrids are much more diverse in net Ps/Rs ratio than are the parents, as would be expected following a period of

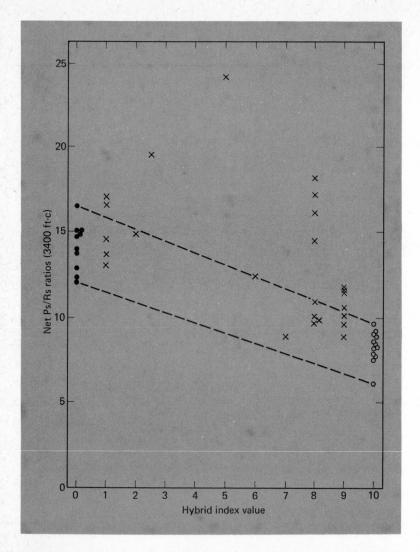

Fig. 14.3 Correlation between hybrid index values and net photosynthetic/dark respiratory ratios (Ps/Rs) at 10°C of *Phlox glaberrima* (●) and *P. maculata* (O) and intermediates (×) at Idaville, Indiana. Broken lines represent projected variation limits of hybrid population based on the parental variation limits. (From Hadley and Levin[196].) (Note that 1 foot candle (f.c.) = approx. 10 lux.)

recombination. None of the hybrids, however, has a lower Ps/Rs ratio than *P. maculata*. All have either intermediate or transgressively superior ratios. Inferior values would be predicted to occur just as often as superior ones, on the basis of recombination theory. It seems reasonable to speculate that the hybrid derivatives which had net Ps/Rs ratios lower than that of *P. maculata* have been eliminated by natural selection in the Idaville site. They would have been unable to compete with their parents and sibling hybrids, and so have left fewer offspring, or possibly no offspring whatever.

Phlox maculata subsp. *pyramidalis* has for some time been suspected to be a stabilized interspecific hybrid of *P. maculata* and *P. glaberrima* on the basis of morphological and chromatographic evidence.[302] In all the physiological characters investigated,[196] subsp. *pyramidalis* was intermediate to varying degrees between its putative parents, and was physiologically indistinguishable from several of the hybrids from the Idaville population. Physiological evidence strongly

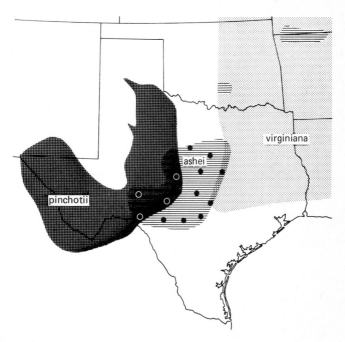

Fig. 14.4 The distributions of *Juniperus ashei, J. pinchotii,* and *J. virginiana.* The samples of the population are indicated by filled circles and include each of the 3 species which was present in that area. (From Adams and Turner.[3])

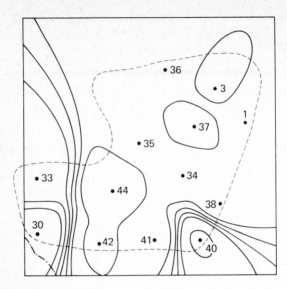

Fig. 14.5 Contour map of %γ-terpinene in 13 populations (indicated by numbers) of *Juniperus ashei* in Texas (dotted line shows Texas distribution). See text for explanation. (From Adams and Turner.[3])

supports the notion of hybrid origin for subsp. *pyramidalis*. Both in the character of optimal temperature for carbon dioxide fixation and in moisture compensation point, subspecies *pyramidalis* closely resembled *P. maculata*. Both taxa inhabit wet places, perhaps emphasizing that the ecological properties of species are the summation of its physiological tolerances.

A classic case of allopatric introgression in *Juniperus*[198] subsequently proved to be more apparent than real, following the application of chemotaxonomic evidence. Hall considered that the variation patterns in *Juniperus ashei* and *J. virginiana* indicate that although these two species are no longer spatially coincident, i.e. do not have sympatric distributions, they must have undergone a phase of introgressive hybridization when their distributions overlapped at some time in the past. They are, in Hall's view,[198] now connected by their hybrid progeny. All the initial signs pointed to such a conclusion. Subsequently Rudloff *et al.*[494] and Flake *et al.*,[160] using chemical evidence in part, were unable to support the idea that hybridization had necessarily occurred or was occurring between these two juniper species, even though they sampled some of the same populations described by Hall.

Adams and Turner analysed the variable *J. ashei* populations in an attempt to uncover the variation pattern in terpenoid constitutents of these widespread, weedy trees.[3] Gas–liquid chromotography revealed 135 terpenoid constituents, comprising 88 terpenoid characters, in three geographically contiguous species, *J. ashei*, *J. virginiana* and a third species *J. pinchotii*. The plants were sampled from thirteen sites in central Texas (Fig. 14.4). Nineteen morphological characters were also studied. To maximize the differences demonstrated between the putative patents in this study, the terpenoids showing the greatest interpopulation differences were statistically detected and then contour-mapped. Figure 14.5 shows such a contour map for the percentage of γ-terpinene in *J. ashei*, Most of the population means were insignificantly different,

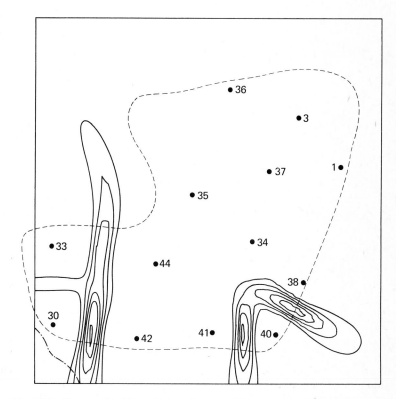

Fig. 14.6   Composite differential contours of 14 terpenoids of *Juniperus ashei*. See text for discussion. (After Adams and Turner.[3])

but populations 40 and 30 both had a significantly higher percentage of γ-terpinene than the other populations. Population 33 had an intermediate value. The results of all fourteen terpenoid contour maps made by Adams and Turner are summarized in Fig. 14.6, which gives the composite differential contours. It is confirmed that changes in terpenoid content are occurring between population 40 and populations 38, 34 and 41 and also between population 30 (and to a lesser extent 33) and the populations to the north and east.

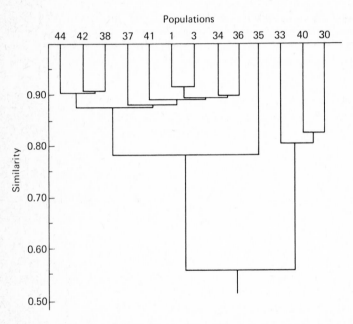

Fig. 14.7 Dendrogram of similarities between 13 populations of *Juniperus ashei*. Single-linkage clustering involving 39 terpenoid characters. (From Adams and Turner.[3])

Adams and Turner calculated similarity measures on the basis of 39 terpenoid characters, and then clustered them by means of the single linkage method to produce the similarity dendrogram shown in Fig. 14.7. Populations 1 and 3 seem to have the greatest affinity, but most of the thirteen populations are more or less equally related at about the 90% similarity level. Populations 30, 33 and 40 are very much less similar, being connected to the other populations only at the 57% level. *J. ashei* is thus a more or less homogeneous species, in its terpenoid content, with the exception of these three peripheral populations. Similar treatment of the morphological characters confirmed the chemical findings. The populations were divided into four sets: (a) populations 1 and 3 (NE. Texas); (b) populations 37, 44, 42, 41, 34, 36, 38 (Central Region); (c) population 35; and (d) the divergent peripheral populations 30, 33 and 40.

On the basis of these extensive chemical and numerical analyses, Adams and Turner consider that the idea of introgression between *J. ashei* and *J. virginiana*, and with *J. pinchotii*, must be abandoned. Populations 40 and 30 are relatively distant, yet they have diverged from the other populations far more than they have diverged from each other. If introgression was taking place, with *J. pinchotii* in population 30 or with *J.virginiana* in population 40, the two populations would be expected to show divergence, not convergence. It is also strange, supposing that alien genes have been or are being introduced to *J. ashei* at these two sites, that there are no characteristic *J. virginiana* or *J. pinchotii* terpenoids in the *J. ashei* chromatograms. Terpenoid characters are known to be heritable, and therefore some at least would be expected to occur in hybrids.

Adams and Turner suggest that the allopatric introgression originally proposed[198] is non-existent or at any rate very rare. They believe that the divergence of the peripheral populations 40, 30 and 33 may arise from the small sample size taken (5 plants per population), or from the existence of an as yet unidentified common selective pressure operating in all three sites. A third possibility, since the directions of wind currents and bird migrations during the pollination and seed dispersal periods are all from the south to the north, is that a genetic outflow, unreplenished from the south, may have effected some differentiation in these peripheral areas, but not elsewhere. In general, *J. ashei* is rather uniform; although the few morphological peculiarities of populations 30, 33 and 40 are backed up by terpenoid evidence, the terpenoid differences are rather small. The differences between the gas–liquid chromatograms of a typical population from central Texas (34) and the aberrant population 40 are of small magnitude only.

For studies of hybridization, and of small-scale variation below the species level, this combination of chemotaxonomy and numerical methods seems to offer a powerful means of analysis. A similar technique has demonstrated that though hybridization between *Juniperus pinchotii* and *J. monosperma* may well occur in the Palo Duro Canyon (Texas Panhandle), introgression does not.[2]

CHEMICAL EVIDENCE, DELIMITATION
AND THE ATTRIBUTION OF RANK

Delimitation of taxa and attribution of rank to taxa are two of the principal occupations of all taxonomists. By contrast those who glean systematic evidence without acting upon it must be classified among the hewers of wood and drawers of water. Chemical data offer further information from which to judge alternative solutions to these two fundamental taxonomic problems. Examples of the use of chemical facts for both purposes occur throughout Part II, but it may be helpful to consider some specific cases from the taxonomic standpoint, rather than in terms of the nature of chemical evidence.

The recognition of species

In 1968 Smith recounted the events following a collection of a curious form of the corn brome-grass (*Bromus secalinus*), from a newly sown roadside.[440] Material of this kind was generally identified as *B. secalinus* var. *hirsutus* Kindberg. Striking similarities with *B. secalinus* were mainly in the nature of the spikelet and florets, which disarticulate only very slowly, after a tight inrolling of the caryopsis and lemma. These features are related to the fact that *B. secalinus* is a weed of wheat and rye fields. Its fruit mimics that of the crop species in size and shape, while the tough rachilla prevents the spikelets from shattering before the crop plants are harvested. Harvested weed seeds are difficult to separate from the crop, and so the weed is disseminated in subsequent sowings of seed wheat or rye. Var. *hirsutus* has all the qualitative peculiarities and adaptations of *B. secalinus*, with the differences that it has smaller fruits and that unlike *B. secalinus* it has hairs on the leaf sheaths. Both features have been regarded as trivial.

As a matter of routine, the seed proteins of the collections of var. *hirsutus* were compared serologically with those of *B. secalinus*. In Chapter 11, Fig. 11.9 shows how unexpectedly different they proved to be. It seemed unlikely that so great a difference indicated only varietal rank for var. *hirsutus*, particularly when it was recalled that *B. secalinus* was serologically homogeneous, and that certain related species showed only quite small seed protein differences from it.

The serological discontinuity was reinforced by a root tip chromosome count which showed var. *hirsutus* to be a diploid taxon, unlike

B. secalinus, which is a tetraploid. On the basis of the serological difference, backed up by the chromosome evidence, it was considered that the morphological differences between *B. secalinus* and its var. *hirsutus* had been underweighted. Var. *hirsutus* was accordingly recognized as a new species—*B. pseudosecalinus*. Subsequently the morphological differences have been scrutinized more closely,[445] and found to be greater than previously thought, while the plant has been located in various parts of Britain. Though still under-collected, like most critical species, it seems to be an occasional contaminant of small-seeded pasture grasses, such as the rye-grasses and fescues, appearing in sown lawns, road verges and leys.

The economy of time and materials connected with this particular change of rank and delimitation should perhaps be mentioned. The plant was collected on a Saturday. One caryopsis sufficed for the preparation of an antigenic solution used in the serological test; another was sown in a petri dish to produce root tips. Both serological and cytological results were available on the following Thursday, by which time the dried specimen had just been admitted to the herbarium.

Chemotaxonomy at tribal and generic levels

Generic concepts differ from one plant group to another, and between taxonomists, but any aid which chemical studies might give to the recognition and stabilization of this often rather artificial category would be welcomed by any taxonomist of any plant group. Often the basic morphological and anatomical data have not been sufficient to convince all taxonomists of the correctness of rank or position assigned to isolated, artificial or refractory genera.

Work on the biology and taxonomy of *Geranium* sections *Anemonifolia* and *Ruberta*[509] appeared in close association with an account of the flavonoid chemotaxonomy of the genus by Bate-Smith.[32] The most recent monograph of *Geranium* (1912) is by Knuth.[274] Chemists should be assured that publications of at least such antiquity are frequently the latest accounts of larger taxonomic groups, owing to the labour involved in their classification on a world basis. Knuth divided *Geranium* into 30 sections, with a further grouping of these into broad geographical types, e.g. the Paleoarctic, and the Mediterranean *Gerania*. Bate-Smith analysed the level of advancement, in phenolic characters, of 60 species. He assigned different scores to primitive and advanced phenolic characters, which have already been referred to in Chapter 5.[204,283] The 'flavonoid score' showed that primitive flavonoid patterns predominate in species of Central Eurasia, and that *Gerania* from areas

peripheral to this have increasingly impoverished flavonoid complements. Reduction in complexity of flavonoid complement is
regarded as an advanced feature. Bate-Smith's data support Yeo's
contention that sections *Ruberta, Anemonifolia, Lucida* and
Unguiculata may all be closely related, in contradiction to the widely
separate positions assigned to them by Knuth. Their flavonoid
patterns are almost the same, so pointing strongly to the need for an
adjustment of Knuth's system for *Geranium*.

Bate-Smith[32] also compared the flavonoid constituents of
Geranium with those of other genera in the Geraniaceae. His most
interesting discovery was that the flavonoid pattern of *Biebersteinia*
was completely unlike that of any other genus in the family, and that
it included a number of unusual, unidentified compounds. This new
chemotaxonomic evidence is interesting because some taxonomists
have previously suggested that *Biebersteinia* should be removed
from the Geraniaceae, even on the basis of traditional taxonomic
characters.[464]

Serological evidence has been considered along with more
orthodox data in attempts to circumscribe the genus *Bromus*.[443] On
the basis of morphology and genetics, sections or subgenera can be
recognized in *Bromus sensu lato*, which have geographical connota-
tions. These infrageneric taxa are sometimes elevated to the rank of
genera (e.g. *Anisantha, Ceratochloa, Trisetobromus*). Between all these
narrower genera there is a strong morphological similarity. When
serological data also showed similarities between these groups,
but not between *Bromus s.l.* and undoubtedly separate genera
such as *Festuca* or *Brachypodium*, it was decided to adopt the
broader generic concept and to regard the infrageneric units as
sections.

During the comparisons of *Bromus* species in the different sections, with other grass species, it soon became clear that there was a
serological gulf between *Bromus* and most other genera. The
exception to this finding was *Boissiera*, a monotypic genus of annual
plants, long supposed to approach *Bromus* in certain morphological
characters. Quite strong serological reactions were shown by seed
antigens of *Boissiera squarrosa* to antisera of a range of different
Bromus species (Fig. 14.8). After a re-evaluation of the morphological evidence it was decided that *Boissiera squarrosa*, far from being a
separate genus, was a specialized member of *Bromus* section *Bromus*.
It shows multiple adaptations to the conditions on arid, heavily
grazed, rocky slopes with thin soils. The genus *Boissiera* has been
abandoned and the single species incorporated in *Bromus* as *B.
pumilio*.[441]

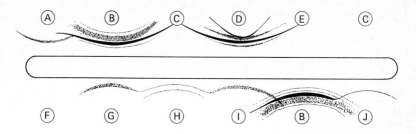

Fig. 14.8 Reaction of antigenic extracts of seeds of species in various grass genera to *Bromus arvensis* antiserum (in centre trough).

A *Agropyron cristatum*
B *Bromus hordeaceus*
C *Agrostis tenuis*
D *Bromus pumilio*
   (Syn. *Boissiera squarrosa*)
E *Avena fatua*

F *Brachypodium sylvaticum*
G *Agropyron spicatum*
H *Hordeum spontaneum*
I *Triticum monococcum*
J *Festuca pratensis*

Generic concepts in bacteria are very different from those in flowering plants and, because of the relative paucity of taxonomic characters, bacterial genera are often more artificial (see Chapter 13). Generic delimitation is nonetheless vital in the bacteria and new chemical evidence has sometimes been of service in making sounder generic boundaries. The evidence of DNA base composition (% GC) has been applied to the classification of the *Micrococcus–Staphylococcus* group.[434] Figure 14.9 shows how well the GC ratio data agree with similarity dendrograms arrived at by numerical analysis of variation in more orthodox characters. Homogeneous *Micrococcus* and *Staphylococcus* groups are indicated by both approaches. Numerical methods classified one strain of *S. lactis* (NCTC 7564) in the genus *Micrococcus*. The high GC ratio of this strain confirms the correctness of this position.

An interesting example of correlation between chemical data and other kinds of taxonomic characters is given in two recent papers on the generic and tribal classification of the Ericaceae. Stevens produced a well-documented case for taxonomic changes in the Ericaceae, arising from his investigations of mainly morphological and anatomical features.[454] Harborne and Williams[212] report work on a survey of the flavonoids and simple phenols of 381 species of Ericaceae and three related families, in which they comment on the re-classification proposals of Stevens.

Table 14.1 shows how the conclusions of Stevens and of Harborne and Williams are mutually confirmatory. Though there are some

Table 14.1 The correlation of Stevens' classification of Ericaceae and the chemical data of Harborne and Williams.

Stevens' classification	Stevens' innovations	Relation of chemical data to innovations	Other chemical indications
Rhododendroideae Bejarieae			Very distinct (no gossypetin; predom. 3,5-O-methyl flavonols and dihydroflavonols)
Rhodoreae			Gossypetin is characteristic
Cladothamneae			Cladothamneae lack all characteristic subfamily markers
Epigaeae	From Andromedeae	AGREE. *Epigaea* has 5-O-methyl flavonols (unlike Andromedeae, but like Rhodoreae)	
Phyllodoceae			Chemically like Rhodoreae *Chamaedaphne* (Phyllodoceae) has rhododendroid leaf scales plus gossypetin; ? transfer to Rhodoreae
Daboecieae	From Phyllodoceae	AGREE. Lacks gossypetin unlike most Phyllodoceae	
Diplarcheae	From Diapensiaceae	AGREE. Has hydroquinone—common in Ericaceae but absent in Diapensiaceae	

Taxon			
Ericoideae			
Ericeae			
Calluneae	*Calluna* separated from *Cassiope*	AGREE. *Calluna* differs from *Cassiope*	
Vaccinioideae			
Arbuteae	Reduced from subfamily	AGREE, though Arbuteae now a distinct, uniform tribe	
Enkiantheae			
Cassiopeae	Includes only *Cassiope* and *Harrimanella*	AGREE on separation of *Calluna*, but *Cassiope* and *Harrimanella* also differ	*Cassiope* and *Harrimanella* might be tribally distinct
Andromedeae			
Vacciniaeae			
Pyroloideae	Reduced from family	AGREE	
Monotropoideae	Reduced from family		Both seem closest to Vaccinioideae (having kaempferol, hydroquinone and methyl hydroquinone)
Wittsteinioideae	From Epacridaceae	No evidence available	

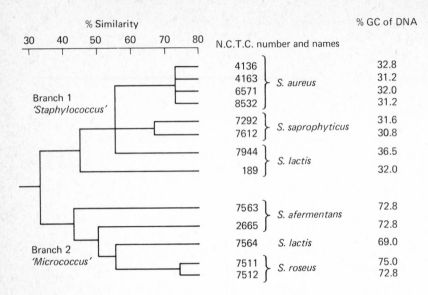

Fig. 14.9 Example of agreement between numerical taxonomy and DNA %GC. *Microccocus-Staphylococcus* group divided into two major groups by numerical taxonomy (see dendrogram with % similarity scale) was confirmed by large differences in DNA base compositions. (From Hill, L. R. in Gibbs, B. M. and Shapton, D. A. (Eds.), *Identification Methods for Microbiologists*, Part B, London, Academic Press, 1968.)

areas where the chemical data indicate a need for further consideration, in almost every place where Stevens recommended a taxonomic adjustment there is independent chemical evidence to support his view.

Clearly the provision of large amounts of diverse chemical evidence offers a powerful method for effecting improvements in classification, and for checking those which have already been suggested. Flavonoid chemistry may not be as useful in all families as it obviously is in the Ericaceae, but chemical facts of some sort can always be obtained quite economically. From Table 14.1 it is seen that no evidence from the phenolic constituents could be brought to bear on Stevens' proposed transfer of *Wittsteinia* to the Ericaceae from the Epacridaceae, because it contained only quercetin (found in all Ericaceae and Epacridaceae) and kaempferol (common in both families). Discontinuities in other chemical constituents, such as terpenoids or proteins, might be sought as evidence for or against this transfer. Parallel investigations of more than one kind of chemical variation (e.g.[385]) are often more than doubly rewarding.

In work on the relationships of tribes and genera of grasses, serological discontinuities matched well with independent evidence obtained from the study of carbohydrates.[442]

Chemical evidence at family and order levels

It is not always remembered that chemical data are useful in defining higher categories. It was mentioned in Chapter 7 that the distinctions between algal divisions, between algae and fungi and between plants and animals rest partly on chemical criteria. In the 'middle' categories of family and order, applications of chemical evidence to circumscription and rank attribution are perhaps less obvious than at either end of the hierarchy.

In recent years there has been an increasing tendency to base chemical studies on the framework of a particular family, for instance the Leguminosae, which is often regarded as an order.[210] Conferences have also followed the theme of particular families—for example the 1974 symposium of the Phytochemical Society on the Cruciferae. On the whole the studies therein reported have not covered the circumscription and rank of the taxon under discussion—these have usually been assumed. There have been numerous serological investigations of family boundaries and relationships, some of which are described in other chapters (e.g. Cornaceae/Nyssaceae;[157] Ranunculaceae;[254] Solanaceae[220]). Serotaxonomists have always investigated the affinities of the taxon under study in respect of what appear on other criteria to be its closest relatives, so gaining a taxonomic perspective. This admirable practice has been adopted by workers on flavonoid variation.[32,212]

Distributions of secondary plant products have provided interesting support for the delimitation of certain families (e.g. the solanaceous alkaloids; isoquinoline alkaloids, especially protopine (in the Papaveraceae); ranunculin in Ranunculaceae[414]).

It is at the level of the order that plant chemotaxonomy has made probably its best-known achievement: the delimitation of the Centrospermae (Caryophyllales) on chemical criteria. Many accounts of the facts have been given but it would be a serious omission not to present a short reference to the situation here.

The betalain pigments (betaxanthins and betacyanins—see Chapter 5) are chemically distinct from the widely distributed anthocyanin and anthoxanthin pigments,[314] and are found to be restricted to ten families of flowering plants, all of which are grouped together in the order Centrospermae (see Table 14.2). The Centrospermae, as classically conceived on morphological, anatomical and embryo features, include the large, important family

Table 14.2 Classification of betalain-containing families according to Hutchinson[243] and Cronquist[104]. (*indicates betalain families).

Hutchinson	Cronquist
Caryophyllales	Caryophyllales
Elatinaceae	*Phytolaccaceae (incl.
Molluginaceae	Agdestidaceae, Barbeiuaceae,
Caryophyllaceae	Petiveriaceae, Stegnospermaceae)
*Aizoaceae	*Nyctaginaceae
*Portulacaceae	*Didiereaceae
	*Cactaceae
Chenopodiales	*Aizoaceae
Barbeuiaceae	Molluginaceae
*Phytolaccaceae	Caryophyllaceae
Gyrostemonaceae	*Portulacaceae
Agdestidaceae	*Basellaceae
*Chenopodiaceae	*Amaranthaceae
*Amaranthaceae	
Cyanocrambaceae	Batales
Batidaceae	Bataceae (= Batidaceae)
*Basellaceae	
	Polygonales
Thymelaeales	Polygonaceae
*Nyctaginaceae	
	Plumbaginales
Pittosporales	Plumbaginaceae
*Stegnospermaceae	
Cactales	
*Cactaceae	
Sapindales	
*Didiereaceae	

Caryophyllaceae. It was discovered that this family, unlike all others in the order, lacked the betalain pigments, and possessed instead the more common anthocyanins and anthoxanthins. At once a clash between traditional and chemical evidence was inevitable in the delimitation of the order. One group of workers considered the betalain evidence so important that they cast out the Caryophyllaceae (incl. Illecebraceae), so weighting the betalain characters more heavily than the orthodox ones.[313] If the Caryophyllaceae are retained as members of the Centrospermae, neither traditional nor chemical evidence alone is sufficient to define the order.

Apart from the controversial position of the Caryophyllaceae, the classification of several other families has been reviewed in the light of the curious distributions of the betalain pigments. The

Cactaceae have for a long time been a puzzling group of plants, at least to taxonomists. On the one hand the vegetative and floral similarities which they display to *Mesembryanthemum* and other genera of Aizoaceae (in the Centrospermae) suggested to some that they should be classified there. On the other hand, these resemblances (tendencies to succulence, proliferation of floral parts, etc.) might have arisen by convergent evolution. Taxonomists who inclined to the second view have usually placed the Cactaceae in a monotypic order (Cactales or Opuntiales). Until the betalains were investigated there was little other evidence to settle the position of the Cactaceae. When the pigments of cacti were eventually analysed and found to be betalains, it was at last unequivocally demonstrated that the Cactaceae belong in the Centrospermae.

The Molluginaceae have usually been included in the Aizoaceae, but Hutchinson considered them to be a discrete family.[243] Betalain data support his attribution of family rank here, because while the Aizoaceae contain betalains, the Molluginaceae do not. Thus if betalains are to be a required character for membership of the Centrospermae, the Molluginaceae must be excluded.

The classificatory positions not only of families but of genera have been investigated with reference to the betalain distribution. *Geocarpon* is a monotypic genus of the south-central United States. *G. minimum* was placed in the Aizoaceae by its author, and has been generally accepted as a member of that family. After a review of the morphological evidence, Steyermark later transferred it to the Caryophyllaceae. Clearly the presence or absence of betalains in *Geocarpon* might settle the matter one way or the other. Bogle *et al.*[58] could detect only anthocyanin pigments in extracts from *Geocarpon minimum*. The complete absence of betalains supports Steyermark's view that *Geocarpon* is a member of Caryophyllaceae.

Other families of presumed affinity to the members of the Centrospermae, and sometimes included in that order, are the Plumbaginaceae, Polygonaceae and the Batidaceae. None of the species in these families which have so far been analysed for their pigments has proved to contain betalains. This does not mean, of course, that they may not be closely related to the Centrospermae, merely that they are perhaps better placed in a different order.

The value of betalain evidence rests heavily on the facts that despite diligent searches no plant of any but clear Centrospermous affinity has been shown to contain betalains, and that betalains and anthocyanins are mutually exclusive. A report that they might possibly co-occur in *Carpobrotus edulis* (Aizoaceae) has been convincingly discounted.[264]

The pigment pecularities of the Centrospermae have stimulated botanists to look for correlated evidence of their distinctness from other groups of plants, which might resolve the conflict between morphological and chemical circumscriptions of the order.

Kendrick and Hillman found that all three members of the Centrospermae which they investigated (*Amaranthus caudatus*, *Mirabilis jalapa* and *Spinacia oleracea*) lacked the phytochrome dark reversion process typical of other dicotyledons.[263] Dark reversion is absent also in monocotyledons. A further physiological indication of a surprising link between Centrospermae and monocotyledons is that members of the Amaranthaceae, Portulacaceae and Chenopodiaceae, almost alone among dicotyledons, resemble certain tropical grasses in having the C_4-dicarboxylic acid photosynthetic pathway.[215] Low carbon dioxide compensation points are a feature of C_4 plants: in the dicotyledons they occur only in the Centrospermae and the Geraniales.[105]

Such close connections with monocotyledons as may be suggested by these data are rather unlikely, though the Centrospermae include some quite primitive plants which may in some ways resemble the ancestral stock from which both dicotyledons and

Table 14.3   Modification of Cronquist's subclass III (Caryophyllidae) by Behnke and Turner.[37]

Subclass IIIa. Caryophyllidae (sieve-tube plastids with ring-shaped bundles of
              proteinaceous filaments).
  1. Caryophyllales (anthocyanins present; betalains absent)
        Caryophyllaceae
        Molluginaceae
  2. Chenopodiales (betalains present; anthocyanins absent)
        Phytolaccaceae
        Stegnospermaceae
        Nyctaginaceae
        Didiereaceae
        Cactaceae
        Aizoaceae
        Portulacaceae
        Basellaceae
        Chenopodiaceae
        Amaranthaceae
Subclass IIIb. Polygonidae (sieve-tube plastids with starch; betalains absent)
  1. Polygonales
  2. Plumbaginales
Subclass IIIc. Batidae (sieve-tube plastids with starch; betalains absent)
  1. Batales

---

monocotyledons arose. Meeuse proposed an origin of 'true Centrospermae' from the Bennettitales, using morphological evidence to support his views.[336]

Further information on the relative positions of Centrospermae and Caryophyllaceae, which lends support to the indications from traditional sources, has recently come from a totally independent source—Behnke's work on the ultrastructure of angiosperm sieve-tube plastids.[36] Most dicotyledons have feebly developed, starch-containing plastids in their sieve-tubes, but Behnke has detected variants of the plastids which contain proteinaceous inclusions of a form specific to particular taxa. Sieve-tube plastids of the Centrospermae, but also of the Caryophyllaceae and Molluginaceae, have protein filaments in ring-shaped bundles. These inclusions are absent from the sieve-tube plastids of Polygonaceae, Plumbaginaceae and Batidaceae. The sieve-tube data hence correlate completely with traditional diagnostic features of the Centrospermae, but less well with the betalain distribution. It is intriguing, but probably without significance to the Centrospermae controversy, that Behnke has detected another group of specific protein bodies in the sieve-tube plastids of certain monocotyledons.

Behnke and Turner[37] propose a modification of Cronquist's classification[104] which attempts to reconcile different lines of evidence bearing on the taxonomy of the Centrospermae and allied families (Table 14.3). In essence the old Centrospermae is replaced by two closely related orders—the Caryophyllales (without betalains) and the Chenopodiales (with betalains).

Chemical evidence in taximetrics

Numerical treatment of characters is obviously important as the number of features attributed to a plant increases with further study. Many of the new characters will in future come from chemotaxonomic research. Numerical methods in taxonomy ('taximetrics') are increasingly applied in attempts to reduce the subjectivity of taxonomic conclusions as far as possible.[446]

There is in principle no reason why a chemical feature, such as occurrence of a particular alkaloid or phenolic constituent, should not be incorporated in a taximetric analysis just as a morphological attribute would be. Chemical characters are already included as a routine in numerical classifications of bacteria, with great success (see Chapter 13). It is of course difficult to ensure that the chemical characters chosen are not polygenic and that they are unlinked, but these problems exist with the use of morphological properties too.

The only problems surround the conversion of chemical evidence into a form which can be used for computerized classification. Presence or absence of spots on a chromatogram, or bands in an electrophoretic pattern, are clearly directly usable as plus or minus characters, but many chemical data are of a greater complexity than this, making it difficult, for instance, to be certain that spots on two protein fingerprints are homologous. *Patterns* of spots or bands have been regarded as more significant, in many cases, than the presence or absence of individual chemical entities. Where macromolecules are being compared by short-cut techniques such as DNA hybridization, it is less easy to see how the data may be validly transformed into facts for the computer. GC ratios clearly relate to the DNA of one species and so may be used as raw numbers, but in DNA hybridization, and in serological work, the data obtained about a taxon are already in the form of a comparison with one or more other taxa.

Faced with the problem of utilizing patterns in numerical investigations, most workers have produced some kind of similarity coefficient giving an index of the resemblance between paired patterns, followed by a clustering technique. This approach was used in the work already described on *Juniperus* gas–liquid chromatogram patterns.[3] Dendrograms or charts of supposed similarities are produced. The technique resolved the chemical differences between the *Ambrosia* ragweed populations previously discussed.[336,385]

Some workers have criticized certain methods used to prepare chemical data for taximetric study.[95,415] Weimarck calls attention to the need to base correlation indices on pattern data obtained only from a wide sampling of the taxa.[495] He also mentions the possible swamping of one significant spot on a chromatogram by the mathematical equality necessarily assigned to the numerous biologically insignificant ones.

If pattern data come from analysis of appropriately sampled populations, and it is not obvious that some of the components of the pattern make more biological sense than others, or vary more than others, it is hard to see why pairwise comparisons of similarity should not be the basis for numerical interpretation of the data. Assumptions about the common biogenesis of the components of the patterns have to be made whatever means of analysis is employed. In the work on junipers and ragweeds numerical treatment of the data seems to have been very illuminating.

Nomenclature of chemical variants

At the levels of species and above, the chemical data which have been obtained have typically shown correlations with other data to a greater or lesser extent. The taxonomic changes which have been suggested by the discrepancies of traditional and chemotaxonomic evidence have been expressible in terms of the standard hierarchical classification. Often the discrepancies have not withstood the subsequent investigation which they have stimulated: thus *Bromus secalinus* var. *hirsutus* proved eventually to be morphologically and cytologically as well as chemically distinct[440]; morphological 'hybrids' of *Tsuga heterophylla* and *T. mertensiana* proved rarely to be chemically intermediate so requiring an alternative explanation of most of the morphological variation.[467] Chemical variants, in the sense of being remarkable for their chemical peculiarity alone, seem to occur only below the species level.

The question of nomenclature for chemical varieties and forms has inevitably arisen. Similar questions of nomenclature for otherwise unrecognizable genetic and cytological variants have been debated for generations.

Tétényi has proposed a formal system for the naming of infraspecific chemical variants.[468,469] There can be little doubt that in the case of medicinal plants there is a clear need for a system by which the chemical variation detected in a species may be described in a controlled fashion, with named categories for ease of reference. Controversy has surrounded proposals to extend such a system of categories into the general hierarchical system because of the difficulty and confusion which would accompany the enormous number of names necessary to accommodate all chemical variants. Where no morphological, cytological or other differences also characterize a chemical variant its formal naming is bound to be resisted.[72] Tétényi asserts that polychemism (biochemical variation) is known in over 600 species, making some formal recognition and nomenclature quite urgent.[468]

The basic difficulty is of assessing how biochemically anomalous an infraspecific variant must be, before a formal name is appropriate. In pharmacognosy, minor variants are no doubt of some importance. In general systematics, it seems sufficient to overlook most minor biochemical variation, or to incorporate it into the formal description of the named taxon to which it belongs (the 'taxonomic profile'[155]) and to give chemical variants the respectability and permanence afforded by a formal name only when they are striking or important. These have always been the reasons for wanting a name for something. Too many names may cloud the recognition of taxa, and serve no useful purpose: perhaps some lichen 'species' should have been regarded only as chemotypes. It should be mentioned that in the past when chemical features have been particularly obvious and have correlated with other characters, there has been no hesitation about indicating the fact in the name of the taxon concerned, e.g. *Iris foetidissima; Tripleurospermum maritimum* subsp. *inodorum; Rumex acetosa; Lactarius rufus.*

A further point is that, like some cytogenetic variants, it is impractical to name minor chemical taxa on the basis of characters which require extensive experimentation to verify the identification. Only rarely will such identifications be worth the time and effort to make them. At least the cytogenetic characters sometimes provide sufficient consequential phenetic variation to make it practical to do so.

CONCLUSION

It is asserted by some botanists that chemistry has so far had so small an impact upon plant systematics that it may be a waste of time for taxonomists to pursue it. Certainly there has been no revolutionary development following the taxonomic applications of chemistry, but it would have been naive to have expected one. Not even the combined activities of Darwin and Mendel caused a revolution in systematics, though for a time it was thought that they should, and therefore that they had. Taxonomy itself, the practice of classification, is perhaps best regarded as a continuous revolution.

Probably the examples cited above reflect the true, increasing contribution which chemotaxonomy has to offer—new facts and new correlations leading to taxonomic reappraisals which may be quite considerable, as well as to a better understanding of adaptation. It is simply untrue to say that chemistry has had little impact on plant classification—its impact has been increasing for two centuries at least. Whatever supposedly new lines of evidence materialize in future, the broad outlines and many of the details of plant systematics have been established after long, skilful scrutiny of so many different characters that it is statistically unlikely that major errors have been overlooked.

15

Macromolecules and Phylogeny

Chemical variation in plant taxa has been investigated not only for purely classificatory (i.e. taxonomic) purposes, but also to gain evidence relating to the phylogeny of different plant groups. All kinds of chemical characters have been employed to support ideas on the relationships of plants, usually with the implication that the relationships are phylogenetic, arising from common ancestry of the plants compared. A phylogeny is the evolutionary history of a taxon.

Botanists have sought diligently for evidence about the course of plant evolution ever since Darwin's publications in the middle of the nineteenth century. The chief source of data about the phylogeny of plants, now as then, is the record provided by fossil-bearing rocks of known age and sequence of deposition. Not only do the plant fossils demonstrate the fact of evolutionary change, but they show additionally the antiquity of particular levels of plant organization. The statement of the phylogeny of a plant or plant group should ideally incorporate the complete sequence of evolutionary changes which link the taxon with its immediate ancestor and then those which link these ancestors back through time to the plants, now extinct, which if they existed today would not be referred to the same taxon as their modern descendant. Thus in Fig. 15.1, the phylogeny of genus B includes four stages intermediate between genus B and the nearest ancestral genus Y. Stages B_2 to B_5 may represent species of B or species of Y, or of intermediate genera, depending on taxonomic opinion and the amount of knowledge available about the variation characterizing the four stages, B and Y. Fewer stages connect C and

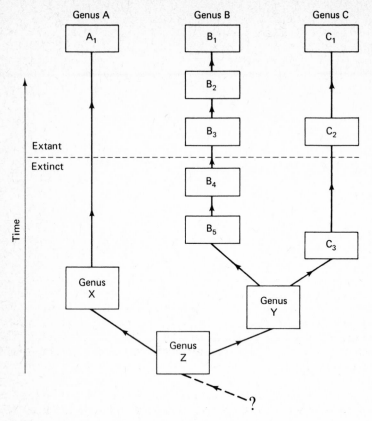

Fig. 15.1 Phylogeny of genera A, B, and C. See text for explanation.

Y, while genus A is unconnected by known intermediates with its ancestor X. Genera X and Y have a common ancestor in genus Z, though clearly they may have arisen from different species of Z. The complete phylogeny of A, B and C, if stated in full, should include all intermediate stages between Z and the ancestors of Z, back through time until all plants which exist or which have existed are connected by a common ancestor. If life arose only once on earth all organisms must have an ultimate common ancestor, presumably in what W. S. Gilbert described as a protoplasmal, primordial globule!

It is unlikely in the extreme that so complete a statement of phylogeny will ever be made for any taxon of extant or extinct plants. The information is simply not available. Intermediate stages between most modern taxa and their extinct ancestors are usually quite unknown; in fact the extinct ancestors themselves are undiscovered. Fossilization, the process by which organisms are preserved after death in something like the form which they had when living, is a complex and very rare event. Most dead organisms, especially those with soft tissues, decay rapidly, or are eaten by scavengers. Only a tiny proportion of the biota of past times is preserved in fossil form, and often this proportion is ecologically biased towards those groups which inhabited places where favourable fossilizing conditions are likely to occur, i.e. the margins of lakes or rivers, or marshes. Of the fossil-bearing rock, only a small proportion is exposed naturally or artificially for our scrutiny.

Phylogenetic study therefore rests heavily on the interpretation of the comparative phenetics of living plants, traditionally on comparative morphology and comparative anatomy. Primitive and advanced features have been determined by reference to whatever sparse fossil floras are obtainable, and by various assumptions. Among these assumptions or principles is included the idea that those plants are advanced which during their development pass through stages resembling the mature form or physiology of other plants. The other plants are, by definition, more primitive. This is essentially a statement that ontogeny may repeat phylogeny. Primitive features *tend* to be simpler than advanced ones but mere complexity is not an absolute guide to advancement because many plants become specialized by reduction of complexity. *Lemna*, though simple in structure, is highly advanced by reduction. Constancy, for instance of floral parts, is usually an indication of advancement, whereas inconstancy of the form or number of homologous parts usually betrays primitiveness.

Primitive organisms may co-exist with more advanced ones of the same line of descent for indefinite periods. Plants may be primitive in some of their features, but highly advanced in some others. Reproductive morphology and behaviour is commonly more primitive than vegetative structure and behaviour in the same plant group. Characters which show little advancement while others appear to undergo relatively rapid evolutionary change are said to be **conservative**. The definition of what is meant by a primitive group therefore becomes partly a matter of time and partly a matter of how far the group has diverged from its ancestor (see Fig. 15.2). Engler[147] supposed that if a group possessed many advanced, specialized features (e.g. the catkin-bearing trees) they must have had a long, isolated evolutionary development, and hence be

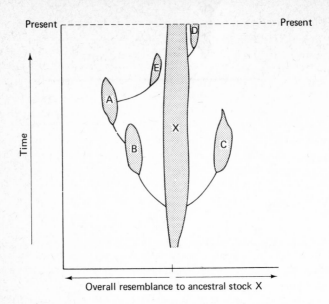

Fig. 15.2 Primitiveness and advancement. Primitive groups are those least modified from their ancestral stock. A is more advanced than B, but neither is necessarily more advanced than C. Though advanced, E shows convergent evolution with X, which might not be detected. Though of recent origin, D is comparatively primitive.

primitive in time of origin. If extrapolated logically this means that groups showing advanced characters must be regarded as primitive, a paradox which is an unacceptable *reductio ad absurdum*. It would mean, for example, that a newly evolved family of blue-green algae must be regarded as more advanced than the Compositae. Cronquist emphasized that groups which most resemble the ancestral prototype must be described as primitive, regardless of their time of origin.[104] Clearly a successful primitive group may persist alongside some of its more advanced descendants, and subsequently give rise to a discrete taxon, of essentially the same level of primitiveness, long after some of the more advanced descendants have become extinct (see Fig. 15.2). The situation is complicated for the student of comparative phenetics because evolutionary convergence, instead of divergence, may occur from time to time. Primitiveness of organisms or features, whether determined from incontrovertible fossil evidence, or by the application of principles of comparative phenetics to living taxa, can be defined on a time basis only when the organisms or features existed before more advanced organisms or features *in the same line of descent.*

Obviously a good deal of intuitive judgement is involved in statements of phylogeny, which can almost all be regarded as speculative to a high degree. There is incomplete agreement between different workers on even the broad principles to be adopted.

Many botanists decry such speculations as unscientific, which many of them are, and point to the fact that, even as hypotheses, they are unusually unproductive and difficult to test by experiments. Such fundamentalists often assert also that the past is, in any case, unknowable, and perhaps best forgotten. Yet the attraction of the subject is so great that the phylogenies, whether expressed as stammbaums, charts of evolutionary history, or phyletic trees, continue to appear. Men have fortunately always reached out from what is possible to what is seemingly impossible or difficult. Chemists as well as biologists have now been attracted to the study of phylogeny, because certain chemical data suggest new ideas and perhaps more objective approaches to the problems. It is quite understandable that the non-biologists have sometimes confused phylogenetic research with taxonomy, the practice of classification. It is interesting and encouraging that they have found plant phylogenetics—the most academic of plant sciences— so attractive. Everyone seems to find evolution a compelling idea,[161,206,480] and there is now a *Journal of Molecular Evolution.*

Before chemical evidence can be applied in phylogenetic research, it must be plainly understood what kind of information is needed to arrive at the statement of the phylogeny of a given group.

PHYLOGENETIC TERMS AND DIMENSIONS

In the angiosperms the fossil record is tantalizingly selective and incomplete. Many plants have soft tissues which fossilize badly, but even those with hard stems or fruits are not well known from fossil remains. Most of the links between angiosperms and their ancestors are missing.[219] Darwin described the origin of angiosperms as 'an abominable mystery' and it remains one to this day. Angiospermous plants appear in quantity as fossils in the Cretaceous period, but so many modern groups can be recognized among them that they must have originated a long time before then. The abominable mystery encompasses also the problem of how the numerous, diverse groups of flowering plants are phylogenetically related to each other. Every taxonomist has ideas about the likely course of past angiosperm evolution. The phylogeny of minor categories such as species and subspecies is sometimes not in dispute, since individuals which are classifiable into particular species and varieties can sometimes be synthesized from other taxa by artificial hybridization and amphidiploidy. In a few cases this extends to genera, e.g. in the grass tribe Triticeae. At family and order level, phylogenetic statements become highly speculative and are sources of fascinating, but often unproductive, controversy.

As we consider evolution further and further back in time, the gaps in our knowledge or suspicion of phylogeny increase in size. Our knowledge or reasonable suspicions of phylogeny often has the structure shown in Fig. 15.1, ending above the genus or family, and before the Cretaceous, with a question mark.

Figure 15.3 relates the two dimensions which phylogeneticists consider; (a) taxonomic differences between living organisms and (b) time. It may be that a few fossils are known, which have been reliably classified into a position in the system of modern plants. These fossils may perhaps have been accurately assigned to a particular geological period and assigned an age based on radiologi-

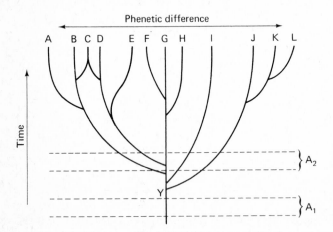

Fig. 15.3 All taxa A–L are *patristically* related, having a common ancestor Y. They show different degrees of *cladistic* relationship. Depending on the taxonomic status assigned to populations at times A_1 and A_2, genus A–L is *monophyletic* or *polyphyletic*. See text for details. (Modified from Davis and Heywood, after Heslop-Harrison, J. (1958), *Phytomorphology*, **8**, 177–184.)

cal (e.g. potassium–argon) dating. Apart from such facts, all other indications of the branching points and branch lengths in a phylogenetic 'tree' must be obtained by extrapolation, assumption and more or less inspired guesswork from the positions assigned by taxonomists to the extant *tips* of the branching network. Taxonomists are of course not infallible. Figure 15.3 shows two kinds of phylogenetic relationship which are recognized. All the taxa A–L are **patristically** related, i.e. have a common ancestry. But they show different degrees of **cladistic** relationship. Cladistic affinity refers to the closeness of the phylogenetic relationship between two taxa, and is represented by the lengths and numbers of the branches by which the two taxa are separated in the diagram. Thus F and G are cladistically more closely related than are F and H.

Two further relevant terms are **monophyly** and **polyphyly**. Though not all definitions agree, both terms are valuable. In Fig. 15.3, taxon A–L is monophyletic if during times A_1 or A_2 the ancestral plants would be regarded as belonging to one taxon of the same or lower rank than taxon A–L. Taxon A–L is polyphyletic if during times A_1 or A_2 the ancestral plants would be regarded as belonging to two or more taxa of at least equal rank to taxon A–L. An example may be the algae. If eukaryotic algae are regarded as a taxon, almost certainly it is polyphyletic since it contains descendants of some blue-green algae and some fungi. A full discussion of monophyly and polyphyly is given by Davis and Heywood[118] and by Simpson.[437]

A fundamental difficulty in the use of phenetic (e.g. morphological) resemblances for determining cladistic relationship arises from the occasional occurrence of convergent evolution. Two taxa of low cladistic affinity, for example E and F in Fig. 15.3, may come to resemble each other closely owing to similar reactions to similar selection pressures. Some succulent plants in unrelated families (e.g. Cactaceae and Euphorbiaceae) look alike for this reason. Often the convergence is by no means so obvious, and may go undetected. The best criterion for determining cladistic relationships is therefore the one which is most free from possible complications caused by evolutionary convergence.

The usual way of minimizing errors in classification due to suspected or possible convergent evolution is to multiply the number of attributes chosen for comparison—that is to make the classification as natural as possible (see Chapters 1 and 14). The argument is that no two taxa will be convergent in all their features. Though their floral morphology may appear almost the same, their anatomy, or their indumentum or their alkaloids should be different. The enormous number of attributes and attribute-states which this approach requires eventually needs a computer analysis of similarities and differences. Such analyses can generate similarity dendrograms like that in Fig. 14.7 (Chapter 14). Superficially these look a little like phylogenetic trees, but it must be remembered that they are based solely on phenetic similarity, and have no time dimension. The hope would be that if sufficient characters are included in the similarity assessment, all errors due to convergent evolution may be avoided. The dendrogram should then indicate the form of a phylogenetic tree, *assuming* that similarities arise from community of descent, and *assuming* also that phenetic dissimilarity of taxa is proportional to the time since they diverged from their common ancestor. Both assumptions may be unjustified.

Another point which should be considered is the rank of ancestral taxa. Presumably when the first plants of a modern species, genus or family appeared originally, they were usually not so radically or consistently different from their own immediately ancestral taxon. Genera become defined by the isolation and divergence of their first few, possibly highly polymorphic, species, just as species are first represented by their first variety and families by their first genus. The discontinuity which separates a taxon at its first appearance is smaller than that which characterizes it subsequently. We assign rank to taxa of fossil plants with the benefit of a clouded hindsight. 'New genera' perhaps exchange genes freely with their ancestors and sibling 'new genera' for some time. Therefore the branching points on the phylogenetic tree drawn for any taxon or taxa have a spurious neatness and clarity. In reality the branching points may be a maze of complex anastomoses not unlike a modern hybridizing complex: they are not junctions but marshalling yards.

Even after two genera have been defined by a period of divergent evolution it is quite possible that one or more of their species may hybridize, forming a new intergeneric hybrid line, and later perhaps a polyploid complex (see C in Fig. 15.3). Hybrid genera are well known in the angiosperms, e.g. × *Raphanobrassica*, × *Festulolium* and × *Ammocalamagrostis*. In phylogenetic terms similar hybrid genera may in the past have evolved into hybrid families, which may not be recognized as such by taxonomists. Perhaps all the families of the Bicarpellatae (Scrophulariaceae, Solanaceae, Labiatae, etc.) arose from a segregating hybrid swarm as long ago as the Triassic. Perhaps the betalain families of the Centrospermae all arose long ago from an aggressively successful mutant with a genetic deficiency for anthocyanin production. Was it a mutant of a long since extinct, anthocyanin-containing member of what has become the protean family Phytolaccaceae? Perhaps it may have been. Phylogenetic possibilities are enormous and intriguing, the evidence either way usually inconclusive, and the temptation to speculate therefore quite irresistible. Chemists, chemotaxonomists and comparative morphologists alike have accordingly been encouraged to apply their own data to the obscurity of plant evolutionary history. Several phylogenetic trees or schemes based on chemical evidence have been described in earlier chapters.

CHEMICAL EVIDENCE OF PHYLOGENETIC RELATIONSHIPS

Two questions which should be asked of chemical approaches to the determination of phylogenies can be summarized with reference to Fig. 15.3: firstly do the data employed lead to substantially the same classification as that arrived at by consideration of other data, and secondly, do they provide a means of determining cladistic relationship in terms of branch lengths and/or the position of branching points? If they do not satisfy both these requirements they are not essentially superior to any other branch of comparative phenetics in suggesting reasonable schemes of phylogeny.

Consideration of supposed primitive and advanced states of metabolism of phenolic compounds[203] or of lipids[361] or of other molecules does little more than provide supplementary evidence for schemes of phylogenetic relationship originally proposed on the basis of supposed primitiveness and advancement in morphology or anatomy. The supplementation or contradiction which the chemical facts offer may be valuable and suggestive, but it is no more conclusive. Hütter and DeMoss rearranged Gäumann's system of fungi (see Fig. 15.4) in the light of chemical evidence from the patterns of enzymes involved in tryptophan biosynthesis,[244] and Bartnicki-Garcia has added further data.[25] There is support for and valuable extension of Gäumann's scheme, for instance in the indication of additional branching points. But the lengths of the branches and the position of the branching points are still vague. If chemical data are to provide real *advances* in phylogenetic study they must do so by ensuring that the phylogenetic trees are as far as possible architecturally accurate and are in all places drawn to the same scale.

Since the nature of the genetic material and the genetic code have been discovered, the taxonomic value of molecular structures which comprise some reflection of the genetic information (semantides) has been increasingly recognized (see Chapters 10, 11, 12). Their

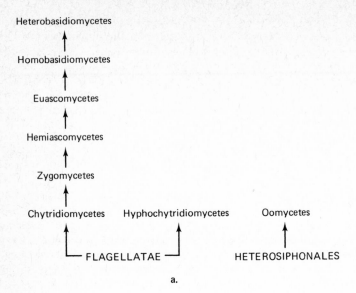

a.

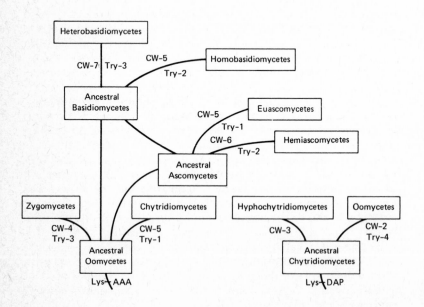

b.

relevance to phylogenetic research has been seen equally clearly. In contrast to small molecules such as amino acids or alkaloids, the mere structures of certain macro-molecules incorporate recognizable translations of parts of the genetic code. Though sometimes large, carbohydrate, phenolic or terpenoid polymers have a repetitive structure which is connected to the properties of synthesizing enzymes, and they do not contain sequences of structures which reflect the lineal genetic information. Macromolecules of particular interest to students of phylogeny are the nucleic acids (DNA and RNA), which are respectively primary semantides and secondary semantides and the proteins (tertiary semantides).[514]

Taxonomic studies of nucleic acids, which have been reviewed in Chapters 12 and 13, rest largely on the short-cut techniques of polynucleotide hybridization and determination of the GC ratio. Only by rather time-consuming methods can the actual sequence of nucleotides, which constitutes the genetic code, be completely and unambiguously elucidated. Phylogenetic speculations based on the evidence of GC ratio and DNA hybridization are often published (see Chapter 12) but they have little intrinsic merit beyond that which also characterizes schemes of evolutionary relationship founded upon comparative morphology.

Proteins seem to be a more promising source of data relating to phylogeny than the other semantides, because the *sequences* of amino acids can be determined with only moderate labour (see Chapter 10). There is also a range of accessory, short-cut techniques which provide contributory, if not conclusive, evidence of the amino acid sequence. Of these the fingerprint and serological methods appear to have most potential. Fingerprint analysis rests on the assumption that the amino acids of the homologous protein from two related species will be in almost the same sequence. Chromatographic and electrophoretic patterns of the peptides released by digestion of selected peptide bonds may therefore indicate sequence similarities to a degree. Serological resemblance indicates the presence of the same or similar determinant groups on the surfaces of the proteins compared. Antigenic determinants are a feature of the tertiary

Fig. 15.4 Modification and extension of a phylogenetic arrangement following the incorporation of chemical data. (a) A representation of the evolutionary arrangement of fungi according to Gäumann, E. A. (1964), *Die Pilze*. Birkhauser, Berlin. (b) Modified scheme after inclusion of chemical data on pathways of lysine synthesis (Lys–AAA/Lys–DAP) from Vogel,[493] density differences of tryptophan synthesizing enzymes (Try–1,2,3,4) from Hütter and DeMoss;[244] and cell-wall polysaccharides (CW–2,3,4,5,6,7) from Bartnicki-Garcia.[25] (After Bartnicki-Garcia.[25])

structure of the protein, which is an important functional attribute of the molecule. Natural selection acts on whatever is the functional property of the protein, usually residing in the tertiary structure, which thereby imposes a conservatism on the amino acid sequence, and at the same time is a manifestation of it. Prager and Wilson calculated an 'immunological distance' (y) between different lysozymes which was always about five times as great as the percentage difference (x) between the known amino acid sequences of the same proteins, i.e. $y \simeq 5x$.[386] If this relationship is more or less constant, serological data can be used as a guide to sequence resemblances more precisely than has previously been thought possible. The equation has been applied also to alkaline phosphatase variations in the Enterobacteriaceae.[94] The findings from immunology agreed fairly well with results from similar work on other enzymes, with fingerprint analyses and with data from DNA hybridization.

It seems that macromolecules, especially proteins, can be made to yield facts which are not just of phenetic significance but which may be of value in phylogenetic studies. Their value to the latter rests on the fact that they mirror the genotype to a greater extent than most phenetic characters. The genotype is the medium of inheritance linking modern organisms with their ancestors and is an obvious source of facts relating to phylogeny. Because of its conservatism and complexity the genotype is the property of the organism least susceptible to direct environmental modification, and convergent evolution.

The interesting and valid results on Enterobacteriaceae[94] raise a problem about the phylogenetic significance of macromolecular correlations. Taxonomists have recognized for a long time that they should look for correlations among phenetic characters. Almost intuitively they have normally valued only those characters which are *independently* correlated. For example if the stem of a plant specimen is unusually thick, and its leaves unusually large, the automatic reaction, initially at least, is to consider that all such size peculiarities arise from one cause, whether it be a mutant allele or particularly rich soil. The different size features might all be recorded together under a note such as 'plant robust'. Though these different size characters correlate, they are probably not independent. Some characters are clearly *dependent* or *necessary correlates*, such as the diameter of a cylindrical stem and its circumference.

Necessarily correlated characters must be carefully watched for in assessments of variation which are to be used in phylogenetic conclusions, perhaps especially where the assessor is not a practising taxonomist with a cynical eye. In macromolecular work, care must be taken not to overvalue correlations of protein data with nucleic acid data or other biochemical data where the same portion of genotype is being compared again and again. The presence of a particular alkaloid, of the enzyme which synthesizes it, of the RNA which codes for the enzyme and of the DNA sequence which codes for the RNA are all manifestations of the same property: all are necessary correlates. In phylogenetic assessments, just as in taxonomy, the different lines of evidence must be seen to be different.

SEQUENCE ANALYSIS OF PROTEINS IN PHYLOGENETIC RESEARCH

The recognition that amino acid sequences might provide useful insights into phylogeny was followed by rapid progress in the study of animal evolution.[119] Partly this was due to the availability of a good fossil record, particularly of vertebrates, with which the results of the molecular approach could be compared. Using relatively small proteins which could be easily purified, zoologists managed to construct phylogenetic trees by various methods,[158] which agreed very well with phylogenetic conclusions based on the comparative phenetics of living organisms and with the fossil data.

In plants, where the fossil record is poor, and the desire for more information accordingly stronger, the application of protein sequence analyses to phylogenetic study has been very recent. There have been difficulties with extracting sufficient quantities of plant proteins for purification. Most of the work on angiosperms has come from Boulter's laboratory[62] and it is mainly this work which is used here to indicate the possibilities and limitations of the method.

Much of the study has involved comparisons of the amino acid sequences of the various cytochromes c. Cytochromes c are complicated, widespread proteins consisting of just over 100 amino acid residues. They are conservative, characteristic proteins showing substantial similarities in a wide range of animals, plants, fungi and bacteria. They are unlikely to have evolved convergently. Cytochromes c have been completely analysed for comparatively few plants, most of them angiosperms, and so the information available is less than adequate. The labour involved in sequencing, and the need to process large quantities of plant material to yield sufficient pure protein for analysis, have undoubtedly delayed the application of the technique. Boulter and his colleagues successfully used automatic sequencing methods, and developed a technique which employs only micro-quantities of the pure protein.[471] The way is now open for a wider adoption of the protein sequencing approach by botanists.

Construction of phylogenetic trees

When the sequences of a number of cytochromes c have been determined they are carefully aligned so that homologous amino acid positions can be compared. If the sequences are of equal length, or if there is some feature along it which confers an unmistakable morphology on the sequence (such as a prosthetic group), the alignment is not difficult. Where deletions or additons of residues have occurred, the molecules may have to be matched up by a computer technique which maximizes the similarity of the two aligned sequences[418] or by X-ray crystallography.[129] Clearly there must be a possibility that, in the alignment process, human error may not altogether be avoided.

The aligned sequences are then subjected to pair-wise comparison of the supposedly homologous amino acid positions, to obtain the number of amino acid differences between each pair of cytochromes. Amino acid differences are then transformed into **minimal mutational distances** between two cytochromes. This is the smallest number of nucleotide substitutions necessary to change the code for one protein into the code for the other. Several possible codons exist for some amino acids and therefore the actual number of nucleotide changes which may have taken place cannot be determined. The minimal mutational distance is based on the smallest number of mutations which are necessary to effect the observed divergence of the compared sequences. This is the only reasonable procedure to adopt, but it means that assumptions, for instance about the frequency of back-mutations, are being made. Occam's razor is sharp and useful, but also dangerous.

When the minimal mutational distances have been determined between all possible pairs of sequences, a phylogenetic tree can be constructed from the data.

Crowson has used a traditional approach to tree construction, classifying the sequences by weighted qualitative characters.[107] Not all possible pairs can be compared by this method, and most workers, including those of Boulter's school, have employed computer procedures to construct the phylogenetic trees.

One computer method is the 'flexible numerical' matrix procedure.[289] Single amino acid sequences are assigned to subsets, which are then combined by selecting from all possible pairs the grouping of protein subsets which gives the lowest average mutational distance between them. When a sequence is incorporated into a group, only the group is considered in further grouping procedures. Many combinations are therefore not examined, and much expensive computer time is saved. The eventual tree represents the order in which the subsets have been joined. A selection of such trees is produced by combining alternative pairs of subsets, and the tree chosen as the best phylogenetic scheme is the one where the distances along its branches agree most closely with the mutational distances originally determined. Figure 15.5 shows a tree constructed by this method, using sequences of cytochromes c from fifteen plant species.

Characteristics of the 'flexible-numerical' method are that it assumes evolution to have occurred by the minimum number of amino acid substitutions, and that the tree finally adopted is the one which is characterized by that minimum number. Not all the possible trees are tested. A further assumption is of a constant rate of evolution of all the taxa represented by their cytochrome c sequences.

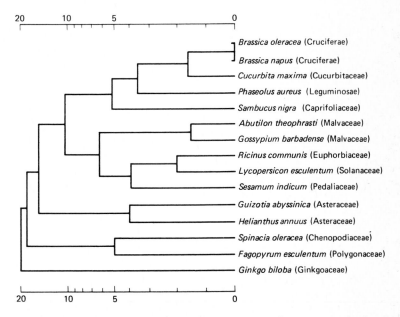

Fig. 15.5 A phylogenetic tree relating fifteen plant species constructed using the 'flexible numerical' method. (After Boulter et al.[65])

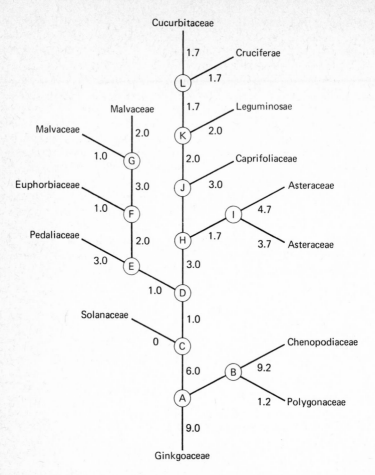

Fig. 15.6   A phylogenetic tree relating species of 12 families, using the 'ancestral sequence' method. Species as in Fig. 15.5. (After Boulter et al.[65])

Boulter's school favour an alternative computer approach to tree construction. It is an 'ancestral sequence' method based on the scheme of Dayhoff and Eck.[121] Figure 15.6 shows a tree constructed in this way, from the same data as Fig. 15.5.

All species are related by the ancestral sequence method: the tree has branches with junctions called **nodes**. Each node has three branches leading either to other nodes or to particular amino acid sequences. The most probable ancestral sequence at each node (a hypothetical sequence) is determined from all the amino acid sequences, starting with any three sequences, and adding the others in all possible positions. When a new sequence has been added on to the existing tree, the most likely ancestral sequence at each node is determined for each of the nodes from the sequences which they join.[65] Like the flexible-numerical system, it assumes that cytochrome c evolution has involved the minimal number of nucleotide substitutions and does not take account of unknown back mutations.

When a sequence has been attached to a point on the tree its position does not change. Though this limits the amount of computation, it means that no account is taken of sequences which may be added to the tree later. To minimize errors arising from this property of the method, a final procedure was to relocate systematically all branches of the final tree into all possible alternative positions, so generating numerous trees for evaluation.

Trees are completed when all the ancestral sequences at the nodes have been calculated and all the sequences determined by experiment have been incorporated. Trees are then evaluated by counting the amino acid differences between adjacent sequences and totalling these for the whole tree. The 'best' tree is the one with the smallest total of differences, i.e. which shows minimal mutational differences, or maximum evolutionary parsimony. Though not all possible trees are tested, the vast amount of computer time which would be necessary to achieve this suggests that the economy is justifiable. Of the 8×10^{12} trees which might be constructed from fifteen sequences of cytochrome c, Boulter et al.[65] considered 10^3.

A great advantage of the ancestral sequence method is that evolutionary rates are not assumed to be constant. Evolutionary rates certainly vary a good deal over short periods, as is shown by the fossil record. Where rates differ, two taxa are likely to be more closely related to their own common ancestor, perhaps accurately represented by the hypothetical ancestral sequence, than to anything else. By chance it is possible that a taxon might evolve so rapidly that it would distort the apparent ancestral sequence, and cause an error in the tree. Only multiplying the number of available sequences can reduce that possibility. In any case there is no reason to suppose that highly conservative proteins such as cytochrome c do not have a rather constant rate of evolution.

A problem with the ancestral sequence method is that it requires some indication of which way up the tree should be placed, i.e. of which sequence is at the earliest point of time. In the work of Boulter's group the inclusion of *Ginkgo* among the other, angiosperm, sequences determines the base of the tree quite convincingly.[65] Fossil records show convincingly that gymnosperms existed before angiosperms.

Conclusions from phylogenetic trees

There are few firm conclusions which can be drawn from the two 'best trees' produced by Boulter's group, because of the small number of sequences available. A sample of 20 or 30 sequences out of more than half a million plant species is simply not adequate. Nevertheless the conclusions which can be drawn are interesting and encouraging.

Firstly the two very different methods of tree-construction give substantially the same results, suggesting that the scheme reflects something with biological meaning, and not, as might otherwise have been feared, a few quirks of mathematics.

Secondly, it is reassuring that plants which are classified close together on orthodox taxonomic criteria, for example spinach and buckwheat (aff. Centrospermae) or cauliflower and rape (Cruciferae), appear close together in the final tree. Of the plants included in the investigation, *Fagopyrum* and *Spinacia* seem to have diverged from the common stock at the earliest period shown for angiosperms. Both have been associated in or near the Centrospermae, which has been regarded by some botanists as an ancient group (see Chapter 14). Boulter *et al.* consider that their ancestral sequence tree (Fig. 15.6) indicates the persistence of a 'basic flowering plant stock' from which various groups have diverged at different times.[65] These groups either remained at a relatively primitive level (such as cauliflower and rape) or became advanced (e.g. sunflower—Compositae). In their view, as in that of most plant evolutionists, time of origin has little to do with advancement of primitiveness, in a particular group.

With respect to the chemical properties of the tree, it is noteworthy that the 68 amino acid changes which it represents can be accomplished by only 80 nucleotide changes. Few of the mutations need therefore require more than one base change. Most known mutations have proved to be single base changes[102] suggesting that the assumption of minimal evolutionary routes may be well-founded in general. The possibility of 'local errors' in the tree still remains.

To what extent does this method of assessing phylogenetic relationships satisfy the two requirements previously described?

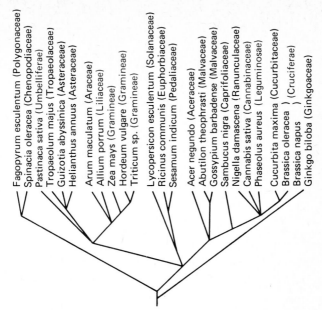

Fig. 15.7 A phylogenetic tree based on cytochrome *c* sequences of 25 species, constructed by the ancestral sequence method. (From Boulter.[63])

So far as the data go, which is admitted by Boulter to be not very far, they do not conflict with the orthodox *classification* of plants. In determination of the branching points of phylogeny, the ancestral sequence method seems rather powerful, although the times when the branches began are not indicated. The lengths of the branches and the 'internodes' are readily indicated by the number of amino acid differences or the minimal mutational distances between successive sequences. Figure 15.7 is of an ancestral sequence tree of 25 species, with the branches drawn to scale in a vertical direction, and with a group of monocotyledons included.[63] If it is assumed again that *Ginkgo* was the earliest taxon to evolve, the monocotyledons seem to have diverged from a dicotyledonous stock at about the same time as the Compositae. It would be interesting to know where the cytochrome *c* sequence of a primitive monocotyledon or dicotyledon would fit on to this tree.

Further indications of the age to be assigned to branching points might come from the inclusion of sequences of other gymnosperms and primitive angiosperms such as those in the Magnoliales. Even a few pteridophytes might show something. The fossil evidence does not, after all, rule out the possibility that some angiosperms existed before *Ginkgo biloba*.

There is, however, another way in which it may be possible to determine the times of origin of groups of organisms from amino acid sequence data. In animal studies, the time of divergence of several groups can be estimated with accuracy from the fossil record. When the amino acid sequences are known, one can derive the average time for an amino acid difference to become fixed on two lines of descent from the dated point. This time is called the 'unit evolutionary period'. Multiplying it by the average number of amino acid differences between two taxa gives a measure of the time since they diverged from a common ancestor. By the application of probability theory, this estimate can be corrected to some extent for back and parallel mutations. It is found that different proteins have different unit evolutionary periods, i.e. different rates of mutation fixation (= evolution). Fitch and Markowitz suggest that, at a given time, only certain parts of a protein can undergo change, i.e. fix mutations, and that the other part at that given time is more or less constant, perhaps because of functional restrictions.[159] The variable part of the sequence, which may not always be the same part, is called the 'concomitantly variable' fraction. Fitch and Markowitz showed that the rates of mutation fixation for the concomitantly variable fraction of cytochrome *c* and fibrinopeptide A were the same, although the evolutionary rates for the whole molecules are different. If mutation fixation rates are indeed uniform, at least in some parts of the molecule, a single accurately dated fossil might serve as the basis for determining times of origin for many other taxa.

Times of origin of plant groups have been estimated by reference to animal fossils and cytochrome *c* data.[391] The angiosperms were shown to pre-date the Cretaceous period considerably, as would have been expected from the advanced nature of the earliest undoubted angiosperm fossils, which caused early palaeobotanists to dub the Cretaceous period as the 'Age of Angiosperms'.

The relevance of sequence analyses

Further work on the amino acid sequences of homologous proteins will perhaps fulfil the promise of these early results. The possibility of comparing a wider range of proteins should be followed up in future. Less conservative, i.e. faster evolving, proteins than cytochrome *c* show larger differences between closely related taxa, which are characterized by very similar or even identical sequences in their cytochrome c. They might resolve the finer detail of phylogeny, at least of recently evolved taxa. Preliminary findings from plastocyanin sequences tend to support the phylogenetic arrangement constructed from the cytochrome c data.[63] A phylogenetic tree based on ferredoxin sequences agreed with expectations from comparative phenetics, but only five green plants were incorporated.[83]

The assumptions made about minimal routes of evolution, in the construction of phylogenetic trees, can be tested only by further research. Many more taxa must be included, and a wider range of their proteins must be sampled. A 'one-fossil' time estimation and a 'one-protein' phylogenetic tree are attractive because of the elegance and economy of the method, but it must be remembered that phylogenies, no less than classifications, will always be suspect if they are postulated on the diversity of only one or very few characters.

The assumption that convergent evolution does not seriously distort the indications of cladistic relationship arrived at from protein sequence data is probably justified in most cases. For only a few non-homologous proteins has there been any suggestion that convergent evolution may explain similarities revealed by sequencing.[433] The complexity of proteins rules out convergent evolution as a likely general explanation for similarities. If more kinds of protein are compared side by side, the extent of any convergence should become obvious. It will be some time before extensive sequence data are available for a diversity of plant proteins, but there is sufficient agreement between the putative vertebrate phylogenies constructed from sequences of cytochrome c, haemoglobin and other animal proteins to suggest that convergent evolution is not a major source of error.[120]

It would, of course, be very easy to produce an accurate phylogenetic tree from sequence data if protein differences arose simply by an accumulation of mutations dependent on time alone. Protein differences would then be strictly proportional to time, and would indicate phylogenies, branching points and branch lengths, and the times of divergence most conveniently. Faith that this situation might exist undoubtedly acted as a spur to the application of sequence data in phylogenetic investigation. It does not exist because natural selection acts upon protein structure quite as remorselessly as on any other character which may affect the efficiency of the individual in the population (see Chapter 10). In fact protein variations are just a matter of elapsed time only if it is possible to rule out selection pressures of different directions and

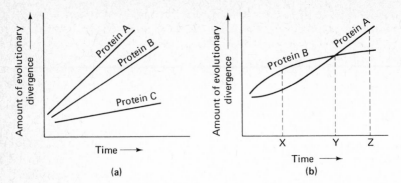

Fig. 15.8 Evolutionary rates of proteins in a hypothetical genus T (see text for details). Proteins assumed to be alike in all species originally. (**a**) Constant rate of evolutionary divergence (change from original state with time) occurs in each protein. C is most conservative of the three. (**b**) Varying rate of evolution characterizes A and B so that they indicate relatively greater discontinuities between species of genus T at some times than at others.

magnitudes. In 'concomitantly variable' protein sequences[159] the apparent uniformity of mutation fixation presumably reflects long-term consistency of selection pressure. It remains to be seen how easy it is to define concomitantly variable sequences in a wide range of proteins from a wide range of organisms, and whether the apparent uniformity of mutation fixation is maintained.

In general, different proteins evolve at different rates, just as different morphological features have been shown by the fossil record to have had non-coincident phases of high or low evolutionary tempo. In Fig. 15.8a, species of genus T will differ more in protein A than in protein B, and least of all in protein C, which is the most conservative of the three. Schemes of cladistic relationships arrived at from sequence data from different proteins should therefore be expected to yield complementary rather than identical information.

Another situation is illustrated in Fig. 15.8b, where the rates of evolution of the proteins are different, but inconstant. Inconstancy of rates is the normal situation. Like any other character, a protein which has been conservative for millenia may start to evolve at a rapid rate following a change in some factor of the environment which impinges on its function. Rates of evolution of other proteins may remain unchanged. At time X the species of genus T would seem more similar in terms of protein A than protein B, while at time Y both A and B would tell much the same story. At time Z, protein A would reveal more interspecific differences than protein B. During the period of evolution in question, the selective pressures would certainly not apply equally to all the species of genus T. Therefore not only the size of the discontinuities between taxa but also their distribution and very existence will be affected by changing evolutionary rates. Phylogenetic trees based on amino acid sequences must in principle vary with the protein chosen for investigation, and when the investigation is made. Since we have no choice about when we investigate the sequence, we are forced to conclude that numerous proteins may have to be examined to minimize the errors due to changing evolutionary rates.

Evolutionary rates can change strikingly in the short term. Over the very long periods of time during which the major taxa originate and evolve it is probably valid to assume that the average evolutionary rate of a character is a constant. In the long term any conservative protein should give substantially the same indication of phylogeny. This is confirmed by the agreement of the various animal phylogenetic trees with each other and with the fossil data. In the long term, varying selection pressures can be ignored. But in the short term, because of changeable rates of evolution like those represented in Fig. 15.8, it is not possible to say that a phylogenetic tree produced from sequence data from one set of homologous proteins is more accurate than a dissimilar tree produced from another set. Many sets will be needed. They will be assessed by the extent to which they agree with external evidence.

For practical reasons of time, labour and finance, these considerations probably limit the phylogenetic use of protein sequence data to the study of taxa which are known to be of great antiquity—in other words those which are of family or higher rank. Fortunately it is the phylogeny of these taxa of which we are most ignorant. The ancestral sequence method can provide a hypothetical sequence for nodal points which beome more accurate every time a new sequence is available. Ancestral sequences will probably never be verified on actual ancestors: missing links usually remain missing. Less conservative proteins, which are in principle suitable for the detection of phylogenetic relationships of taxa of low rank, will produce trees subject to greater errors caused by variable evolutionary rates, and which may not always agree with each other.

Changes in protein sequences, changes in the genetic code and changes in the mature phenotype of the organism are by no means necessarily proportional. Genes may change without affecting amino acid sequence, since the code is degenerate. A coding change which has no consequence for the structure of a protein probably has no significance, but cannot be detected by sequencing techniques. Therefore some mutations are not allowed for in the phylogenetic trees. Small protein changes may, however, be of enormous consequences for the intact organism, and this is not directly reflected by the equal weighting necessarily given them in the tree construction methods. The hope would be that these enormous consequences would include some detectable sequence changes. Large changes in amino acid sequence presumably have important consequences for the organism, particularly if they are scattered throughout the protein. A major deletion of residues might have no consequence if it involved a non-functional part of the molecule. Many proteins have non-functional sequences, which may be quite large, but which can be removed without loss of activity. Perhaps these non-functional parts, which must be matched by at least as much 'molecular junk' in the nucleotide complement of the organism, represent earlier functional states of the molecules which have not yet been totally obscured. In future it may be possible to produce evidence about past evolution by studying how ontogeny repeats phylogeny even at the molecular level.

The promise of protein analyses, in terms of the estimation of cladistic relationships, can be realized only by a massive increase in the number of proteins which have been investigated. In view of the number of different proteins and of different species, and taking even a cautiously optimistic view of resources available for phylogenetic research, it is unrealistic to suppose that sequencing alone can provide the information desired. Even with automated procedures it will be laborious, often boring work.

All supplementary short-cut techniques must also be involved. This demands a major effort to establish the relationships, both general and particular, between amino acid sequence, the immuno-electrophoretic properties of proteins, and their fingerprint characteristics.

16

Some   Conclusions

Chemotaxonomy is a field of knowledge which transgresses the boundaries of several others, most notably chemistry, biochemistry and taxonomy. Taxonomy itself is a transgressive subject. Chemotaxonomy can provide data which may be useful in the study of phylogeny. All these fields cover diverse kinds of knowledge and philosophy. It is therefore inevitable that the principles and methods of chemotaxonomy should in part be borrowed from other disciplines, and also that its findings should sometimes be harshly or hastily judged by taxonomists on the one hand and by chemists on the other. Though of long ancestry, chemotaxonomy has become a major growth area of systematic research mainly because the availability of simple, rapid and cheap techniques of analysis has coincided with a ferment of new thought about the characteristics and purposes of taxonomy.

Though much of interest to taxonomists has come from the long application of chemical data in taxonomy, it is not surprising, following a new burst of activity, that there are more questions about the possibilities offered by cheomotaxonomic approaches than there are answers.

Obtaining the chemical facts is the first requirement. Taxonomists will probably have to cooperate much more closely with chemists in future, if they are to get the facts in sufficient number and at a satisfying speed. Another requirement is that taxonomists must increasingly be trained in chemistry and physiology. Both these developments are already under way. The corollary is that chemists who are interested in taxonomy or in phylogeny must recognize their need of fundamental insights into the sources and nature of biological variation and how it is treated by taxonomists.

How may chemical facts be evaluated? Taxonomists have great experience in distinguishing what characters may or may not be significant in morphology and anatomy, but significance is not so obvious to them in chemistry. They have to evaluate the evidence from macromolecules and micromolecules, and to detect which are reliable chemical methods, and which ones dubious. The value of results depends on the power of the techniques used to gain them. Taxonomists have to determine how much weight to place on the chemical facts elicited by an enormous range of different methods.

There is no simple answer to questions about the value of particular kinds of evidence. All depends on the purpose for which taxonomic information is required, and the kind of classification which is wanted. Macromolecules were once thought to be of greatest value because of their associations with the genotype and relative freedom from environmental modification. But they are often difficult to study, and the variations which they exhibit cannot always be shown to have a functional significance. Taxonomists have always felt more confident about characters which can be associated, even if only doubtfully, with a function. Macromolecules nevertheless seem to hold great promise in terms of the detection of phylogenetic relationships of taxa of high rank, as well as of species and genera where there is a worldly relevance to information about evolutionary relationships.

Small molecules have in the past been regarded as excessively affected by environmental and developmental variations, and to have distributions possibly reflecting convergent evolution. A further suspicion was that they were waste products of metabolism, thus lacking positive functions.

In modern investigations, most of these doubts about the taxonomic validity of characters based on the distribution and occurrence of small molecules can confidently be set aside. Samples of sufficient size, taken in different habitats and at different times, are usually adequate to assess the extent of any environmental variation which can then be taken into account. Analyses of juvenile and mature plants, and intervening stages, provide data about the degree to which developmental variations may obscure taxonomic similarities and differences. Better knowledge of the genetics of characters involving micromolecules, such as terpenoids and phenolics, has emphasized that these compounds, no less than macromolecules, obey the usual laws of inheritance. Like macromolecules, they too therefore can be used as a guide to the genotype, albeit only a small portion of it. Enzymes which produce the micromolecules, most of which fall into the category of 'secondary substances', can be extracted and investigated. Complex pathways of synthesis, governed by several or many loci, are often found to precede the formation of the micromolecular end-product. If the pathway of synthesis of a simple compound is shown to be the same in two or more taxa, it is unlikely that the taxonomic resemblance arises from convergent evolution. Pathway research will be increasingly important in the application of micromolecular characters in taxonomy.

It has become increasingly obvious over the past ten years that many secondary substances discharge a valuable function in the life of the plant. Though some may possibly have been waste products originally, many seem to have gained a function as the habitat of the plant has changed with time. Alkaloids, phenolics, glycosides and many other secondary materials may often help to determine palatability of foliage, perhaps thereby discouraging excessive grazing. Volatile constituents often serve as attractants to insects, while some may discharge phytotoxic functions. Other secondary substances may have phytoalexin properties, like the isoflavonoid pisatin in *Pisum*, or act as wound-healing agents (resins and rubbers). Turner comments on substances from fungi which cause stomatal opening.[482] To the extent that different plant taxa inhabit different ecological niches, interact with different competitors, predators and pests, and possess different pollination and dispersal syndromes, their array of secondary substances will display a variation as discontinuous as their ecology. This variation is likely to be of taxonomic value. It is surely not without significance that most aquatics produce only a small range of secondary constituents in comparison to terrestrial plants.[328] Perhaps among the reasons for the success of the angiosperms as land dwellers is the biochemical virtuosity which enables them to evolve chemical defence and attack systems, giving them a competitive edge over plants able to withstand the diverse pressures of the land environment less well. Perhaps some secondary substances will be found to have complicated feed-back effects on the plant which produces them.

Further research sometimes shows apparent discontinuities in the distribution of secondary substances to be spurious. Such findings are, of course, not at all limited to chemotaxonomic data. Bulk assay showed that 'rare' free amino acids might in reality be widespread in minute quantities.[168] Findings of this kind are a commonplace of taxonomic research and do not detract from the general value of secondary substances as taxonomic characters. In the case of the amino acids, the significant fact is that in some cases the 'rare' state of the character is common in a particular group—i.e. certain related plants synthesize the rare compound in vast quantity. Exceptions like this abound in biology and are one reason for its intellectual challenge. Some dicotyledons have only one cotyledon, while some monocotyledons have two, or apparently none, according to the opinion of some morphologists. Sycamores often produce three cotyledons. These observations in no way detract from the general interest and value of the observation of the cotyledon character. No-one proposes to ignore or undervalue the vessel-less characteristics of many dicotyledonous aquatics and many monocotyledons, because a vessel or two may be found in *Nelumbo*. Increasing refinement of techniques and their wider application often complicates what appeared previously to be simple. The scanning electron microscope has shown some 'glabrous' surfaces to be hairy: like the amino acid distribution, it is basically a matter of magnification.

It is axiomatic that further research in biochemical ecology will inform and encourage the application of chemical data in taxonomy. Taxonomists must be as mindful of ecological research in future as they have been in the past.

The final evaluation of particular kinds of chemotaxonomic evidence will be possible only after much further work. When a restricted distribution of some compound has been detected, subject to further sampling, every new record of its occurrence takes on an added meaning and interest. Thus the distribution of betalain pigments is seen now to be significant, following the indication that they are associated with the Centrospermae. Previously they were of unknown significance. Biflavonyls are associated with gymnosperms: further work alone will decide whether their significance is understated or overstated at present.

It is exciting to note that there does not appear to be any kind of chemical data or technique which does not have some bearing on taxonomic or on phylogenetic study. Where restrictions are imposed by technical difficulties, it is virtually certain that technological progress will eventually lift them. New techniques are continually discovered and existing ones are improved (e.g. a recently announced revolution in liquid chromatography).[132] Biochemical shortcuts grow surer and shorter.

Time will solve many of the current difficulties which taxonomists feel in the use of biochemical data. Characters will be better understood and the methods of presentation of biochemical data will improve. There is a formidable blockage of communication between natural historians and chemists. 'Affinity indices', 'similarity measures', 'immunological distances', and the various kinds of phylogenetic diagrams are attempts to convert raw chemical data into a form which taxonomists can assimilate. The validity and success of these transformations can only improve with further work. Standard methods of presenting chemotaxonomic data will gradually evolve from the range of existing techniques which are illustrated in earlier chapters.

The judgement of the future on the chemotaxonomy of the twentieth century may be that the methods were crude, rashly applied with inadequate controls, and used to draw premature conclusions. Nevertheless, much good may be seen to have come from it. The area for taxonomic research, and for phylogenetic enquiry, is so vast that a chemotaxonomic 'boom' is inevitable. Like most human beings, taxonomists have always rushed into things, unlikely though that may seem to outsiders! But they have never abandoned the philosophies or methods of the past completely. The gas chromatograph and the automatic sequenator join the razor, the microscope, the hand-lens and the vasculum in the laboratory of the Complete Taxonomist.

References

1. ABBOTT, H. C. de S. (1886). Certain chemical constituents of plants considered in relation to their morphology and evolution. *Bot. Gaz.*, **11**, 270–272.
2. ADAMS, R. P. (1972). Chemosystematic and numerical studies of natural populations of *Juniperus pinchotii* Sudw. *Taxon*, **21**, 407–427.
3. ADAMS, R. P. and TURNER, B. L. (1970). Chemosystematic and numerical studies of natural populations of *Juniperus ashei* Buch. *Taxon,* **19**, 728–751.
4. ALLARD, H. A. (1918). Effects of various salts, acids, germicides, etc. upon the infectivity of the virus causing the mosaic disease of tobacco. *J. agric. Res.*, **13**, 619–637.
5. ALLARD, R. W., KAHLER, A. L. and WEIR, B. S. (1972). The effect of selection on esterase allozymes in a barley population. *Genetics*, **72**, 489–503.
6. ALSTON, R. E. (1964). The genetics of phenolic compounds. In Harborne, J. B. (Ed.) *Biochemistry of Phenolic Compounds,* pp. 171–204. Academic Press, London and New York.
7. ALSTON, R. E. (1967). Biochemical Systematics. In Dobzhansky, T., Hecht, M. K. and Steere, W. C. (Eds.) *Evolutionary Biology*, I, pp. 197–305. Appleton–Century–Crofts, New York.
8. ALSTON, R. E., RÖSLER, H., NAIFEH, K. and MABRY, T. J. (1965). Hybrid compounds in natural interspecific hybrids. *Proc. natn. Acad. Sci. U.S.A.*, **54**, 1458–1465.
9. ALSTON, R. E. and TURNER, B. L. (1959). Applications of paper chromatography to systematics: Recombination of parental biochemical components in a *Baptisia* hybrid population. *Nature, Lond.*, **184**, 285–286.
10. ALSTON, R. E. and TURNER, B. L. (1962). New techniques in analysis of complex natural hybridisation. *Proc. natn. Acad. Sci. U.S.A.*, **48**, 130–137.
11. ALSTON, R. E. and TURNER, B. L. (1963a). Natural hybridization among four species of *Baptisia* (Leguminosae). *Am. J. Bot.*, **50**, 159–173.
12. ALSTON, R. E. and TURNER, B. L. (1963b). *Biochemical Systematics.* Prentice-Hall, New Jersey.

13. AMBLER, R. P. (1967). Species differences in the amino acid sequences of bacterial proteins. In Hawkes, J. G. (Ed.) *Chemotaxonomy and Serotaxonomy*, pp. 57–64. Academic Press, New York and London.

14. AMBLER, R. P. (1972). Sequence data acquisition for the study of phylogeny. In Previero, A., Pechere, J-F. and Colleti-Previero, M-A. (Eds.) *Recent Developments in the Chemical Study of Protein Structure,* pp. 289–305. Montpelier Colloquium, 1971.

15. ANDERSON, D. M. W., DEA, I. C. M., KARAMALLA, K. A. and SMITH, J. F. (1968). Studies on uronic acid materials. XXIV. An analytical study of different forms of the gum from *Acacia senegal* Willd. *Carbohyd. Res.,* **6**, 97–103.

16. ANDERSON, D. M. W. and DEA, I. C. M. (1969). Chemotaxonomic aspects of the chemistry of *Acacia* gum exudates. *Phytochemistry,* **8**, 167–176.

17. ANDERSON, D. M. W. and MUNRO, A. C. (1969). An analytical study of gum exudates from the genus *Araucaria* Jussieu (Gymnospermae). *Carbohyd. Res.,* **11**, 43–51.

18. BACON, J. S. D. (1960). The oligofructosides. *Bull. Soc. Chim. biol.,* **42**, 1441–1449.

19. BAKER, E. A. and HOLLOWAY, P. J. (1970). The constituent acids of angiosperm cutins. *Phytochemistry,* **9**, 1557–1562.

20. BAKER, J. E. and NORRIS, D. M. (1967). A feeding stimulant for *Scolytus multistriatus* (Coleoptera: Scolytidae) isolated from the bark of *Ulmus americana. Ann. ent. Soc. Am.,* **60**, 1213–1215.

21. BAKER, R. T. and SMITH, H. G. (1902, 1920). *A Research on the Eucalypts, especially in Regard to their Essential Oils* (Edns. 1 and 2). Sydney: Tech. Mus. Bull. 13, N.S.W. Tech. Educn. Serv.

22. BAKER, W. and OLLIS, W. D. (1961). Biflavonyls. In Ollis, W. D. (Ed.) *Recent Developments in the Chemistry of Natural Phenolic Compounds,* pp. 152–184. Pergamon Press, Oxford.

23. BALDWIN, I. L. FRED, E. B. and HASTINGS, E. G. (1927). Grouping of legumes according to the biological reaction of their seed proteins. *Bot. Gaz.,* **83**, 217–243.

24. BARBER, G. A. (1965). Nucleotides and carbohydrate metabolism. A summary. In Pridham, J. B. and Swain, T. (Eds.) *Biosynthetic Pathways in Higher Plants,* pp. 117–121. Academic Press, London and New York.

25. BARTNICKI-GARCIA, S. (1970). Cell wall composition and other biochemical markers in fungal phylogeny. In Harborne, J. B. (Ed.) *Phytochemical Phylogeny,* pp. 81–103. Academic Press, London and New York.

26. BASU, N. and RASTOGI, R. P. (1967). Triterpenoid saponins and sapogenins. *Phytochemistry,* **6**, 1249–1270.

27. BATE-SMITH, E. C. (1948). Paper chromatography of anthocyanins and related substances in petal extracts. *Nature, Lond.,* **161**, 835–838.

28. BATE-SMITH, E. C. (1958). Plant phenolics as taxonomic guides. *Proc. Linn. Soc.,* **169**, 198–211.

29. BATE-SMITH, E. C. (1961). Chromatography and taxonomy in the Rosaceae, with special reference to *Potentilla* and *Prunus. J. Linn. Soc. (Bot.),* **58**, 39–54.

30. BATE-SMITH, E. C. (1962). The phenolic constituents of plants and their taxonomic significance. *J. Linn. Soc. (Bot.),* **58**, 95–173.

31. BATE-SMITH, E. C. (1972). Attractants and repellents in higher animals. In Harborne, J. B. (Ed.) *Phytochemical Ecology,* pp. 45–56. Academic Press, London and New York.

32. BATE-SMITH, E. C. (1973). Chemotaxonomy of *Geranium. Bot. J. Linn. Soc.,* **67**, 347–359.

33. BATE-SMITH, E. C., DAVENPORT, S. M. and HARBORNE, J. B. (1967). A correlation between chemistry and plant geography in the genus *Eucryphia*. *Phytochemistry*, **6**, 1407–1414.

34. BATE-SMITH, E. C. and RIBEREAU-GAYON, P. (1959). Leucoanthocyanins in seeds. *Qual. Pl. Mater. veg.*, **5**, 189–198.

35. BATE-SMITH, E. C. and SWAIN, T. (1966). The asperulosides and the aucubins. In Swain, T. (Ed.) *Comparative Phytochemistry*, pp. 159–174. Academic Press, London and New York.

36. BEHNKE, H.-D. (1969). Über Siebröhren-Plastiden und Plastiden-filamente der Caryophyllales. Untersuchungen zum Feinbau und sur Verbreitung eines weiteren spezifischen Plastiden-typs. *Planta*, **89**, 275–283.

37. BEHNKE, H.-D. and TURNER, B. L. (1971). On specific sieve-tube plastids in Caryophyllaceae. *Taxon*, **20**, 731-737.

38. BELL, E. A. (1958). Canavanine and related compounds in Leguminosae. *Biochem. J.*, **70**, 617–619.

39. BELL, E. A. (1962). Associations of ninhydrin reacting compounds in the seeds of 49 species of *Lathyrus. Biochem. J.*, **83**, 225–229.

40. BELL, E. A. (1966). Amino acids and related compounds. In Swain, T. (Ed.) *Comparative Phytochemistry*, pp. 195–209. Academic Press, London and New York.

41. BELL, E. A. (1971). Comparative biochemistry of the non-protein amino acids. In Harborne, J. B. *et al.* (Eds.) *Chemotaxonomy of the Leguminosae*, pp. 179–206. Academic Press, London and New York.

42. BELVAL, H. and CUGNAC, A. de (1941). Le contenu glucidiques des bromes et des fétuques et la classification. *Bull. Soc. Chim. biol.*, **23**, 74–77.

43. BELZER, N. F. and OWNBEY, M. (1971). Chromatographic comparison of *Tragopogon* species and hybrids. *Am. J. Bot.*, **58**, 791–802.

44. BEMIS, W. P., RHODES, A, M., WHITAKER, T. W. and CARMER, S. J. (1970). Numerical taxonomy applied to *Cucurbita* relationships. *Am. J. Bot.*, **57**, 404–412.

45. BENDICH, A. J. and BOLTON, E. T. (1967). Relatedness among plants as measured by the DNA-agar technique. *Pl. Physiol., Lancaster*, **42**, 959–967.

46. BENDICH, A. J. and McCARTHY, B. J. (1970a). DNA comparisons among barley, oats, rye, and wheat. *Genetics*, **65**, 545–565.

47. BENDICH, A. J. and McCARTHY, B. J. (1970b). DNA comparisons among some biotypes of wheat. *Genetics*, **65**, 567–573.

48. BENDICH, A. J. and McCARTHY, B. J. (1970c). Ribosomal DNA homologies among distantly related organisms. *Proc. natn. Acad. Sci. U.S.A.*, **65**, 349–356.

49. BERAHA, L. and GARBER, E. D. (1971). Avirulence and extracellular enzymes of *Erwinia carotovora. Phytopath. Z.*, **70**, 335–344.

50. BERTARELLI, E. (1902). Il metodo biologico e le sue applicazioni alla diagnosi differenziale delle farine delle leguminose. *G. Accad. Med. Torino*, **8**, 489–492.

51. BIDWELL, R. G., KROTKOV, S. G. and REED, G. B. (1952). Paper chromatography of sugars in plants. *Can. J. Bot.*, **30**, 291–305.

52. BIRCH, A. J. (1963). Biosynthetic pathways. In Swain, T. (Ed.) *Chemical Plant Taxonomy*, pp. 141–166. Academic Press, London and New York.

53. BIRDSONG, B. A., ALSTON, R. E. and TURNER, B. L. (1960). Distribution of canavanine in the family Leguminosae as related to phyletic groupings. *Can. J. Bot.*, **38**, 499–505.

54. BISWAS, S. B. and SARKAR, A. K. (1970). Deoxyribonucleic acid base composition of some angiosperms and its taxonomic significance. *Phytochemistry*, **9**, 2425–2430.

55. BJÖRKMAN, O. (1968). Further studies on differentiation of photosynthetic properties in sun and shade ecotypes of *Solidago virgaurea*. *Physiol. Plant.*, **21**, 84–99.

56. BLACKMAN, F. F. (1921). The biochemistry of carbohydrate production in the higher plants from the point of view of systematic relationship. *New Phytol.*, **21**, 2–9.

57. BLAGOVESCHCHENSKI, A. V. (1967). *Biochemistry of Leguminous Plants*. Akad. Nauk. SSSR.

58. BOGLE, A. L., SWAIN, T., THOMAS, R. D. and KOHN, E. D. (1971). *Geocarpon*: Aizoaceae or Caryophyllaceae? *Taxon*, **20**, 473–477.

58a. BOHLOOL, B. B. and SCHMIDT, E. L. (1974). Lectins: A possible basis for specificity in the *Rhizobium*—root nodule symbiosis. *Science, N.Y.*, **185**, 269–271.

59. BONNER, J. (1950). *Plant Biochemistry*. Academic Press, New York.

60. BONNER, J. (1967). Rubber biogenesis. In Bernfeld, P. *Biogenesis of Natural Compounds*, pp. 727–737. Pergamon Press, Oxford.

61. BOTTONE, E. and SCHNEIERSON, S. S. (1972). *Erwinia* species: an emerging human pathogen. *Am. J. clin. Pathol.*, **57**, 400–405.

62. BOULTER, D.(1972). Protein structure in relationship to the evolution of higher plants. *Sci. Prog., Oxf.*, **60**, 217–229.

63. BOULTER, D. (1974). The evolution of plant proteins with special reference to higher plant cytochrome *c. Current Advances in Plant Science*: Commentary No. 8, pp. 1–16.

64. BOULTER, D. and DERBYSHIRE, E. (1971). Taxonomic aspects of the structure of legume proteins. In Harborne, J. B., Boulter, D. and Turner, B. L. (Eds.) *Chemotaxonomy of the Leguminosae*, pp. 285–308. Academic Press, London and New York.

65. BOULTER, D., RAMSHAW, J. A. M., THOMPSON, E. W., RICHARDSON, M. and BROWN, R. H. (1972). A phylogeny of higher plants based on the amino acid sequence of cytochrome *c* and its biological implications. *Proc. R. Soc., B*, **181**, 441–455.

66. BOULTER, D. and THOMPSON, E. W. (1971). The amino-acid sequence of *Phaseolus aureus* (Mung bean) cytochrome *c* with reference to phylogeny. In Harborne, J. B. *et al.* (Eds.) *Chemotaxonomy of the Leguminosae*, pp. 543–548. Academic Press, London and New York.

67. BOULTER, D., THURMAN, D. A., and DERBYSHIRE, E. (1967). A disc electrophoretic study of globulin proteins of legume seeds with reference to their systematics. *New Phytol.*, **66**, 27–36.

68. BOYDEN, A. (1942). Systematic serology: a critical appreciation. *Physiol. Zool.*, **15**, 109–145.

69. BOYDEN, A. A. (1954). The measurement and significance of serological correspondence among proteins. In Cole, W. H. (Ed.) *Serological Approaches to Studies of Protein Structure and Metabolism*, pp. 74–97. Rutgers Univ. Press.

70. BOYDEN, A. A. (1965). A review of the present status of systematic serology. Part I. *Bull. serol. Mus., New Brunsw.*, **33**, 5–8.

71. BREED, R. S., MURRAY, F. G. D. and HITCHENS, A. P. (1957). *Bergey's Manual of Determinative Bacteriology*, 7th edn. Williams & Wilkins, Baltimore.

72. BREHM, B. G. and ALSTON, R. E. (1964). A chemotaxonomic study of *Baptisia leucophaea* var. *laevicaulis* (Leguminosae). *Am. J. Bot.*, **51**, 644–650.

73. BREHM, B. G. and OWNBEY, M. (1965). Variation in chromatographic patterns in the *Tragopogon dubius–pratensis–porrifolius* complex (Compositae). *Am. J. Bot.*, **52**, 811–818.

74. BRENNER, D. J., FANNING, G. R. and STEIGERWALT, A. G. (1972). DNA relatedness among species of *Erwinia* and between *Erwinia* species and other enterobacteria. *J. Bact.*, **110**, 12–17.

75. BRIESKORN, C. H. (1956). Eigenschaften und Verbreitung einiger im Pflanzenreich vorkommender pentacyclischer Triterpene. *Pharmaz. Z.*, **95**, 235–247.

76. BRISOU, J., TYSSET, J. and VACHER, B. (1959). Étude d'une souche d'*Erwinia* (*Erwinia salmonis* nv. sp.) isolée d'une truite commune (*Salmo fario* L.). *Ann. Inst. Pasteur*, **97**, 241–244.

77. BRITTEN, R. J. and KOHNE, D. E. (1968). Repeated sequences in DNA. *Science, N.Y.*, **161**, 529–540.

78. BROWN, S. A. (1964). Lignin and tannin biosynthesis. In Harborne, J. B. (Ed.) *Biochemistry of Phenolic Compounds*, pp. 361–398. Academic Press, London and New York.

79. BROWNLEE, G. G. (1972). *Determination of Sequences in RNA.* North–Holland/American Elsevier, Amsterdam, London and New York.

80. BRÜCHER, O., WECKSLER, M., LEVY, A., PALOZZO, A. and JAFFÉ, W. G. (1969). Comparison of phytohaemagglutinins in wild beans (*Phaseolus aborigineus*) and in common beans (*P. vulgaris*) and their inheritance. *Phytochemistry*, **8**,1739–1743.

81. BULL, L. B., CULVENOR, C. C. J. and DICK, A. T. (1968). *The Pyrrolizidene Alkaloids.* North–Holland, Amsterdam.

82. CADMAN, C. H. (1960). Inhibition of plant virus infection by tannins. In Pridham, J. B. (Ed.) *Phenolics in Plants in Health and Disease*, pp. 101–105. Pergamon Press, Oxford.

83. CAMMACK, R., HALL, D. and RAO, K. (1971). Ferredoxins: are they living fossils? *New Scient.* **51**, 696–698.

84. CAMPBELL, L. L. and POSTGATE, J. R. (1965). Classification of spore-forming sulphate reducing bacteria. *Bact. Rev.*, **29**, 359–363.

85. CANDOLLE, A. P. de (1804). *Essai sur les propriétés medicales des Plantes, comparées avec leur formes extérieures et leur classification naturelle*, Edn. 1. Méquignon, Paris.

86. CARR, N. G. and CRAIG, I. W. (1970). The relationship between bacteria, blue-green algae and chloroplasts. In Harborne, J. B. (Ed.) *Phytochemical Phylogeny*, pp. 119–143. Academic Press, London and New York.

87. CASIDA, J. E. (Ed.) (1973). *Pyrethrum. The Natural Insecticide.* Academic Press, New York and London.

88. CHALLICE, J. S. (1972). Phenolics of *Pyrus* interspecific hybrids. *Phytochemistry*, 11, 3015–3018.

89. CHATTERJEE, A. K. and STARR, M. P. (1972). Genetic transfer of episomic elements among *Erwinia* species and other enterobacteria: F'lac⁺. *J. Bact.*, **111**, 169–176.

90. CHESTER, K. S. (1937). A critique of plant serology. *Q. Rev. Biol.*, **12**, 19–46; 165–190; 294–321.

91. CHOOI, W. Y. (1971a). Variation in nuclear DNA content in the genus *Vicia*. *Genetics*, **68**, 195–211.

92. CHOOI, W. Y. (1971b). Comparison of the DNA of six *Vicia* species by the method of DNA–DNA hybridization. *Genetics*, **68**, 213–230.

93. CHURCH, R. B. and McCARTHY, B. J. (1968). Related base sequences in the DNA of simple and complex organisms. II. The interpretation of DNA/RNA hybridization studies with mammalian nucleic acids. *Biochem. Genet.*, **2**, 55–73.

93a. CLARKE, A. E., KNOX, R. B. and JERMYN, M. A. (1975). Localization of lectins in legume cotyledons. *J. Cell Sci.*, **19**, 157–167.

94. COCKS, G. T. and WILSON, A. C. (1972). Enzyme evolution in Enterobacteriaceae. *J. Bact.*, **110**, 793–802.

95. COLLESS, D. H. (1967). An examination of certain concepts in phenetic taxonomy. *Syst. Zool.*, **16**, 6–27.

96. CONKLIN, M. E. and SMITH. H. H. (1971). Peroxidase isozymes: a measure of molecular variation in ten herbaceous species of *Datura*. *Am. J. Bot.*, **58**, 688–696.

97. CONSDEN, R., GORDON, A. H. and MARTIN, A. J. P. (1944). Qualitative analysis of proteins: a partition chromatographic method using paper. *Biochem. J.*, **38**, 387–400.

98. CONSTANCE, L. (1957). Plant taxonomy in an age of experiment. *Am. J. Bot.*, **44**, 88–92.

99. COWAN, S. T. (1967). An assessment of the value of biochemical and serological techniques in microbial taxonomy. In Hawkes, J. G. (Ed.) *Chemotaxonomy and Serotaxonomy*, pp. 269–278. Academic Press, London and New York.

100. CRANMER, M. and TURNER, B. L. (1967). Systematic significance of Lupine alkaloids with particular reference to *Baptisia* (Leguminosae). *Evolution, Lancaster, Pa.*, **21**, 508–517.

101. CRAWFORD, D. J. (1972). The morphology and flavonoid chemistry of synthetic infraspecific hybrids in *Coreopsis mutica* (Compositae). *Taxon*, **21**, 27–38.

102. CRICK, F. H. C. (1963). The recent excitement in the coding problem. *Progr. Nucleic Acid Res.*, **1**, 163–217.

103. CROMWELL, B. T. (1967). The biogenesis of the piperidine alkaloids. In Pridham, J. B. and Swain, T. (Eds.) *Biosynthetic Pathways in Higher Plants*, pp. 147–157. Academic Press, London and New York.

104. CRONQUIST, A. (1968). *The Evolution and Classification of Flowering Plants*. Nelson, London and Edinburgh.

105. CROOKSTON, R. K. and MOSS, D. N. (1970). The relation of carbon dioxide compensation and chlorenchymatous vascular bundle sheaths in leaves of dicots. *Pl. Physiol., Lancaster*, **46**, 564–567.

106. CROWLE, A. J. (1961). *Immunodiffusion*. Academic Press, New York and London.

107. CROWSON, R. A. (1972). A systematist looks at cytochrome *c*. *J. molec. Evol.*, **2**, 28–37.

108. CRUCKSHANK, I. A. M. and PERRIN, D. R. (1964). Pathological function of phenolic compounds in plants. In Harborne, J. B. (Ed.) *Biochemistry of Phenolic Compounds*, pp. 511–544. Academic Press, London and New York.

109. CULBERSON, W. L. (1969). The use of chemistry in the systematics of the lichens. *Taxon*, **18**, 152–166.

110. CUMMINS, C. S. (1962). Chemical composition and antigenic structure of cell walls of *Corynebacterium, Mycobacterium, Nocardia, Actinomyces* and *Arthrobacter. J. gen. Microbiol.*, **28**, 35–50.

111. CUMMINS, C. S. and HARRIS, H. (1956). The chemical composition of the cell wall in some Gram-positive bacteria and its possible value as a taxonomic character. *J. gen. Microbiol.*, **14**, 583–600.

112. CUMMINS, C. S. and HARRIS, H. (1958). Studies on the cell-wall composition and taxonomy of Actinomycetales and related groups. *J. gen. Microbiol.*, **18**, 173–189.

113. DADAY, H. (1954). Gene frequencies in wild populations of *Trifolium repens*. I. Distribution by altitude. *Heredity*, **8**, 61–78.

114. DADAY, H. (1955). Cyanogenesis in strains of White Clover. *J. Br. Grassld. Soc.*, **10**, 266–274.

115. DANIELSSON, C. E. (1949). Seed globulins of the Gramineae and Leguminosae. *Biochem. J.*, **44**, 387–400.

116. DARWIN, C. (1859). *The Origin of Species by Means of Natural Selection etc.* Murray, London.

117. DAVIDSON, J. N. (1972). *Biochemistry of the Nucleic Acids.* Chapman and Hall, London.

118. DAVIS, P. H. and HEYWOOD, V. H. (1963). *Principles of Angiosperm Taxonomy.* Oliver and Boyd, Edinburgh and London.

119. DAYHOFF, M. O. (1969). *Atlas of Protein Sequence and Structure*, Vol. 4. National Biomedical Foundation, Maryland, U.S.A.

120. DAYHOFF, M. O. (1972). *Atlas of Protein Sequence and Structure*, Vol. 5. National Biomedical Foundation, Maryland, U.S.A.

121. DAYHOFF, M. O. and ECK, R. V. (1966). *Atlas of Protein Sequence and Structure*, Vol. 2. National Biomedical Foundation, Maryland, U.S.A.

122. DELEUIL, M. G. (1950). Mise en évidence de substances toxiques pour les thérophytes dans les associations du Rosmarino-Ericion. *C. r. hebd. Séanc. Acad. Sci., Paris*, **230**, 1362–1364.

123. DELEUIL, M. G. (1951a). Origine des substances toxiques du sol des associations sans thérophytes du Rosmarino-Ericion. *C. r. hebd. Séanc. Acad. Sci., Paris*, **232**, 2038–2039.

124. DELEUIL, M. G. (1951b). Explication de la présence de certaines thérophytes rencontrés parfois dans les associations du Rosmarino-Ericion. *C. r. hebd. Séanc. Acad. Sci., Paris*, **232**, 2476–2477.

125. DE LEY, J. (1968). DNA base composition and hybridization in the taxonomy of phytopathogenic bacteria. *A. Rev. Phytopath.*, **6**, 63–90.

126. DE LEY, J. (1969). Compositional nucleotide distribution and the theoretical prediction of homology in bacterial DNA. *J. theor. Biol.* **22**, 89–116.

127. DESBOROUGH, S. and PELOQUIN, S. J. (1969). Acid disc gel electrophoresis of tuber proteins from *Solanum* species. *Phytochemistry*, **8**, 425–429.

128. DIAS, F. F. (1967). Isolation of pectinolytic strains of *Aerobacter aerogenes. Appl. Microbiol.*, **15**, 1512–1513.

129. DICKERSON, R. E. (1971). Sequence and structural homologies in bacterial and mammalian-type cytochromes. *J. molec. Biol.*, **57**, 1–15.

130. DICKERSON, R. E. and GEIS, I. (1969). *The Structure and Action of Proteins.* Harper & Row, New York.

131. DIXON, R. O. D. (1969). *Rhizobia* (with particular reference to relationships with host plants). *A. Rev. Microbiol.*, **23**, 137–158.

132. DONE, J. N., KENNEDY, G. J. and KNOX, J. H. (1972). Revolution in liquid chromatography. *Nature, Lond.*, **237**, 77–81.

133. DOUGLAS, A. G. and EGLINTON, G. (1966). The distribution of alkanes. In Swain, T. (Ed.) *Comparative Phytochemistry*, pp. 57–77. Academic Press, London and New York.

134. DREIDING, A. S. (1961). The betacyanins, a class of red pigments in the Centrospermae. In Ollis, W. D. (Ed.) *Recent Developments in the Chemistry of Natural Phenolic Compounds*, pp. 194–211. Pergamon Press, Oxford.

135. DREWS, G. and MEYER, H. (1964). Untersuchungen zum chemischen Aufbau der Zellwände van *Anacystis nidulans* und *Chlorogloea fritschii. Arch. Mikrobiol.*, **48**, 259–267.

136. DUBNAU, D., SMITH, J., MORRELL, P. and MARMUR, J. (1965). Gene conservation in *Bacillus* species. I. Conserved genetic and nucleic acid base sequence homologies. *Proc. natn. Acad. Sci. U.S.A.*, **54**, 491–498.

137. DUFF, R. B. and KNIGHT, A. H. (1963). The occurrence of apiose in *Lemna* (Duckweed) and other Angiosperms. *Biochem. J.*, **88**, 33–34.

138. DUNBAR, W. P. (1910). Über das serologische Verhalten der Geschlechtzellen. *Z. Immunforsch. exp. Ther.*, **4**, 740–760; **7**, 454–497.

139. DUNCAN, U. K. (1970). *Introduction to British Lichens*. Buncle, Arbroath.

140. DYE, D. W. (1969). A taxonomic study of the genus *Erwinia*. IV. 'Atypical' *Erwinias*. *N.Z. Jl. Sci.*, **12**, 833–839.

141. EDELMAN, J. and JEFFORD, T. G. (1968). The mechanism of fructosan metabolism in higher plants as exemplified in *Helianthus tuberosus*. *New Phytol.*, **67**, 517–531.

142. EDELMAN, M., SWINTON, D., SCHIFF, J. A., EPSTEIN, H. T. and ZELDIN, B. (1967). Deoxyribonucleic acid of the blue-green algae (Cyanophyta). *Bact. Rev.*, **31**, 315–331.

143. EGLINTON, G., GONZALES, A. G., HAMILTON, R. J. and RAPHAEL, R. A. (1962). Hydrocarbon constituents of the wax coatings of plant leaves; a taxonomic survey. *Phytochemistry*, **1**, 89–102.

144. EHRLICH, P. (1891). Experimentelle Untersuchung über Immunität. I Über Ricin. II Über Abin. *Dt. med. Wschr.*, **17**, 976 and 1218.

145. ELEK, S. D. (1948). The recognition of toxicogenic bacterial strains *in vitro*. *Br. med. J.*, **1**, 493–496.

146. ELTON, G. A. H. and EWART, J. A. D. (1962). Starch gel electrophoresis of cereal proteins. *J. Sci. Fd. Agric.*, **13**, 62–72.

147. ENGLER, A. (1926). *Die naturlichen Pflanzenfamilien* (2nd edn.), **14a**, 136–137. Engelmann, Leipzig.

148. ENSGRABER, A. (1958). Die Phytohämagglutinine und ihre Funktion in der Pflanze also Kohlenhydrat-Transportsubstanzen. *Ber. dt. bot. Ges.*, **71**, 349–361.

149. ENSLIN, P. E. and REHM, S. (1958). The distribution and biogenesis of the cucurbitacins in relation to the taxonomy of the Cucurbitaceae. *Proc. Linn. Soc. Lond.*, **169**, 230–238.

150. EPSTEIN, C. J. and SCHECHTER, A. N. (1968). An approach to the problem of confirmational isozymes. *Ann. N.Y. Acad. Sci.*, **151**, 85–101.

151. ERDTMAN, H. (1963). Some aspects of chemotaxonomy. In Swain, T. (Ed.) *Chemical Plant Taxonomy*, pp. 89–125. Academic Press, London and New York.

152. ERGLE, D., KATTERMAN, F. R. H. and RICHMOND, W. (1964). Aspects of nucleic acid composition in *Gossypium*. *Pl. Physiol., Lancaster*, **39**, 145–150.

153. EYKMAN, J. F. (1888). Notes phytochimiques. *Annls. Jard. bot. Buitenz.*, **7**, 224–234.

154. FAHSELT, D. and OWNBEY, M. (1968). Chromatographic comparison of *Dicentra* species and hybrids. *Am. J. Bot.*, **55**, 334–345.

155. FAIRBROTHERS, D. E. (1967). Chemosystematics with emphasis on systematic serology. In Heywood, V. H. (Ed.) *Modern Methods in Plant Taxonomy*, pp. 141–174. Academic Press, London and New York.

156. FAIRBROTHERS, D. E. and JOHNSON, M. A. (1961). The precipitin reaction as an indicator of relationships in some grasses. *Recent Advances in Botany*, pp. 116–120. Univ. of Toronto Press.

157. FAIRBROTHERS, D. E. and JOHNSON, M. A. (1964). Comparative serological studies within the families Cornaceae (Dogwood) and Nyssaceae (Sour Gum). In Leone, C. A. (Ed.) *Taxonomic Biochemistry and Serology*, pp. 305–318. Ronald Press, New York.

158. FITCH, W. M. and MARGOLIASH, E. (1967). Construction of phylogenetic trees. *Science, N.Y.*, **155**, 279–284.

159. FITCH, W. M. and MARKOWITZ, E. (1970). An improved method for determining codon variability in a gene and its application to the rate of fixation of mutations in evolution. *Biochem. Genet.*, **4**, 579–593.

160. FLAKE, R. H., VON RUDLOFF, E. and TURNER, B. L. (1969). Quantitative study of clinal variation in *Juniperus virginiana* using terpenojd data. *Proc. natn. Acad. Sci. U.S.A.*, **64**, 487–494.

161. FLORKIN, M. (1966). *A Molecular Approach to Phylogeny*. Elsevier, Amsterdam, London and New York.

162. FLUCK, H. (1963). Intrinsic and extrinsic factors affecting the production of secondary plant products. In Swain, T. (Ed.) *Chemical Plant Taxonomy*, pp. 167–186. Academic Press, London and New York.

163. FOULDS, W. and GRIME, J. P. (1972). Response of cyanogenic and acyanogenic phenotypes of *Trifolium repens* to soil moisture supply. *Heredity*, **28**, 143–146.

164. FOWDEN, L. (1954). The nitrogen metabolism of groundnut plants: the role of γ-methylene-glutamine and γ-methylene-glutamic acid. *Ann. Bot.*, **18**, 417–440.

165. FOWDEN, L. (1958a). New amino acids of plants. *Biol. Rev.*, **33**, 393–441.

166. FOWDEN, L. (1958b). δ-Acetylornithine: a constituent of some common grasses. *Nature, Lond.*, **182**, 406–407.

167. FOWDEN, L. (1962). The non-protein amino acids of plants. *Endeavour*, **21**, 35–42.

168. FOWDEN, L. (1972). Amino acid complement of plants. *Phytochemistry*, **11**, 2271–2276.

169. FOWDEN, L. and BELL, E. A. (1965). Cyanide metabolism by seedlings. *Nature, Lond.*, **206**, 110–112.

170. FOWDEN, L. and STEWARD, F. C. (1957). Nitrogenous compounds and nitrogen metabolism in the Liliaceae. I. The occurrence of soluble nitrogenous compounds. *Ann. Bot.*, **21**, 53–67.

171. FRAENKEL, G. S. (1959). The raison d'etre of secondary plant substances. *Science, N.Y.*, **129**, 1466–1470.

172. FRELICH, J. R. and MARTEN, G. C. (1973). Quick test for Reed Canarygrass (*Phalaris arundinacea* L.) Alkaloid concentration. *Crop Sci.*, **13**, 548–551.

173. FREY-WYSSLING, A. and BLANK, F. (1943). Untersuchungen über die Physiologie des Anthocyans in Keimlinger von *Brassica oleracea* L. var *capitata* L. f. *rubra* L. *Ber. schweiz. bot. Ges.*, **53A**, 550–578.

174. FRÖST, S. and BOSE, S. (1966). An investigation of the phenolic compounds in two species of jute (*Corchorus olitorius* and *C. capsularis*) and their supposed hybrid, using the thin-layer chromatographic technique. *Hereditas*, **55**, 183–187.

175. GAILLARD, B. D. E. (1965). Comparison of the hemicelluloses from plants belonging to two different plant families. *Phytochemistry*, **4**, 631–634.

176. GALSTON, A. W. (1969). Flavonoids and photomorphogenesis in peas. In Harborne, J. B. and Swain, T. (Eds.) *Perspectives in Phytochemistry*, pp. 193–204. Academic Press, London and New York.

177. GELL, P. G., HAWKES, J. G. and WRIGHT, S. T. C. (1960). The application of immunological methods to the taxonomy of species within the genus *Solanum*. *Proc. R. Soc., B*, **151**, 364–383.

178. GIBBS, R. D. (1963). History of chemical taxonomy. In Swain, T. (Ed.) *Chemical Plant Taxonomy*, pp. 41–88. Academic Press, London and New York.

179. GIBBS, R. D. (1974). *Chemotaxonomy of Flowering Plants*. McGill–Queen's University Press, Montreal.

180. GILG, E. and SCHURHOFF, P. H. (1926). Die Serodiagnostik in der Verwandschaftsforschung. *Bot. Jb.*, **60**, 439–450.

181. GOLDBERG, R. B., BEMIS, W. P. and SIEGEL, A. (1972). Nucleic acid hybridization studies within the genus *Cucurbita*. *Genetics*, **72**, 253–266.

182. GOLDOVSKII, A. H. 1960. Evolutionary changes in fat biosynthesis in organisms. *Russian Rev. Biol.*, **50**, 127–141.

183. GOODWIN, T. W. (1966). The carotenoids. In Swain, T. (Ed.) *Comparative Phytochemistry*, pp. 121–137. Academic Press, London and New York.

184. GOODWIN, T. W. (1967). The biological significance of terpenes in plants. In Pridham, J. B. (Ed.) *Terpenoids in Plants*, pp. 1–23. Academic Press, London and New York.

185. GOODWIN, T. W. (Ed.) (1970). *Natural Substances formed biologically from Mevalonic Acid.* Academic Press, London and New York.

186. GOULD, H. J. (1967). Evolution of ribosomal RNA. In Hawkes, J. G. (Ed.) *Chemotaxonomy and Serotaxonomy*, pp. 131–156. Academic Press, London and New York.

187. GRABAR, P. and WILLIAMS, C. A. (1953). Méthode permettant l'étude conjuguée des propriétés électrophorétiques et immunochimiques d'un mélange de protéines. *Biochim. biophys. Acta*, **10**, 193–194.

188. GREEN, B. R. and DICK, M. W. (1972). DNA base composition and the taxonomy of Oomycetes. *Can. J. Microbiol.*, **18**, 963–968.

189. GREENE, R. A. and FOSTER, E. O. (1933). The liquid wax of *Simmondsia californica. Bot. Gaz.*, **94**, 826–828.

190. GREGORY, W. C. (1941). Phylogenetic and cytological studies in the Ranunculaceae. *Trans. Am. Phil. Soc.*, N.S., **31**, 443–521.

191. GRESHOFF, M. (1891). Aperçu du premier rapport du laboratoire chimico-pharmacologique du Jardin Botanique de l'Etat de Buitenzorg. *Annls. Jard. bot. Buitenz.*, **9**, 247–260.

192. GRESHOFF, M. (1909). Phytochemical investigations at Kew. *Bull. misc. Inf. R. bot. Gdns. Kew*, **10**, 397–418.

193. GREW, N. (1673). *An Idea of a Phytological History Propounded.* Chiswell, London.

194. GUPTA, A. S. and CHAKRABARTY, M. M. (1964). Constitutive studies of some seed fats of Indian Arid Zone with particular reference to the influence of environmental and genetic factors. *Indian J. appl. Chem.*, **27**, 49–61.

195. GUPTA, V. and STEBBINS, G. L. (1969). Peroxidase activity in hooded and awned barley at successive stages of development. *Biochem. Genet.*, **3**, 15–24.

196. HADLEY, E. B. and LEVIN, D. A. (1969). Physiological evidence of hybridization and reticulate evolution in *Phlox maculata. Am. J. Bot.*, **56**, 561–570.

197. HALE, M. E. (1974). *The Biology of Lichens* (2nd edn.). Arnold, London.

198. HALL, M. T. (1952). A hybrid swarm in *Juniperus. Evolution, Lancaster, Pa.*, **6**, 347–366.

199. HALL, O. (1959). Immunoelectrophoretic analyses of allopolyploid rye–wheat and its parental species. *Hereditas*, **45**, 495–504.

200. HALLAM, N. D. (1967). *An electron microscope study of the leaf waxes of the genus Eucalyptus L'Héritier.* Ph. D. thesis, Univ. of Melbourne.

201. HARBORNE, J. B. (1963). Distribution of anthocyanins in Higher Plants. In Swain, T. (Ed.) *Chemical Plant Taxonomy*, pp. 359–388. Academic Press, London and New York.

202. HARBORNE, J. B. (Ed.) (1964). *Biochemistry of Phenolic Compounds.* Academic Press, London and New York.

203. HARBORNE, J. B. (1966). The evolution of flavonoid pigments in plants. In Swain, T. (Ed.) *Comparative Phytochemistry*, pp. 271–295. Academic Press, London and New York.

204. HARBORNE, J. B. (1967a). *Comparative Biochemistry of the Flavonoids.* Academic Press, London and New York.

205. HARBORNE, J. B. (1967b). Luteolin-5-glucoside and its occurrence in the Umbelliferae. *Phytochemistry*, **6**, 1569–1573.
206. HARBORNE, J. B. (Ed.) (1970). *Phytochemical Phylogeny.* Academic Press, London and New York.
207. HARBORNE, J. B. (1971). Terpenoid and other low-molecular weight substances of systematic interest in the Leguminosae. In Harborne, J. B., Boulter, D. and Turner, B. L. (Eds.) *Chemotaxonomy of the Leguminosae*, pp. 257–283. Academic Press, London and New York.
208. HARBORNE, J. B. (Ed.) (1972). *Phytochemical Ecology.* Academic Press, London and New York.
209. HARBORNE, J. B. (1974). *Phytochemical Methods.* Chapman and Hall, London.
210. HARBORNE, J. B., BOULTER, D. and TURNER, B. L. (1971). *Chemotaxonomy of the Leguminosae.* Academic Press, New York and London.
211. HARBORNE, J. B. and SIMMONDS, N. W. (1964). The natural distribution of the phenolic aglycones. In Harborne, J. B. *Biochemistry of Phenolic compounds*, pp. 77–127. Academic Press, London and New York.
212. HARBORNE, J. B. and WILLIAMS, C. A. (1973). A chemotaxonomic survey of flavonoids and simple phenols in leaves of the Ericaceae. *Bot. J. Linn. Soc.,* **66**, 37–54.
213. HARDER, R., and DÖRING, B. (1935). Über die Farbänderung der Blüten, von *Dahlia variabilis. Nachr. Ges. Wiss. Göttingen,* **VI(2)**, 89–95.
214. HARMATHA, J., SAMEK, Z., NOVOTNY, L., HEROUT, V. and ŠORM, F. (1968). The structure of adenostylone and isoadenostylone: two furoeremophilanes from *Adenostyles alliariae. Tetrahedron Lett.,* **12**, 1409–1412.
215. HATCH, M. D. and SLACK, C. R. (1970). Photosynthetic CO_2-fixation pathways. *A. Rev. Pl. Physiol.,* **21**, 141–162.
216. HATHWAY, D. E. (1958). Oak-bark tannins. *Biochem. J.,* **70**, 34–42.
217. HAWKES, J. G. and LESTER, R. N. (1966). Immunological studies on the tuber-bearing *Solanums.* II. Relationships of North American species. *Ann. Bot.,* **30**, 270–290.
218. HAWKES, J. G. and LESTER, R. N. (1968). Immunological studies on the tuber-bearing *Solanums.* III. Variability within *S. bulbocastanum. Ann. Bot.,* **32**, 165–186.
219. HAWKES, J. G. and SMITH, P. M. (1965). Continental drift and the age of angiosperm genera. *Nature, Lond.,* **207**, 48–50.
220. HAWKES, J. G. and TUCKER, W. G. (1968). Serological assessment of relationships in a flowering plant family (Solanaceae). In Hawkes, J. G. (Ed.) *Chemotaxonomy and Serotaxonomy*, pp. 77–88. Academic Press, London and New York.
221. HEGNAUER, R. (1962–1969). *Chemotaxonomie der Pflanzen*, Vols. 1–5. Birkhauser, Basel.
222. HEGNAUER, R. (1963). The taxonomic significance of alkaloids. In Swain, T. (Ed.) *Chemical Plant Taxonomy*, pp. 389–427. Academic Press, London and New York.
223. HEGNAUER, R. (1966). Comparative Phytochemistry of Alkaloids. In Swain, T. (Ed.) *Comparative Phytochemistry*, pp. 211–230. Academic Press, London and New York.
224. HEGNAUER, R. (1967). Chemical characters in plant taxonomy: some possibilities and limitations. *Pure appl. Chem.,* **14**, 173–187.
225. HEMINGWAY, J. S., SCHOFIELD, H. J. and VAUGHN, J. G. (1961). Volatile mustard oils of *Brassica juncea* seeds. *Nature, Lond.,* **192**, 993.

226. HENDERSHOTT, C. H. and WALKER, D. R. (1959). Identification of a growth inhibitor from extracts of dormant peach flower buds. *Science, N.Y.*, **130**, 798–799.

227. HENRY, T. A. (1949). *The Plant Alkaloids*. J. and A. Churchill, London.

228. HERBIN, G. A. and ROBINS, P. A. (1968). Studies on plant cuticular waxes. I. The chemotaxonomy of alkanes and alkenes of the genus *Aloe* (Liliaceae). *Phytochemistry*, **7**, 239–255.

229. HEROUT, V. and ŠORM, F. (1969). Chemotaxonomy of the sesquiterpenoids of the Compositae. In Harborne, J. B. and Swain, T. (Eds.) *Perspectives in Phytochemistry*, pp. 139–165. Academic Press, London and New York.

230. HEYWOOD, V. H. (1967). *Plant Taxonomy*. Arnold, London.

231. HEYWOOD, V. H. (1971a). Chemosystematic studies in *Daucus* and allied genera. *Boissiera*, **19**, 289–295.

232. HEYWOOD, V. H. (Ed.) (1917b). *Biology and Chemistry of the Umbelliferae.* Academic Press, London and New York.

233. HEYWOOD, V. H. and McNEILL, J. (1964). *Phenetic and Phylogenetic Classification.* Systematics Association, London.

234. HILDITCH, T. P. (1952). The seed and fruit fats of plants. *Endeavour*, **1**, 173–182.

235. HILDITCH, T. P. (1956). *The Chemical Constitution of Natural Fats*, 3rd edn. Chapman and Hall, London.

236. HILL, A. S. and MATTICK, L. R. (1966). The *n*-alkanes of cabbage (var. Copenhagen) and sauerkraut. *Phytochemistry*, **5**, 693–697.

237. HILLIS, W. E. (1956). Leucoanthocyanins as the possible precursors of extractives in woody tissues. *Aust. J. biol. Sci.*, **9**, 263–280.

238. HILLIS, W. E. (1958). Formation of condensed tannins in plants. *Nature, Lond.*, **182**, 1371.

239. HIRST, E. L. and REES, D. A. (1965). The structure of alginic acid. Part V. Isolation and unambiguous characterization of some hydrolysis products of the methylated polysaccharide. *J. chem. Soc.*, 1182–1187.

240. HOLLIGAN, P. M. and DREW, E. A. (1971). Routine analysis by gas–liquid chromatography of soluble carbohydrates in extracts of plant tissues. II. Quantitative analysis of standard carbohydrates, and the separation and estimation of soluble sugars and polyols from a variety of plant tissues. *New Phytol.*, **70**, 271–297.

241. HOYER, B. H., McCARTHY, B. J. and BOLTON, E. T. (1964). A molecular approach in the systematics of higher organisms. *Science, N.Y.*, **144**, 959–967.

242. HUBBARD, C. E. (1948). Gramineae. In Hutchinson, J. *British Flowering Plants*, pp. 284–348. Gawthorn, London.

243. HUTCHINSON, J. (1959). *Families of Flowering Plants*. Clarendon Press, Oxford.

244. HÜTTER, R. and DeMOSS, J. A. (1967). Organization of the tryptophan pathway: a phylogenetic study of the fungi. *J. Bact.*, **94**, 1896–1907.

245. IKAWA, M. (1964). Cell wall composition in relation to the classification of lactic acid bacteria. In Leone, C. A. (Ed.) *Taxonomic Biochemistry and Serology*, pp. 599–605. Ronald Press, New York.

246. IMAI, S., TOTOSATO, T., FUJICK, S., SAKAI, M. and SATO, Y. (1968). Screening of plants for compounds with insect moulting activity. *Chem. pharm. Bull., Tokyo*, **17**, 335–339.

247. INGHAM, J. L. (1972). Phytoalexins and other natural products as factors in plant disease resistance. *Bot. Rev.*, **38**, 343–424.

248. INGLE, J., PEARSON, G. G. and SINCLAIR, J. (1973). Species distribution and properties of nuclear satellite DNA in higher plants. *Nature, Lond.*, **242**, 193–197.

249. JACKSON, P., MILTON, J. M. and BOULTER, D. (1967). Fingerprint patterns of the globulin fraction obtained from the seeds of various species of the Fabaceae. *New Phytol.*, **66**, 47–56.

250. JAMIESON, G. R. and REID, E. H. (1969). The leaf lipids of some members of the Boraginaceae family. *Phytochemistry*, **8**, 1489–1493.

251. JAMIESON, G. R. and REID, E. H. (1971). The leaf lipids of some members of the Caryophyllaceae. *Phytochemistry*, **10**, 1575–1577.

252. JANZEN, D. H. (1966). Co-evolution of mutualism between ants and Acacias in Central America. *Evolution, Lancaster, Pa.*, **20**, 249–275.

253. JEFFREY, D. C., ARDITTI, J. and KOOPOWITZ, H. (1970). Sugar content in floral and extrafloral exudates of orchids: Pollination, myrmecology and chemotaxonomy implication. *New Phytol.*, **69**, 187–195.

254. JENSEN, U. (1968). Serologische Beitrage zur Systematik der Ranunculaceae. *Bot. Jb.*, **88**, 204–268.

255. JOHNSON, B. L. (1972). Seed protein profiles and the origin of the hexaploid wheats. *Am. J. Bot.*, **59**, 952–960.

256. JOHNSON, B. L. and HALL, O. (1965). Analysis of phylogenetic affinities in the *Triticinae* by protein electrophoresis. *Am. J. Bot.*, **52**, 506–513.

257. JOHNSON, B. L. and THEIN, M. M. (1970). Assessment of evolutionary affinities in *Gossypium* by protein electrophoresis. *Am. J. Bot.*, **57**, 1081–1092.

258. JONES, D. A. (1972). Cyanogenic glycosides and their function. In Harborne, J. B. (Ed.) *Phytochemical Ecology*, pp. 103–124. Academic Press, London and New York.

259. JONES, D. and SNEATH, P. H. A. (1970). Genetic transfer and bacterial taxonomy. *Bact. Rev.*, **34**, 40–81.

260. KABAT, E. A. (1968). *Structural Concepts in Immunology and Immunochemistry.* Holt, Reinhart and Winston, New York and London.

261. KAUFFMANN, F. (1954). *Enterobacteriaceae.* Ejnar Munksgaard, Copenhagen.

262. KEDDIE, R. M., LEASK, B. G. S. and GRAINGER, J. M. (1966). A comparison of coryneform bacteria from soil and herbage: cell wall composition and nutrition. *J. appl. Bact.*, **29**, 17–43.

263. KENDRICK, R. E. and HILLMAN, W. S. (1971). Absence of phytochrome dark reversion in seedlings of the Centrospermae. *Am. J. Bot.*, **58**, 424–428.

264. KIMLER, L., MEARS, J., MABRY, T. J. and RÖSLER, H. (1970). On the question of the mutual exclusiveness of betalains and anthocyanins. *Taxon*, **19**, 875–878.

265. KIRK, J. T. O. (1967). Effect of methylation of cytosine residues on the buoyant density in caesium chloride solution. *J. molec Biol.*, **28**, 171–172.

266. KITAGAWA, M. and MONOBE, S. (1933). Studies on a diamino acid, canavanin. III. The constitution of canalin. *J. Biochem., Tokyo*, **18**, 333–343.

267. KLEESE, R. S. and FREY, K. J. (1964). Serological predictions of genetic relationships among oat varieties and corn inbreds. *Crop Sci.*, **4**, 379–383.

268. KLOZ, J. (1971). Serology of the Leguminosae. In Harborne, J. B., Boulter, D. and Turner, B. L. (Eds.) *Chemotaxonomy of the Leguminosae*, pp. 309–365. Academic Press, London and New York.

269. KLOZ, J., KLOZOVA, E. and TURKOVA, V. (1966). Chemotaxonomy and genesis of protein characters with special reference to the genus *Phaseolus*. *Preslia*, **38**, 229–236.

270. KLOZ, J. and KLOZOVA, E. (1968). Variability to proteins I and II in the seeds of species of the genus *Phaseolus*. In Hawkes, J. G. (Ed.) *Chemotaxonomy and Serotaxonomy*, pp. 93–102. Academic Press/Systematics Association, London.

271. KLOZ, J., TURKOVA, V. and KLOZOVA, E. (1960). Serological investigation of the taxonomic specificity of proteins in various organs in some taxons of the family Viciaceae. *Biologia Pl.*, **2**, 126–137.

272. KLOZ, J. and TURKOVA, V. (1963). Legumin, Vicilin and proteins similar to them in the seeds of some species of the Viciaceae (a comparative serological study). *Biologia Pl.*, **5**, 29–40.

273. KNOX, R. B., WILLING, R. R. and ASHFORD, A. E. (1972). The role of pollen-wall proteins as recognition subspecies in interspecific incompatibility in Poplars. *Nature, Lond.*, **237**, 328–383.

274. KNUTH, R. (1912). Geraniaceae. In Engler, A. and Gilg, L. *Das Pflanzenreich,* **53**, Heft (iv), Part 129. 640pp. Engelmann, Leipzig.

275. KOHNE, D. E. (1967). Taxonomic applications of DNA hybridization techniques. In Hawkes, J. G. (Ed.) *Chemotaxonomy and Serotaxonomy*, pp. 117–130. Academic Press, London and New York.

276. KOOIMAN, P. (1960). On the occurrence of amyloids in plant seeds. *Acta bot. neerl.*, **9**, 208–219.

277. KOOIMAN, P. (1961). The constitution of *Tamarindus*-amyloid. *Recl. Trav. chim. Pays-Bas Belg.*, **80**, 849–865.

278. KOOIMAN, P. (1967). The constitution of the amyloid from seeds of *Annona muricata* L. *Phytochemistry*, **6**, 1665–1673.

279. KOSTYTSCHEV, S. and WENT, F. A. F. S. (1931). *Lehrbuch der Pflanzenphysiologie*. Springer, Berlin.

280. KOWARSKI, A. (1901). Über den Nachweis von pflanzlichem Eiweiss auf biologischem Wege. *Dt. med. Wschr.*, **27**, 442.

281. KRAUS, R. (1897). Über specifische Reactionen in keimfreien Filtraten aus *Cholera, Typhus* und pestbouillon Culturen erzeugt durch homologes Serum. *Wien. klin. Wschr.*, **10**, 736–738.

282. KRZEMINSKI, L. F., WHITE, H. B., Jr., and QUACKENBUSH, F. W. (1960). Conversion of some ^{14}C-labelled compounds into the neutral lipid of *Neurospora crassa*. *J. Am. chem. Soc.*, **37**, 371–373.

283. KUBITSKI, K. (1968). Flavonoide und Systematik der Dilleniaceen. *Ber. dt. bot. Ges.*, **81**, 238–251.

284. KULSHRETHA, M. J., KULSHRETHA, D. K. and RASTOG, R. P. (1972). The triterpenoids. *Phytochemistry*, **11**, 2369–2381.

285. KÜHN, R. and LOW, I. (1949). Morphologie und Chemie der Staubgefässe von *Forsythia*. *Chem. Ber.*, **82**, 474–479.

286. KUPCHAN, S. M., ZUMMERMAN, J. H. and AFONSO, A. (1961). The alkaloids and taxonomy of *Veratrum* and related genera. *Lloydia*, **24**, 1–26.

287. KWAPINSKI, J. B. G. (1969). *Analytical Serology of Micro-organisms*. Wiley, New York.

288. LAIRD, C. D. and McCARTHY, B. J. (1968). Magnitude of interspecific nucleotide sequence variability in *Drosophila*. *Genetics*, **60**, 303–332.

289. LANCE, G. N. and WILLIAMS, W. T. (1967). A general theory of classificatory sorting strategies. I. Hierarchical systems. *Comput. J.*, **9**, 373–380.

290. LANGENHEIM, J. H. (1969). Amber: a botanical enquiry. *Science, N.Y.*, **163**, 1167–1169.

291. LARSEN, P. O. (1969). *Free Amino Acids in Cruciferae and Resedaceae*. Riso Report 189. Danish Atomic Energy Commission, Riso.

292. LASZLO, H. de and HENSHAW, P. S. (1954). Plant materials used by primitive peoples to affect fertility. *Science, N.Y.*, **119**, 626–631.

293. LAVA-SANCHEZ, P. A., AMALKI, F. and LA POSTA, A. (1972). Base composition of ribosomal RNA and evolution. *J. molec. Evol.*, **2**, 44–45.

294. LEE, D. W. and FAIRBROTHERS, D. E. (1967). Serological and disc-electrophoretic studies of North American *Typha*. *Am. J. Bot.*, **54**, 660 (Abstr.).

295. LEE, K. Y., WAHL, R. and BARBU, E. (1956). Contenu en bases puriques et pyrimidiques des acides désoxyribonucléiques des bactéries. *Ann. Inst. Pasteur*, **91**, 212–224.

296. LEETE, E. (1956). The biogenesis of nicotine and anabasine. *J. Am. chem. Soc.*, **78**, 3520–3523.

297. LEETE, E. (1967). Alkaloid biosynthesis. *A. Rev. Pl. Physiol.*, **18**, 179–196.

298. LEMCKE, R. M. (1965). A serological comparison of various species of mycoplasma by an agar gel double-diffusion technique. *J. gen. Microbiol.*, **38**, 91–100.

299. LEONE, C. A. (1952). Effect of multiple injections of antigen upon the specificity of antisera. *J. Immunol.*, **69**, 285–295.

300. LESTER, R. N. (1965). Immunological studies on the tuber-bearing *Solanums*. I. Techniques and South American species. *Ann. Bot.*, **29**, 609–624.

301. LESTER, R. N., ALSTON, R. E. and TURNER, B. L. (1965). Serological studies in *Baptisia* and certain other genera of the Leguminosae. *Am. J. Bot.*, **52**, 165–172.

302. LEVIN, D. A. (1966). Chromatographic evidence of hybridization and evolution in *Phlox maculata*. *Am. J. Bot.*, **53**, 238–245.

303. LEVIN, D. A. (1967). An analysis of hybridization in *Liatris*. *Brittonia*, **19**, 248–260.

304. LEWIS, J. H. and WELLS, H. G. (1925). The immunological properties of alcohol-soluble vegetable proteins. The biological reactions of the vegetable proteins IX. *J. biol. Chem.*, **66**, 37–48.

305. LINDERSTRØM-LANG, K. (1937). Proteine und proteolytische Enzyme. *Collegium*, **10**, 561–569.

306. LINDSTEDT, G. and MISIORNY, A. (1951). Constituents of pine heartwood. XXV. Investigation of forty-eight *Pinus* species by paper partition chromatography. *Acta chem. scand.*, **5**, 121–128.

307. LOENING, U. E. (1968). Molecular weights of RNA in relation to evolution. *J. molec. Biol.*, **38**, 355–365.

308. LOOMIS, W. D. (1967). Biosynthesis and metabolism of monoterpenes. In Pridham, J. B. (Ed.) *Terpenoids in Plants*, pp. 60–82. Academic Press, London and New York.

309. LUCKNER, M. (1972). *Secondary Metabolism in Plants and Animals*. Chapman and Hall, London.

310. LUND, B. M. (1965). A comparison by the use of gel electrophoresis of soluble protein components and esterase enzymes of some group D streptococci. *J. gen. Microbiol.*, **40**, 413–419.

311. MABRY, T. J. (1966). The betacyanins and betaxanthins. In Swain, T. (Ed.) *Comparative Phytochemistry*, pp. 231–244. Academic Press, New York and London.

312. MABRY, T. (1970). Infraspecific variation of sesquiterpene lactones in *Ambrosia* (Compositae): Applications to evolutionary problems at the population level. In J. B. Harborne (Ed.) *Phytochemical Phylogeny*, pp. 269–300. Academic Press, London and New York.

313. MABRY, T. J., TAYLOR, A. and TURNER, B. L. (1963). The betacyanins and their distribution. *Phytochemistry*, **2**, 61–64.

314. MABRY, T. J., WYLER, H., SASSU, G., MERCIER, M., PARIKH, J. and DREIDING, A. s. (1962). Die Struktur des Neobetanidin. Über die Konstitution des Randen-farbstoffes Betanin. *Helv. chim. Acta*, **45**, 640–647.

315. MACEY, M. and BARBER, H. N. (1969). Chemical genetics of nonacosan-15-one and related compounds in *Brassica oleracea*. *Nature, Lond.*, **222**, 789–790.

316. MAGNUS, W. (1908). Weitere Ergebnisse der Serum-diagnostik für die theoretische und angewandte Botanik. *Ber. dt. bot. Ges.*, **26a**, 532–539.

317. MANDEL, M. (1969). New approaches to bacterial taxonomy: perspective and prospects. *A. Rev. Microbiol.*, **23**, 239–274.

318. MANSKE, R. H. F. (1937). The natural occurrence of acetyl-ornithine. *Can. J. Res.*, **15B**, 84–87.

319. MANSKE, R. H. F. (1944). The alkaloids. *A. Rev. Biochem.*, **13**, 535–548.

320. MANSKE, R. H. F. and HOLMES, H. (1950–1958). *The Alkaloids*. Academic Press, New York.

321. MARMUR, J., ROWND, R. and SCHILDKRAUT, C. L. (1963). Denaturation and renaturation of deoxyribonucleic acid. *Progr. Nucleic Acid Res.*, **1**, 231–300. Academic Press, New York.

322. MARTIN, J. T. and JUNIPER, B. E. (1970). *The Cuticles of Plants*. Edward Arnold, London.

323. MARTIN, P. and RADEMACHER, B. (1960). Studies on the mutual influences of weeds and crops. In Harper, J. L. (Ed.) *The Biology of Weeds. Br. Ecol. Soc. Symp.*, **1**, 143–152. Blackwell Scientific Publications, Oxford.

324. MARTIN-SMITH, M., SUBRAMANIAN, G. and CONNOR, H. E. (1967). Surface wax components of five species of *Cortaderia* (Gramineae)—a chemo-taxonomic comparison. *Phytochemistry*, **6**, 559–572.

325. MATSUDA, K., SIEGEL, A. and LIGHTFOOT, D. (1970). Variability in com-plementarity for chloroplastic and cytoplasmic ribosomal ribonucleic acids among plant nuclear deoxyribonucleic acids. *Pl. Physiol., Lancaster*, **46**, 6–12.

326. MAURER, P. H. and WEIGLE, W. (1954). The cross reactions between albumins of different species and gamma-globulins of different species. *J. Immunol.*, **72**, 119–122.

327. MAZLIAK, P. (1968). Chemistry of plant cuticles. In Reinhold, L. and Liwschitz, Y. (Eds.) *Progress in Phytochemistry*, Vol. 1, pp. 49–111. Interscience, New York.

328. McCLURE, J. W. (1970). Secondary constituents of aquatic Angiosperms. In Harborne, J. B. (Ed.) *Phytochemical Phylogeny*. pp. 233–268. Academic Press, London and New York.

329. McHALE, J. and ALSTON, R. E. (1964). Utilization of chemical patterns in the analysis of hybridization between *Baptisia leucantha* and *B. sphaerocarpa*. *Evolution, Lancaster, Pa.*, **18**, 304–311.

330. McNAIR, J. B. (1929). The taxonomic and climatic distribution of oils, fats and waxes in plants. *Am. J. Bot.*, **16**, 832–841.

331. McNAIR, J. B. (1935a). The taxonomic and climatic distribution of alkaloids. *Bull. Torrey bot. Club*, **62**, 219–226.

332. McNAIR, J. B. (1935b). Angiosperm phylogeny on a chemical basis. *Bull. Torrey bot. Club*, **62**, 515–532.

333. MEARA, M. L. (1958). The fats of higher plants. In Ruhland, W. (Ed.) *Encycl. Pl. Physiol.* VII, pp. 10–49. Springer, Berlin.

334. MEARS, J. A. and MABRY, T. J. (1971). Alkaloids in the Leguminosae. In Harborne, J. B. *et al.* (Eds.) *Chemotaxonomy of the Leguminosae*. Academic Press, London and New York.

335. MECKLENBURG, H. C. (1966). Inflorescence hydrocarbons of some species of *Solanum* L. and their possible taxonomic significance. *Phytochemistry*, **5**, 1201–1209.

336. MEEUSE, A. D. J. (1963). From ovule to ovary: a contribution to the phylogeny of the megasporangium. *Acta Biotheor.*, **16**, 9–182.
337. MEZ, C. and ZIEGENSPECK, H. (1926). Der Konigsberger serodiagnostische Stammbaum. *Bot. Arch.*, **13**, 483–485.
338. MILLER, H. E., MABRY, T. J., TURNER, B. L., and PAYNE, W. W. (1968). Infraspecific variation of sesquiterpene lactones in *Ambrosia psilostachya* (Compositae). *Am. J. Bot.*, **55**, 316–324.
339. MILLER, R. W., VAN ETTEN, C. H., McGREW, C., WOLFF, I. A. and JONES, Q. (1962). Amino acid composition of seed meals from forty-one species of Cruciferae. *J. Agric. Fd. Chem.*, **10**, 426–430.
340. MIROV, N. T. (1938). Phylogenetic relations of *Pinus jeffreyi* and *P. ponderosa*. *Madrono*, **4**, 169–171.
341. MIROV, N. T. (1956). Composition of turpentine of lodgepole × jack pine hybrids. *Can. J. Bot.*, **34**, 443–457.
342. MIROV, N. T. (1961). *Composition of Gum Turpentines of Pines*. U.S.D.A. Tech. Bull. **1239**, Washington.
343. MOEWUS, F. (1951). Die Sexualstoffe von *Chlamydomonas eugametos*. *Ergebn. Enzymforsch.*, **12**, 173–206.
344. MORITZ, O. (1933). Serologische Untersuchungen an Getreidebastarden. *Ber. dt. bot. Ges.*, **51**, 52–57.
345. MORITZ, O. (1934). Die botanische Serologie. *Beitr. Biol. Pfl.*, **22**, 51–90.
346. MORITZ, O. (1958). The serology of plant proteins. In Ruhland, W. (Ed.) *Encycl. Pl. Physiol.* VIII, pp.356–414. Springer, Berlin.
347. MORITZ, O. and VOM BERG, H. (1931). Serologische Studien über das Rinswickenproblem. *Biol. Zbl.*, **51**, 290–307.
348. MOTHES, K. (1955). Physiology of alkaloids. *A. Rev. Pl. Physiol.*, **6**, 393–432.
349. MOTHES, K. (1960). Alkaloids in the plant. In Manske, R. H. F. (Ed.) *The Alkaloids*, **6**, pp. 1–29. Academic Press, New York.
350. MOTHES, K. (1966). Zur Problematik der metabolischen Exkretion bei Pflanzen. *Naturwissenschaften*, **53**, 317–323.
351. MOTHES, K. and SCHUTTE, H. R. (1969). *Biosynthese der Alkaloide*. VEB Deutsche Verlag der Wissenschaften, Berlin.
352. MULLER, C. H. and CHOU, C-H. (1972). Phytotoxins: An ecological phase of phytochemistry. In Harborne, J. B. (Ed.) *Phytochemical Ecology*, pp. 201–216. Academic Press, London and New York.
353. MÜLLER, K. O. and BÖRGER, H. (1941). Experimentelle Untersuchungen über die *Phytophthora*-Resistenz der Kartoffel, *Arb. biol. Anst. (Reichsanst) Berl.*, **23**, 189–231.
354. MURRAY, M. J. (1960a). The genetic basis for the conversion of menthone to menthol in Japanese mint. *Genetics*, **45**, 925–929.
355. MURRAY, M. J. (1960b). The genetic basis for a third ketone group in *Mentha spicata* L. *Genetics*, **45**, 931–937.
356. NAKANISHI, K. (1968). Conference on insect–plant interactions. *BioScience*, **18**, 791–799.
357. NEAMTU, G. and BODEA, C. (1969). Chemotaxonometrische Untersuchungen an höheren Pflanzen. I Carotinoid-farbstoffe der gattung *Astragalus*. *Revue roum. Biochem.*, **6**, 157–161.
358. NELSON, C. I. and BIRKELAND, J. M. (1928). A serological ranking of some wheat hybrids as an aid in selecting for certain genetic characters. *J. Am. Agric. Res.*, **38**, 169–181.
359. NEVINS, D. J., ENGLISH, P. D. and ALBERSHEIM, P. (1967). The specific nature of plant cell wall polysaccharides. *Pl. Physiol.*, Lancaster, **42**, 900–906.
360. NICHOLS, B. W. (1965). The lipids of a moss (*Hypnum cupressiforme*) and of the leaves of green holly (*Ilex aquifolium*). *Phytochemistry*, **4**, 769–772.

361. NICHOLS, B. W. (1970). Comparative lipid biochemistry of photosynthetic organisms. In Harborne, J. B. (Ed.) *Phytochemical Phylogeny*, pp. 105–118. Academic Press, London and New York.

362. NICHOLS, B. W. and JAMES, A. T. (1968). Acyl lipids and fatty acids of photosynthetic tissue. In Reinhold, L. and Liwschitz, Y. (Eds.) *Progress in Phytochemistry*, Vol. I, pp. 1–48. Interscience, New York.

363. NOVOTNY, L., TOMAN, J., STARY, F., MARQUEZ, A. D., HEROUT, V. and ŠORM, F. (1966). Contribution to the chemotaxonomy of some European *Petasites* species. *Phytochemistry*, 5, 1281–1287.

364. NOWACKI, E. (1963). Inheritance and biosynthesis of alkaloids in lupin. *Genet. Polon.*, 4, 161–202.

365. NUTTALL, G. H. F. (1901). The new biological test for blood in relation to zoological classification. *Proc. R. Soc., B*, 69, 150–153.

366. OSBORNE, T. B. (1924). *The Vegetable Proteins*. Longmans, London.

367. OUCHTERLONY, O. (1948) . *In vitro* method for testing the toxin-producing capacity of diphtheria bacteria. *Acta path. microbiol. scand.*, 25, 189–191.

368. OUDIN, J. (1956). Méthode d'analyse immunochimique par précipitation spécfique in milieu gélifié. *C.r. hebd. Séanc. Acad. Sci., Paris*, 222, 117–116.

369. PANDEY, K. K. (1967). Origin of genetic variability: combination of peroxidase isozymes determine multiple allelism of the S gene. *Nature, Lond.*, 213, 669–672.

370. PANDEY, K. K. (1973). Heat sensitivity of esterase isozymes in the styles of *Lilium* and *Nicotiana. New Phytol.*, 72, 839–850.

371. PARIS, R. (1963). The distribution of plant glycosides. In Swain, T. (Ed.) *Chemical Plant Taxonomy*, pp. 337–358. Academic Press, London and New York.

372. PAYNE, R. C. and FAIRBROTHERS, D. E. (1973). Disc electrophoretic study of pollen proteins from natural populations of *Betula populifolia* in New Jersey. *Am. J. Bot.*, 60, 182–189.

373. PENFOLD, A. R. and MORRISON, F. R. (1927). The occurrence of a number of varieties of *Eucalyptus dives* as determined by chemical analysis of the essential oils. I. *J. Proc. R. Soc. N.S.W.*, 61, 54–67.

374. PENFOLD, A. R. and MORRISON, F. R. (1934). The essential oils of *Eucalyptus micrantha* including a form rich in piperitone. *J. Proc. R. Soc. N.S.W.*, 67, 351–355.

375. PENFOLD, A. R., MORRISON, F. R. and McKERN, H. H. G. (1948). Studies of physiological forms of the Myrtaceae. I. *Leptospermum citratum. Mus. Techn. and Appl. Sci. Res. on the Essential Oils of the Australian Flora*, I, 12–17.

376. PERCIVAL, E. (1966). The natural distribution of plant polysaccharides. In Swain, T. (Ed.) *Comparative Phytochemistry*, pp. 139–158. Academic Press, London and New York.

377. PERCIVAL, M. S. (1961). Types of nectar in angiosperms. *New Phytol.*, 60, 235–281.

378. PETIVER, J. (1899). Some attempts made to prove that herbs of the same make or class for the generality, have the like virtue and tendency to work the same effects. *Phil. Trans. R. Soc.*, 21B, 289–294.

379. PIATELLI, M., MINALE, L. and PROTA, G. (1964). Isolation, structure and absolute configuration of indicaxanthin. *Tetrahedron*, 20, 2325–2329.

380. PICKERING, J. L. and FAIRBROTHERS, D. E. (1967). A serological and disc electrophoretic investigation of *Magnolia* taxa. *Bull. Torrey bot. Club*, 94, 468–479.

381. PLESHKOV, B. P., SHMYREVA, T. B. and IVANKO, S. (1959). The free amino acid content of leaves and roots of maize as related to nutritional conditions. *Plant Physiol. (Russia)*, **6**, 674–683.

382. PLOUVIER, V. (1955). Sur le sorbitol des Rosacées. *C.r. hebd. Séanc. Acad. Sci., Paris*, **241**, 1220–1222.

383. PLOUVIER, V. (1963). Distribution of aliphatic polyols and cyclitols. In Swain, T. (Ed.) *Chemical Plant Taxonomy*, pp. 313–336. Academic Press, London and New York.

384. POSSINGHAM, J. V. (1956). The effect of mineral nutrition on the content of free amino acids and amides in tomato plants. I. *Aust. J. biol. Sci.*, **9**, 539–551.

385. POTTER, J. L. and MABRY, T. J. (1972). Origins of the Texas Gulf coast island populations of *Ambrosia psilostachya*: a numerical study using terpenoid data. *Phytochemistry*, **11**, 715–723.

386. PRAGER, E. M. and WILSON, A. C. (1971). The dependence of immunological cross-reactivity upon sequence resemblance among lysozymes. I. Microcomplement fixation. *J. biol. Chem.*, **246**, 5979–5989.

387. PRICE, J. R. (1963). The distribution of alkaloids in the Rutaceae. In Swain, T. (Ed.) *Chemical Plant Taxonomy*, pp. 429–452. Academic Press, London and New York.

388. PRIEST, F. G., SOMERVILLE, H. J., COLE, J. A. and HOUGH, J. S. (1973). The taxonomic position of *Obesumbacterium proteus*, a common brewery contaminant. *J. gen. Microbiol.*, **75**, 295–307.

389. QUILLET, M. (1956). Sur le métabolisme glucidique des Hépatiques: Jungermanniales et Marchantiales. *C.r. hebd. Séanc. Acad. Sci., Paris*, **242**, 2656–2658.

390. RADLER, F. (1965). The surface waxes of the sultana vine (*Vitis vinifera* cv. Thompson Seedless). *Aust. J. biol. Sci.*, **18**, 1045–1056.

391. RAMSHAW, J. A. M., RICHARDSON, D. L., MEATYARD, B. T., BROWN, R. H., RICHARDSON, M., THOMPSON, E. W. and BOULTER, D. (1972). The time of origin of the flowering plants determined by using amino-acid sequence data of cytochrome *c*. *New Phytol.*, **71**, 773–779.

392. RAMSTED, E. and AGURELL, S. (1964). Alkaloid Biogenesis. *A. Rev. Pl. Physiol.*, **15**, 153–168.

393. RAO, S. L. N., RAMACHANDRAN, L. K. and ADIGA, P. R. (1963). The isolation and characterisation of L-homoarginine from seeds of *Lathyrus sativus*. *Biochemistry*, **2**, 298-300.

394. RASMUSSEN, R. A. and WENT, F. W. (1965). Volatile organic material of plant origin in the atmosphere. *Proc. natn. Acad. Sci. U.S.A.*, **53**, 215–230.

395. REDDI, V. and PHIPPS, J. B. (1972). Free amino-acids as taxonomic characters in the tribe Arundinelleae (Gramineae). *Brittonia*, **24**, 403-414.

396. REHR, S. S., BELL, E. A., JANZEN, D. H. and FEENEY, P. P. (1973). Insecticidal amino acids in legume seeds. *Biochem. Syst.*, **1**, 63–67.

397. REICHERT, E. T. (1919). A biochemic basis for the study of problems of taxonomy, heredity, evolution etc., with especial reference to the starches and tissues of parent-stocks and hybrid-stocks and the starches and haemoglobins of varieties, species and genera. *Publs Carnegie Instn.* No. **270**. Part I, 1–376; Part II, 377–834.

398. RENNERFELT, E. and NACHT, G. (1955). The fungicidal activity of some constituents from heartwood of conifers. *Svensk bot. Tidskr.*, **49**, 419–432.

399. REPKE, K., EST, M. and PORTIUS, H. I. (1965). Über die Ursache der Species unterschiede in der Digitalis empfindlichkeit. *Biochem. Pharmac.*, **14**, 1785–1802.

400. RESSLER, C. (1962). Isolation and identification from common vetch of the neurotoxin β-cyanoalanine, a possible factor in lathyrism. *J. biol. Chem.*, **237**, 733–735.

401. REUTER, G. (1957). Die Hauptformen des loslichen Stickstoffs in vegetativen pflanzlichen speicherorganen und ihre systematische Bewertbarkeit. *Flora, Jena,* **145,** 326–338.

402. RIBEREAU-GAYON, P. (1972). *Plant Phenolics.* Oliver and Boyd, Edinburgh.

403. RICHARDSON, M., RICHARDSON, D., RAMSHAW, J. A. M., THOMPSON, E. W. and BOULTER, D. (1970). Isolation and purification of cytochrome *c* from some species of higher plants. *Phytochemistry,* **9,** 2271–2280.

404. RIGHTER, F. I. (1945). *Pinus:* the relationship of seed size and seedling size to inherent vigor. *J. For.,* **43,** 134–137.

405. RIVES, L. (1923), Sur l'emploi du serodiagnostic pour la détermination de Taffinité au greffage des hybrides de vigne. *C. r. hebd. Séanc. Acad. Agric. Fr.,* **9,** 43–47.

406. ROBERTS, E. A. H., WIGHT, W. and WOOD, D. J. (1958) Paper chromatography as an aid to the taxonomy of the Thea Camellias. *New Phytol.,* **57,** 211–225.

407. ROBINSON, A. M. and ROBINSON, R. (1932). Synthetical experiments on the nature of betanin and related nitrogenous anthocyanins. *J. chem. Soc.,* 1439–1445.

408. ROBINSON, E. and BROWN, R. (1952). The development of the enzyme complement in growing root cells. *J. exp. Bot.,* **3,** 356–374.

409. ROBINSON, K. (1966). An examination of *Corynebacterium* spp. by gel electrophoresis. *J. appl. Bact.,* **29,** 179–184.

410. ROTHSCHILD, M. (1972). Some observations on the relationship between plants, toxic insects and birds. In Harborne, J. B. (Ed.) *Phytochemical Ecology,* pp. 1–12. Academic Press, London and New York.

411. ROTTINK, B. A. and HANOVER, J. W. (1972). Identification of blue spruce cultivars by analysis of cortical oleoresin monoterpenes. *Phytochemistry,* **11,** 3255–3257.

412. ROWSON, J. M. (1945). Increased alkaloidal contents of induced polyploids of *Datura, Atropa* and *Hyoscyamus. Q. Jl. Pharm. Pharmac.,* **18,** 175–193.

413. ROWSON, J. M. (1958). Alkaloids and plant taxonomy. *Proc. Linn. Soc. Lond.,* **169,** 212–216.

414. RUIJGROK, H. W. L. (1966). The distribution of ranunculin and cyanogenetic compounds in the Ranunculaceae. In Swain, T. (Ed.) *Comparative Phytochemistry,* pp. 175–186. Academic Press, London and New York.

415. RUNEMARK, H. (1968). Critical comments on the use of statistical methods in chemotaxonomy. *Bot. Notiser,* **121,** 29–43.

416. RYAN, E. and FOTTRELL, P. F. (1972). Electrophoretic and chromatographic differences between aspartate amino-transferases from *Rhizobiums. J. gen. Microbiol.,* **70,** 395–397.

417. RYGH, O., RYGH, A. and LALAND, P. (1932). Chemische Untersuchungen über das antiskorbutische Vitamin. I. *Z. physiol. Chem.,* **204,** 105–111.

418. SACKIN, M. J. (1971). Cross-association: a method of comparing protein sequences. *Biochem. Genet.,* **5,** 287–313.

419. SAINT-PAUL, M. (1961). Les haemagglutinines végétales. *Transfusion,* **4,** 3–37.

420. SAITO, A. (1970). Electrophoretic comparison of soluble pollen proteins of *Alnus* in relation to inter- and intra-specific identification. *J. Jap. For. Soc.* **52,** 291–295.

421. SALTON, M. R. J. (1964). *Microbial Cell Walls.* Wiley, New York.

422. SANDERMANN, W. (1962). Terpenoids: structure and distribution. In Florkin, M. and Mason, H. S. (Eds.) *Comparative Biochemistry,* Vol. III, pp. 503–630. Academic Press, New York.

423. SANTAMOUR, F. S., Jr. (1965). *U.S.D.A. Forest Service Res. Notes,* NE 38 and 39. Cited by Langenheim (1969).

424. SANWAL, G. G. and KRISHNAN, P. S. (1961). The phosphatases of cactus. II. Purification and properties. *Enzymologia*, **23**, 85–93.

425. SAUNDERS, P. P. and BROQUIST, H. P. (1966). Saccharopine, an intermediate of the aminoadipic acid pathway of lysine biosynthesis. *J. biol. Chem.*, **241**, 3435–3440.

426. SCHILDKRAUT, C. L., MARMUR, J. and DOTY, P. (1962). Determination of the base composition of deoxyribonucleic acid from its buoyant density in CsCl. *J. mol. Biol.*, **4**, 430–443.

427. SCHLEIFER, K. H. and KANDLER, O. (1972). Peptidoglycan types of bacterial cell walls and their taxonomic implications. *Bact. Rev.*, **36**, 407–477.

428. SCOGIN, R. (1969). Isoenzyme polymorphism in natural populations of the genus *Baptisia* (Leguminosae). *Phytochemistry*, **8**, 1733–1737.

429. SCOTT-MONCRIEFF, R. (1931). The chemical effect of a Mendelian factor for flower colour. *Nature, Lond.*, **127**, 974–975.

430. SENEVIRATNE, A. S. and FOWDEN, L. (1968). The amino acids of the genus *Acacia*. *Phytochemistry*, **7**, 1039–1045.

431. SHAW, C. (1970). Sporopollenin. In Harborne, J. B. (Ed.) *Phytochemical Phylogeny*, pp. 31–58. Academic Press, London and New York.

432. SHORLAND, F. B. (1963). The distribution of fatty acids in plant lipids. In Swain, T. (Ed.) *Chemical Plant Taxonomy*, pp. 253–311. Academic Press, London and New York.

433. SHOTTON, D. M. and HARTLEY, B. S. (1970). Amino acid sequence of porcine pancreatic elastase and its homologies with other serine proteinases. *Nature, Lond.*, **225**, 802–806.

434. SILVESTRI, L. G. and HILL, L. R. (1965). Agreement between deoxyribonucleic acid base composition and taxometric classification of Gram-positive cocci. *J. Bact.*, **90**, 136–140.

435. SIMOLA, L. K. (1967). The effect of some non-protein amino acids on pollen germination and pollen-tube growth in five species of the Vicieae. *Planta*, **77**, 287–297.

436. SIMONSEN, J. L. and RAU, M. G. (1922). The constituents of some Indian essential oils. Parts 1–7. *Indian Forest Rec.*, **9**(iv), 111–146.

437. SIMPSON, G. G. (1960). Diagnosis of the classes Reptilia and Mammalia. *Evolution, Lancaster, Pa.*, **14**, 388–392.

438. SLOPEK, S. (1969). Analytical serology of *Shigella*. In Kwapinski, J. B. G. *Analytical Serology of Micro-organisms*, pp. 137–180. Wiley, New York.

439. SMITH, P. M. (1968a). The *Bromus mollis* aggregate in Britain. *Watsonia*, **6**, 327–344.

440. SMITH, P. M. (1968b). Serological distinctness of *Bromus pseudosecalinus* P. Smith sp. nov. *Reprium nov. Spec. Regni veg.*, **77**, 61–64.

441. SMITH, P. M. (1969a). Serological relationships of *Bromus* L. and *Boissiera* Hochst. ex Steud. *Reprium nov. Spec. Regni veg.*, **79**, 337–345.

442. SMITH, P. M. (1969b). Serological relationships and taxonomy in certain tribes of the Gramineae. *Ann. Bot.*, **33**, 591–613.

443. SMITH, P. M. (1971). The taxonomy and nomenclature of the brome-grasses. *Notes R. bot. Gdn Edinb.*, **30**, 361–375.

444. SMITH, P. M. (1972). Serology and species relationships in annual bromes (*Bromus* L. sect. *Bromus*). *Ann. Bot.*, **36**, 1–30.

445. SMITH, P. M. (1973). Observations on some critical brome-grasses. *Watsonia*, **9**, 319–332.

446. SOKAL, R. R. and SNEATH, P. H. A. (1963). *Principles of Numerical Taxonomy*. Freeman, San Francisco and London.

447. SONDHEIMER, E. and SIMEONE, J. B. (1970). *Chemical Ecology*. Academic Press, New York and London.

448. STAHL, E. (1952). Über die Farbe des ätherischen Öles von *Artemisia absinthium* L. und das Proazulen. *Naturwissenschaften*, B, **39**, 571.

449. STANIER, R. Y. (1968). Biochemical and immunological studies on the evolution of a metabolic pathway in bacteria. In Hawkes, J. G. (Ed.) *Chemotaxonomy and Serotaxonomy*, pp. 201–225. Academic Press, London and New York.

450. STARR, M. P. and CHATTERJEE, A. K. (1972). The genus *Erwinia*: enterobacteria pathogenic to plants and animals. *A. Rev. Microbiol.*, **26**, 389–426.

451. STEBBINS, G. L. (1956). Cytogenetics and evolution of the grass family. *Am. J. Bot.*, **43**, 890–905.

452. STEBBINS, G. L. (1968). The effect of asexual reproduction on higher plant genera with special reference to *Citrus*. *Proc. 1st Int. Citrus Symposium*, **1**, 455–458.

453. STEBBINS, G. L., HARVEY, B. L., COX, E. L., RUTGER, J. N., JELENKOVIC, G. and YAGIL, E. (1963). Identification of the ancestry of an amphiploid *Viola* with the aid of paper chromatography. *Am. J. Bot.*, **50**, 830–839.

454. STEVENS, P. F. (1971). A classification of the Ericaceae: subfamilies and tribes. *Bot. J. Linn. Soc.*, **64**, 1–53.

455. STOCKELL, A. (1961). Comparative studies on tryptic digests of myoglobins. *J. molec. Biol.*, **3**, 362–366.

456. STOLOFF, L. (1962). Algal classification—an aid to improved industrial utilisation. *Econ. Bot.*, **16**, 86–94.

457. STORCK, R. and ALEXOPOULOS, C. J. 1970) Deoxyribosenucleic acid of fungi. *Bact. Rev.*, **34**, 126–154.

458. STRANSKY, K., STREIBL, M. and HEROUT, V. (1967). On natural waxes. VI. Distribution of wax hydrocarbons in plants at different evolutionary levels. *Colln Czech. chem. Commun. Engl. Edn.*, **32**, 3213–3220.

459. SUEOKA, N. (1961). Variation and heterogeneity of base composition of deoxyribonucleic acids: a compilation of old and new data. *J. molec. Biol.*, **3**, 31–40.

460. SUNG, M. L. and FOWDEN, L. (1969). Azetidine-2-carboxylic acid from the legume *Delonix regia. Phytochemistry*, **8**, 2095–2096.

461. SUTHERLAND, M. D. and PARK, R. J. (1967). Sesquiterpenes and their biogenesis in *Myoporum deserti* A. Cunn. In Pridham, J. B. (Ed.) *Terpenoids in Plants*, pp. 147–157. Academic Press, London and New York.

462. SUTTON, D. D., ARK, P. A. and STARR, M. P. (1960). The causal agent of bacterial brown rot of *Cypripedium* orchids. *Phytopathology*, **50**, 182–186.

463. SYLUSORENKO, A. G., POPOV, L. S., ANTONOV, A. S. and BELOZERSKII, A. N. (1972). Nucleotide composition of DNA of certain members of the class Liliatae. (In Russian.) *Dokl. Akad. Nauk. SSSR*, **205**, 727–730.

464. TAKHTAJIAN, A. L. (1969). *Flowering Plants: Origin and Dispersal*. Oliver and Boyd, Edinburgh.

465. TAPPER, B. A. and BUTLER, G. W. (1971). Oxines, nitriles and 2-hydroxynitriles as precursors in the biosynthesis of cyanogenic glucosides. *Biochem. J:*, **124**, 935–941.

466. TAVORMINA, P., GIBBS, M. H. and HUFF, J. B. (1956). The utilization of β-hydroxy-β-methyl-δ-valerolactone in cholesterol biosynthesis. *J. Am. chem. Soc.*, **78**, 4498–4499.

467. TAYLOR, R. J. (1972). The relationship and origin of *Tsuga heterophylla* and *Tsuga mertensiana* based on phytochemical and morphological interpretations. *Am. J. Bot.*, **59**, 149–157.

468. TÉTÉNYI, P. (1968). The nomenclature of infraspecific chemical taxa. *Taxon*, **17**, 261–264.

469. TÉTÉNYI, P. (1970). *Infraspecific Chemical Taxa of Medicinal Plants*. Akad. Kiadó, Budapest.

470. TEWFIK, E. M. and BRADLEY, S. G. (1967). Characterisation of deoxyribose nucleic acids from Streptomycetes and Nocardiae. *J. Bact.*, **94**, 1994–2000.

471. THOMPSON, E. W., LAYCOCK, M. V., RAMSHAW, J. A. M. and BOULTER, D. (1970). The amino acid sequence of *Phaseolus aureus* L. (Mung-Bean) cytochrome *c*. *Biochem. J.*, **117**, 183–192.

472. THURMAN, D. A. (1971). Comparative studies of legume enzymes. In Harborne, J. B. *et al.* (Eds.) *Chemotaxonomy of the Leguminosae*, pp. 463–483. Academic Press, London and New York.

473. THURMAN, D. A., BOULTER, D., DERBYSHIRE, E. and TURNER, B. L. (1967). Electrophoretic mobilities of formic and glutamic dehydrogenases in the Fabaceae: A systematic survey. *New Phytol.*, **66**, 37–45.

474. TOMS, G. C. and WESTERN, A. (1971). Phytohaemagglutinins. In Harborne, J. B. *et al.* (Eds.) *Chemotaxonomy of the Leguminosae*, pp. 367–462. Academic Press, London and New York.

475. TREWAVAS, A. J. and GIBSON, I. (1968). Ribosomal RNA nucleotide sequence homologies in plants. *Pl. Physiol., Lancaster*, **43**, 445–447.

476. TRIBE, I. S. (1967). Cited by Martin & Juniper (1970) as personal communication.

477. TRIBE, I. S., GAUNT, J. K. and WYNN PARRY, D. (1968). Cuticular lipids in the Gramineae. *Biochem. J.*, **109**, 8p–9p.

478. TSCHIERSCH, B. and HANELT, P. (1967). Die freien Amino-sauren der Samen von *Vicia* L. und die systematische Gliederung der Gattung. *Flora, Jena*, **157**, 389–406.

479. TSO, T. C. and McMURTREY, J. E. (1960). Mineral deficiency and organic constituents in tobacco plants. II. Amino acids. *Pl. Physiol., Lancaster*, **35**, 865–870.

480. TURNER, B. L. (1967). Plant chemosystematics and phylogeny. *Pure appl. Chem.*, **14**, 189–213.

481. TURNER, B. L. and HARBORNE, J. B. (1967). Distribution of canavanine in the plant kingdom. *Phytochemistry*, **6**, 863–866.

482. TURNER, N. C. (1972). Stomatal behaviour of *Avena sativa* treated with two phytotoxins, Victorin and Fusicoccin. *Am. J. Bot.*, **59**, 133–136.

483. URANO, K. (1959). Serological investigations with the phytogenetic relationship among inbred lines in maize. *Maize Gen. Coop. Newsletter*, **33**, 82–84.

484. URITANI, I. and AKAZAWA, T. (1959). Alteration of the respiratory pattern in infected plants. In Horsfall, J. G. and Dimond, A. K. (Eds.) *Plant Pathology I*, pp. 349–390. Academic Press, London and New York.

485. URMENYI, A. M. C. and FRANKLIN, A. W. (1961). Neonatal death from pigmented coliform infection. *Lancet*, **1**, 313–315.

486. VALADON, L. R. G. and MUMMERY, R. S. (1967). Carotenoids of certain Compositae flowers. *Phytochemistry*, **6**, 983–988.

487. VARNS, J. L., KUC, J. and WILLIAMS, E. B. (1971). Terpenoid accumulation as a biochemical response of the Potato tuber to *Phytophthora infestans. Phytopathology*, **61**, 174–177.

488. VAUGHN, J. G. (1968). Seed protein studies of *Brassica* and *Sinapis* species. In Hawkes, J. G. (Ed.) *Chemotaxonomy and Serotaxonomy*, pp. 103–110. Systematics Association and Academic Press, London and New York.

489. VÉRON, M. (1966). Taxonomie numérique des vibrions et de certaines bactéries comparable. II. Correlation entre les similitudes phénétiques et la composition en bases de l'ADN. *Ann. Inst. Pasteur*, **111**, 671–709.

490. VICKERY, J. R. (1971). The fatty acid composition of the seed oils of Proteaceae: a chemotaxonomic study. *Phytochemistry*, **10**, 123–130.

491. VIRTANEN, A. K. and LINKO, P. (1955). The occurrence of free ornithine and its *N*-acetyl derivative in plants. *Acta chem. scand.*, **9**, 531–532.

492. VODKIN, M. and KATTERMAN, F. R. H. (1972). Divergence of ribosomal RNA sequences within Angiospermae. *Genetics*, **69**, 435–451.

493. VOGEL, H. J. (1964). Distribution of lysine pathways among fungi: evolutionary implications. *Am. Nat.*, **98**, 435–446.

494. VON RUDLOFF, E., IRVING, R. and TURNER, B. L. (1967). Re-evaluation of allopatric introgression between *Juniperus ashei* and *J. virginiana* using gas chromatography. *Am. J. Bot.*, **54**, 660 (Abstr.).

495. WEIMARCK, G. (1972). On 'numerical chemotaxonomy'. *Taxon*, **21**, 615–619.

496. WELLS, A. G. and OSBORNE, T. B. (1915). The anaphylaxis reaction with so-called proteoses of various seeds. The biological reactions of the vegetable proteins VI. *J. inf. Dis.*, **17**, 259–275.

497. WET, J. M. J. de and SCOTT, B. D. (1965). Essential oils as taxonomic criteria in *Bothriochloa*. *Bot. Gaz.*, **126**, 209–214.

498. WHITAKER, T. W. and BEMIS, W. P. (1965). Evolution in the genus *Cucurbita*. *Evolution, Lancaster, Pa.*, **18**, 553–559.

499. WHITE, E. and TOWERS, G. H. N. (1967). Comparative biochemistry of the Lycopods. *Phytochemistry*, **6**, 663–667.

500. WHITE, J. N. and STARR, M. P. (1971). Glucose fermentation products of *Erwinia* species and other enterobacteria. *J. appl. Bact.*, **34**, 459–475.

501. WHITTAKER, R. H. (1970). The biochemical ecology of higher plants. In Sondheimer, E. and Simeone, J. B. *Chemical Ecology*, pp. 43–70. Academic Press, New York and London.

502. WHITTENBURY, R. (1965). The differentiation of *Streptococcus faecalis* and *S. faecium*. *J. gen. Microbiol.*, **38**, 279–287.

503. WILLIAMS, C. M. (1970). Hormonal interactions between plants and insects. In Sondheimer, E. and Simeone, J. B. *Chemical Ecology*, pp. 103–132. Academic Press, New York and London.

504. WITHERING, W. (1776). *A Botanical Arrangement*. Swinney, Birmingham.

505. WITHERING, W. (1785). *An Account of the Foxglove and some of its Medical Uses*. Swinney, Birmingham.

506. WOLFF, I. A. and KWOLEK, W. F. (1971). Lipids of the Leguminosae. In Harborne, J. B., Boulter, D. and Turner, B. D. (Eds.) *Chemotaxonomy of the Leguminosae*, pp. 231–255. Academic Press, London and New York.

507. WOOLHOUSE, H. W. (1970). Environmental and enzyme evolution in plants. In Harborne, J. B. (Ed.) *Phytochemical Phylogeny*, pp. 207–231. Academic Press, London and New York.

508. WORK, E. and DEWEY, D. L. (1953). The distribution of α-ε-diaminopimelic acid among various microorganisms. *J. gen. Microbiol.*, **9**, 394–406.

509. YEO, P. F. (1973). The biology and systematics of *Geranium*, sections *Anemonifolia* Knuth and *Ruberta* Dum. *Bot. J. Linn. Soc.*, **67**, 285–346.

510. ZADE, A. (1914). Serologische Studien an Leguminosen und Gramineen. *Z. PflZücht.*, **2**, 101–151.

511. ZADRAZIL, S. (1972). Sekvenci analysa nukleorych kyselin. *Chemické Listy*, **66**, 825–852.

512. ZAVARIN, F., COBB, F. W., BERGOT, J. and BAWBER, H. W. (1971). Variation of the *Pinus ponderosa* needle oil with season and needle age. *Phytochemistry*, **10**, 3107–3114.

513. ZEITOUN, F. M. and WILSON, E. E. (1966). Serological comparisons of *Erwinia nigrifluens* with certain other *Erwinia* species. *Phytopathology*, **56**, 1381–1385.

514. ZUCKERKANDL, E. and PAULING, L. (1965). Molecules as documents of evolutionary history. *J. theor. Biol.*, **8**, 357–366.

Index

DATE DUE